The Professional Pilot's Manual

The Professional Pilot's Manual

Phil Croucher

Airlife
England

Dedication and Thanks

What you're about to read is the result of all the mistakes I made because there wasn't a book like this one to refer to. It contains all the items I often needed in an Operations Manual but was never able to find, either because they weren't there or the Manual itself was badly organized. My thanks are due to all the long-suffering people I have met in my career, especially to Tony Boulter who gave me the chance to make all the mistakes in the first place!

Several beers are also owed to Peter Godwin, Peter Boitel-Gill, Rufus Foster, Colin Heathcote, Arthur Mitchell, John Wood, Kevin Bodley, John Marsden, Chalky White, Graeme Matthews, Mike Barringer, The Thruxton Flight Centre and several others (including some CAA members, who must remain nameless) for their assistance, and David Richards for the preafrooding.

This book is for Kate, whose favourite bird is a Harrier.

Copyright © Phil Croucher, 1990

First published in the UK in 1990
by Airlife Publishing Ltd.

British Library Cataloguing in Publication Data available

ISBN 1 85310 082 X

Printed in England by Livesey Ltd., Shrewsbury.

Airlife Publishing Ltd.

101 Longden Road, Shrewsbury, England.

Contents

Chapter 6 General Aircraft Operations 87

Chapter 7 Special Aircraft Operations 154

Chapter 8 Technical Matters 200

Preface

Despite its title, *The Professional Pilot's Manual* has very little to do with flying. It has, however, everything to do with being a pilot — and the sort of training and information you're not given at flying school but should be. If you work, or are going to work, for a small charter company, then this book is mainly written with you in mind, but that's not to say that people working in larger outfits (or even airlines) won't find anything useful in it, as most of what goes on in those sort of companies is repeated further down the line, only on a much smaller scale, of course.

Smaller companies cannot afford to spend too much time or money on training, although naturally they do meet minimum requirements (the emphasis being on minimum). Not only that, they tend to be rather short on staff as well, needing people who can be quite versatile. You could frequently find yourself (especially in a helicopter company) out in the field dealing directly with customers and making decisions on your company's behalf.

Would you feel up to this task? It's hard enough to maintain basic flying skills, let alone take on some of the functions of management as well. It's well known that what customers think of your company depends not only on how you fly the aircraft, but also on how you interact with them. As a famous aviation advert once said, there's nothing like a curly sandwich to make your passengers query your ability as a pilot! They will expect **you** to know the answers to all their questions, which will range from how long the aircraft can fly on full tanks to the type of form required at Customs for the goods they wish to import.

You might not think it's fair, but you will rapidly find that you're not really a pilot at all — you'll also be expected to be a combination of Handling Agent, Freight Agent, Manager and Salesman, amongst other things. Mastering the aircraft is only half the job!

This book is meant to catch the newly qualified pilot at the same point as when he left school — that is, where his education really begins. It is hoped that more senior pilots may be able to pick up a point or two, as well as Operations staff who quite often have to make decisions on behalf of pilots, such as inspecting and approving Pleasure Flying sites. There is also the Corporate pilot to be considered, somebody who may have no Public Transport experience to fall back on but is nevertheless faced with operating an aircraft by himself.

One day, some of you reading this will be Chief Pilots, or at least have a hand in running a company, however large. That's why there are some parts of the book, such as *Obtaining an Air Operator's Certificate* or *Running Things* (which take you over to the Management side of the fence) that may not seem relevant at this point in your career. Take time to read these chapters anyway. They will give you a greater insight into what your employer had to do in order to get himself into a position to pay your salary; in addition, they will help you understand how your company works — maybe they will assist you to set up your own when the time comes.

Also not necessarily relevant at this stage is Section 11, *Going for a Job*. Like most other pilots, you will find after a few years that your CV will read like a patchwork quilt. Usually, this is no fault of yours, but Management often don't see things the same way as Real People, so you may find something useful in there that will help.

Whatever parts you read (and I hope you read them all), this book is geared to helping you become a more Professional Pilot.

Good luck!

Chapter 1
Your Company — A Guided Tour

What sort of company do you keep?

If you're anything like the average pilot starting out on a new career, and are keen to fly, it's just possible that you may take the first job that comes along (that is, of course, unless you're absolutely hell-bent on doing a particular one, in which case you can skip this bit). However, you may find it useful to know what you could be letting yourself in for and maybe change your mind . . . .

Wherever you end up, you will rapidly have to get used to your position as having no real significance apart from your influence when actually flying. In other words, you may be The Boss when in your own office (the cockpit), but it will seem that everyone else in the Company will be in charge of you otherwise. This is especially so in the smaller companies, where you may well end up amending publications, etc as a secondary duty, amongst others (you're being paid anyway, so when not actually flying, you end up in the pool of cheap labour — no sitting at home when you're not needed!).

Companies differ in what they allow you to get away with. For instance, in some companies, being away from base with a problem may mean ringing Operations up before you make any kind of a move. On the other hand, sometimes you can make decisions on their behalf there and then. This is true everywhere in Aviation, airlines included (some of these won't even allow personal items or conversation in the cockpit).

There are three types of flying according to the Air Navigation Order: Public Transport, Aerial Work and Private. Being a professional, you will only be concerned with the first two.

Public Transport is flying where payment (usually by a passenger) is given for the use of an aircraft; 'use of an aircraft' in this context means in the same sense as a taxi, as opposed to self-drive car hire. You need to be aware that there is considerable legal argument involved as to when a flight is considered to be Public Transport, and you will find some of it summarized later in Chapter 9. As it is such a complex subject, any further discussion will be continued there.

Aerial Work covers situations outside this where payment is still given, but the aircraft is used in specialized roles not involving the usual passenger or freight carrying, such as photography or flying instruction, or any other situation where you're getting paid to fly.

Private flying is fairly self-explanatory, the most distinguishing feature being that no payment exists, other than by the pilot for the right to use the aircraft in the first place, although this in itself could cause problems (see Chapter 9).

Within the above limits, the sort of companies you could get involved with will also fall (broadly) into three categories with a little bit of blurring in between: Scheduled Flying, Charter Flying and Corporate Flying.

Scheduled Flying is a legal definition describing services that run at predefined times with certain conditions imposed on them, such as being open to all classes of passenger and the flights running even though they may be empty. This would mean that although holiday flights and North Sea helicopters do indeed move at predefined times, they are not subject to the other restrictions and therefore cannot technically be regarded as 'Scheduled'. I'll cheat though, and include them all in one, because the difference is transparent to the average user. Let's just say that they are regular services.

Similarly, whilst airlines can provide charter services, the word 'charter' is commonly thought of as covering the sort of services provided by the Air Taxi companies that exist within General Aviation (the term 'General Aviation' itself is nebulous: it usually means anything below 5700 kg Maximum All-Up Weight encompassing Air Taxi, Flying Club and personally owned aircraft. The ICAO definition excludes aerial work, though).

Scheduled flying is often said to be boring, but it does have one major advantage — it's usually organized and set anything up to four weeks in advance so that you at least have the opportunity of some sort of planning in other areas of your life (this is now strictly enforced by the CAA — see Chapter 3). The only qualification to this depends on the size of the Company.

As the size of the operation decreases, and sometimes with it the aptitude of the Operations Department, you will no doubt end up wondering why they bother issuing duty rosters at all. Very often, in this sort of company, rosters are thrown straight into the bin, as the crews know they bear no resemblance to what will actually happen.

Congratulations! You are probably working for a Charter Company (or a flying club) disguised as an Airline, of which there are several, unfortunately. You will need a well-developed sense of humour in this case, as the worst aspects of both types of company will come to the fore, namely little time to yourself and very little information filtering down to the coal face, i.e. you.

Let me explain. If scheduled flying can be compared to bus driving, then **Charter Flying** is taxi driving. As such you are on call twenty-five hours a day and everything is geared to giving an instant response to the customer, thus leaving you unable to plan very much. Don't get me wrong; this can be fun with plenty of variety and challenge in the flying — but the downside is an Ops Department that lets you do all the work yourself, and being left hanging around airports or muddy fields while your passengers are away (with the consequent missed meals, getting home late, etc).

Charter Flying is also an area where your other skills as Salesman and/or Diplomat come into play, as you will be very much involved with your passengers. You will discover that they are more than just self-loading freight!

Thus, while you can move relatively easily from Charter to Scheduled, it's not so straightforward the other way around. As an airline pilot, you rarely see your passengers, and the type of flying is also very different. Charter (or Air Taxi) is intensive, single-handed and stressful work in the worst weather (you can't fly over it), in aircraft that have the least accurate instruments and equipment. It can be quite a culture shock for an airline pilot, looking forward to pottering around in a small aircraft till he retires, to find that he's doing at least twice as much work as he's ever done before, and doing it all at the same time!

As a pilot, therefore, you can have two types of working day, depending on the type of flying you do. In Scheduled, there is relatively little to do before departure as a lot of it is done by other staff — for instance ground staff check in and weigh the passengers whilst engineers check the aircraft (nevertheless, you still have to have a working knowledge of what they do, because in Aviation the buck stops at the bottom). It's still left to you, though, to check the weather, Notams, etc.

A day flying charter, however, is a different story. You could be working at almost any time, provided that Duty Hour limits are not exceeded (again, see Chapter 3). Departures are inevitably very early, as businessmen need to be where they're going at approximately the start of the working day and return at the end of it. Thus, some days can be very long.

As you're only allowed a certain number of hours on duty, there's a continual race to minimize them — sometimes it can mean working like a one-armed paper-hanger in order to keep up with everything! The flight plan has to be filed, the weather checked (as well as the performance and the aircraft itself), the passengers' coffee and snacks must be prepared and they must be properly briefed and looked after (and that's just the start). Usually, the only thing that can usefully be done the day before is place the fuel on board, and even that can be difficult if the aircraft is away somewhere else.

The flight itself is busy, too. As it is single-pilot, you do the flying, navigation and liaison with ATC.

By contrast, the time spent at your destination is very quiet. After you've escorted your passengers through security and seen them safely on their way (the terminal is naturally miles away from the General Aviation park), you have to walk back to tidy up the aeroplane, supervise the refuelling and have your own coffee (if there's any left), while trying to prepare for the return journey.

If you're in a place you haven't been to before, you could always see the sights, but airfields are usually well away from anything interesting, with very little public transport to get you there anyway. After a while, all you will remember will be the same shops, so the general thing is to join the rest of the 'airport ghosts' (other charter pilots in the same boat as you) and find a quiet corner to read a book. You may as well go to the terminal, because you have to meet your passengers there, but constant loudspeaker announcements could drive you out to the aeroplane again.

However, while you may be on time to meet them, your passengers will very rarely be on time to meet you.

In Charter, it is also a luxury to plan to have more than one day off in a row, and those you do get are those you have to have by law (they must be rostered seven days ahead) or surprise ones where you don't fly if business is bad. Some companies have a policy of not allowing leave at all during Summer, which is in the height of the busy season, and only two weeks at a stretch if you do get it (the busy season, by the way, is between April-October, with a quiet period in August).

Corporate Flying, where you work or run the Flight Department for a private company, is similar to Charter but is out of the Public Transport sphere, so the requirements (and the paperwork!) are not as strict. Having said that, most Corporate Flight Departments are run to Public Transport standards, or better, and there is, naturally, no excuse for letting your own standards slip. One major distinguishing feature of this type of flying is the way that the Corporate world regulates itself — you frequently get situations where high performance intercontinental aircraft are under essentially the same controls as single-engined General Aviation ones. It's a credit to the people in Corporate flying that it runs so well.

In the Corporate world there are two types of company. The first is the large conglomerate, where the aircraft is just as much a business tool as a typewriter. You are genuinely a Company employee, people are used to the aircraft, you collect customers and move Company personnel around, from the Chairman at the top to the 'muddy boots' people at the bottom, and your decisions as a professional are respected. There is a great deal of job satisfaction to be gained in this type of work, especially as you will build up relationships with regular passengers.

On the other hand, there is the sort of company where the aircraft is the personal chariot of the Chairman, with you as its chauffeur (or if you look at the company books carefully, a gardener!). In this case, nobody else gets to use it, and what you think doesn't matter because the type of person who is dynamic enough to run a large company single-handed is also the type who thinks the weather will change just for him, and you are continually under pressure to try and find his house in bad weather, which naturally hasn't got a navigation aid within miles of the place.

Unless you can establish a good personal relationship with your passenger, or have an extremely strong character, you are unlikely to get a lot of job satisfaction in this sort of employment.

Having said that, there are some decisions that are not yours to take, no matter who you work for. Unfortunately, you are only In Command as far as technical flying matters are concerned. If it's legal to fly then, strictly speaking, it's nothing to do with you as to whether it's sensible or not from their point of view. It becomes an operational decision and not technical. If the Chairman (or Ops) wants you to fly and therefore risks being left to walk in a muddy field if conditions get too bad, then it's entirely up to them — it's their money.

Please note that I'm not advocating flying in bad weather as a normal procedure. Take as an example a typical situation: you check the weather the night before and advise your passengers to go by car, because while the destination and departure points are going to be OK, the bit in the middle is iffy and there's no real way of knowing what it's like unless you go there and have a look (this is assuming a VFR flight in a helicopter, although the same principles apply to anything larger). They must get there and the timings are such that there's no chance of delaying things till the weather gets better, so it's the car or flying — a straight choice. If your man wants to try and fly, and risk missing the meeting at the other end because you refuse to either start or carry on when it becomes impossible, then that, I suggest, is up to him in the final analysis.

One major plus point about working in Corporate Aviation is the fact that they tend to spend money on their flagship. It's a curious fact that despite the higher standards that are meant to be involved in Public Transport, I have never yet seen a badly maintained Corporate aircraft and very few badly run Corporate Flight Departments. In many cases decidedly the opposite has been the case.

Corporate work sometimes pays the most, at least as far as the smaller aircraft are concerned, but the jobs are also less stable, as the aircraft is usually the first thing to go when the Company gets into financial difficulties.

The Operations Manual

Aside from colleagues etc, almost the first thing you will encounter on arrival at your new company will be the Operations Manual. This is usually fairly badly written, being a copy of somebody else's which will no doubt include their bad English! ('Acquiring' Ops Manuals is a favourite form of Industrial Espionage.) You'll probably also find items in the most illogical places, which have been added willy-nilly over the years with no thought to content. In fairness, though, it must be said that writing an Operations Manual is best left to a professional technical writer, which most pilots are not.

It wouldn't be so bad if you were given time to read it, but you are usually expected to do so overnight, at the same time as learning the rest of the Company procedures and the details for the exams you will no doubt also be expected to sit the following morning (as you have probably discovered already, everything is expected to happen by yesterday).

The Operations (or Ops) Manual can be compared to the Standing Orders issued by any military unit. It's a book of instructions that are constant, so that Company policy can be determined by reference to it on (almost) any question, containing information and instructions that enable all Operating Staff (i.e. you) to perform their duties. As part of the Operating Staff of a Company, you are subject to the rules and requirements contained in it, and it's your responsibility to be fully conversant with it at all times. You will be expected to read it at regular intervals, if only because it gets amended from time to time.

The Chief Pilot is usually responsible for contents and amendment policy (he may well have written it as well, so be careful when you criticise the English!). Amendments, when they are issued, consist of dated replacement pages on which the text affected is marked, ideally by a vertical line in the margin. On receipt of an amendment list, persons responsible for copies of the Manual incorporate the amendment in theirs and record it on the amendment list in the front.

The CAA's prime objective in requiring the Manual to be written in the first place is to promote safety in Company flying operations. As the CAA are involved, it is thus compiled in accordance with requirements laid down by law (in fact, as far as you are concerned it is the law) and all flights should be conducted to the Public Transport standards laid down in it.

Some parts of the Manual apply even when a flight could be thought of as being private, because the aircraft will still be operated by what is known as an **air transport undertaking**. There should be an indication of what bits apply to what types of flight, but most Companies just apply the same rules to everything — it makes life easier.

Usually consisting of several parts, the Manual can be as little as one A5 book with a small operator or as large as several A4 volumes in an outfit the size of the average airline (a small tip for budding Chief Pilots — this book is laid out very generally in a suggested format suitable for a small operator's Operations Manual, which is why at times I seem to be stating the obvious or repeating myself. The bits that appear to be written in legalese can be extracted and slotted straight into your own future Manual — where you **can** read it, just change the wording to make it incomprehensible).

The separate parts will consist of the main volume, which will be the Company operating policy; the Training Manual (sometimes included in the main one if there's room); the Flight Manuals and performance schedules for each type of aircraft operated by the Company, and whatever Flight Guides (Jeppesen, Aerad, etc) they may use.

Manuals are notoriously difficult to navigate around. It may help you to find your way round this book if I explain that it's meant to take you as far as possible through the various stages of a flight, in that you join the Company and find your way around (Chapter 1), get trained (Chapter 2), become subject to duty hours limitations and weather minima (Chapters 3 and 4), plan a flight (Chapter 5) and operate it in a general or a specialized way (Chapters 6 and 7). Everything else is then tacked on the end.

Not all statutory instructions and orders will be mentioned. It doesn't mean that you should ignore those that aren't, but being acquainted with all regulations, orders and instructions issued by the CAA and everybody else is all part of your job. Naturally, references made to any publication (such as the Air Navigation Order 1985) should be taken as meaning the current editions as amended.

Somewhere there will be a declaration of who you're actually working for. This may sound daft, but many companies trade under several aliases and they will be pinned down as to their real identity somewhere in the first few pages. There should also be a definition of Public Transport.

There will be several copies of the Operations Manual distributed around, the numbers issued differing with the size of the Company, but the typical distribution list given below should be regarded as a minimum. Note that each aircraft will also have its own copy, which should also be specified. All copies must be clearly marked for amendment purposes.

1 Master Copy — Operations Manager
2 CAA (Flight Operations Inspectorate)
3 Chief Pilot
4 Training Captain
5 Maintenance Organisation

Operating Regions

The AOC Operating Regions of your Company will be specified for the types of aircraft flown and will be shown by a map. Each area is enclosed by rhumb lines joining points of latitude and longitude; for instance, Area 'A' is England, Scotland and Wales. There are several other areas covering other parts of the world and different rules apply if you wish to operate in particular ones.

Examples of all those available for operations will be found in the back of CAP 360 Part 1. They may be modified as necessary, for example to exclude the Eastern Bloc countries.

Company Personalities

An effective management structure is regarded as essential, especially in the Operations Department (it's a mistake, by the way, to skimp on Operations: if you ever start your own company, by all means spend money on decent pilots, but not at the expense of a good Operations Manager).

The Company will have appointed certain people to undertake particular tasks, and you will find most of these described below. Naturally, some will change depending on the setup of your Company, and one person's functions may be combined with another's.

Most Companies will be laid out as follows, bearing in mind that names of appointment holders will normally be included.

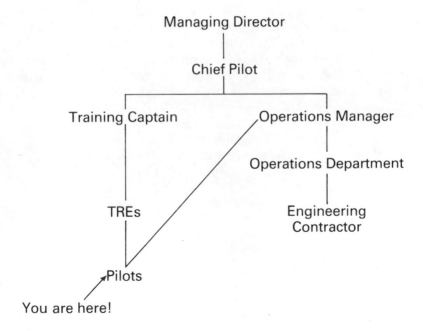

The Managing Director

This person will have the **ultimate** responsibility for everything, which means the efficiency, organization, discipline and welfare of the Company, ensuring that all activities are safe and legal and that the Company is commercially viable. This will therefore include marketing and the projection of the Company image.

The Chief Pilot

Next in line is the **Chief Pilot**, who is the main point of reference that Flight Operations Inspectors (see Chapter 10) and other officials will relate to, and they will expect to see him with some measure of control of the day-to-day happenings of the Company, although technically his job is just to keep things legal. However, in order to do that, he will have to get involved in the more commercial aspects of what goes on. He is responsible to the Managing Director for monitoring on his behalf the overall safety, legality, efficiency and economy of flying operations by the establishment of proper drills and procedures, and for ensuring that employees are properly qualified for their tasks.

Whilst the Managing Director is responsible for the administrative acceptability or otherwise of work, the Chief Pilot has the technical side of things to worry about.

He keeps control of the Flight Time and Duty Hours Scheme (sometimes by random inspection of returned flight documentation) in addition to supervising aircrew currency, maintaining aircrew records, compiling and updating the Operations Manual, raising occurrence reports, Flying Staff Instructions and Crew Notices.

Randomly inspecting returned flight documents is a real chore, and is done for two reasons, the first being to ensure that you are doing your job properly, and the second so that the Chief Pilot doesn't get any nasty surprises when the CAA come to check the paperwork. You will greatly endear yourself to your Chief Pilot if you make sure that **all** boxes on **all** forms are filled in (whether or not you think they are really relevant), especially on the Technical Log (Chapter 6), Loadsheet (8) and Navigation Log (5).

With regard to these three items, where a signature is required, produce one, and always ensure that your departure fuel in the Tech Log agrees with the fuel load indicated in the Load Sheet (all tanks) and the Nav log, and that the fuel usage throughout the flight is consistent with time, e.g. that you are not using mysterious amounts of fuel which would indicate that someone is fiddling the books. Naturally, your arrival fuel should match that on the Nav Log. Especially make sure that the fuel loads on the Tech Log and Load Sheet are above the fuel required for the trip noted on the Nav Log.

The same rules apply to passenger and freight loads and you should **always** check your figures, especially when adding up in hours, minutes and seconds!

Lastly, don't write defects down on the Nav Log as the flight progresses and neglect to put them in the Tech Log at the end of the sector — that's a dead giveaway to your Inspector. It's strange how almost every aircraft goes unserviceable on arrival back at base as if programmed (here's a chance to use simple psychology — occasionally use the deferred procedure away from base, not forgetting to use a new Tech Log sheet, then the Inspector may think that the Company procedures are working well. Then again, he may not).

The Chief Pilot also liaises with the Maintenance Contractor on airworthiness matters.

He may designate a suitable person within the Company (guess who!) to carry out, or be responsible for, any of the above duties. That person would be directly responsible to the Chief Pilot (as is everybody else from now on).

He may have the secondary function of **Flight Safety Officer**, in which case he operates the Mandatory Occurrence Reporting Scheme and maintains a vigorous Flight Safety policy. That entails collecting information from the various sources that publish it, and spreading it around the Company, probably by giving lectures and convening regular meetings with management. He will also most likely be the one to conduct internal investigations when somebody has an accident.

The Chief Training Captain

This person co-ordinates all flying training (the FSO may do Emergency and Survival), arranges periodical checks and examinations, selects training staff and ensures that all aspects of flying training meet statutory requirements, if necessary by liaising with the CAA. He also compiles and maintains flying training records.

Where TREs (see Chapter 2) are thinly spread between companies, the Chief Training Captain may be merely the Chief Pilot wearing another hat. This is to provide some consistency, as the Chief Pilot is in the Company all the time and thus able to keep a constant eye on things (you don't have to be a TRE to be a Training Captain, though of course it does help).

The Maintenance Contractor

The **Maintenance Contractor** (who must be specified) maintains and valets Company aircraft in accordance with directions and laid-down procedures. As to what laid-down procedures is a good question, since it primarily depends on agreements between your Company and whoever does your maintenance. More about this at the end of Chapter 8.

The Operations Manager

Although the **Operations Manager** is technically under the Chief Pilot, in practice you will find that they are both of equal status (however, despite their position in the Chain of Command, Operations Staff still have to bear in mind your ultimate authority as aircraft Commander).

He provisionally accepts work, and in liaison with the Chief Pilot, confirms and accepts it. As a result, he is in charge of organizing the flying programme, including pilot duty and rest days, so you want to keep on his good side! He ensures that duty times are in limits by keeping a record of flight crew flying and duty hours.

He is supposed to ensure that the Commander of each flight receives a written briefing (including Notams, etc) before he goes anywhere and that all passenger and cargo manifests and tickets are completed as required.

It's his job to keep in touch with the Maintenance Contractor to ensure scheduling for statutory maintenance checks, forwarding completed Technical Log sheets and other relevant documents to them at the end of each flight. This is not the same function as mentioned for the Chief Pilot, who does this on a more lofty level — all the Ops Manager is expected to do is monitor the aircraft hours so that nothing gets behind.

He also maintains all carnets and aircraft documents (collectively referred to as aircraft libraries), an up to date stock of maps, route guides and aeronautical charts covering all areas of Company operations, Flight Information Publications (such as Notams, Air Pilot, AICs, Royal Flights, the Landing Site Register, etc), and arranges exemptions and clearances for particular tasks.

Although he is nominally meant to ensure the validity of all licences, medicals, periodical checks and training, it doesn't absolve you of the responsibility for keeping your own up to date.

He ensures that Company accident and incident procedures are followed as necessary, processes amendments of the Operations Manual, assesses landing sites, categorizes airfields, calculates specific weather minima, obtains meteorological forecasts for planned routes and destinations, and arranges overnight accommodation for night stops, amongst other things. Most importantly, he arranges an accurate and up-to-date flight watch of all Company aircraft movements and stand-by telephone coverage outside normal working hours.

A company which succeeds in getting the Ops Manager to do all that is actually setting quite a high standard. Naturally, all the above duties may be delegated.

The Company Pilot
In small companies, it will be policy to operate on a single crew basis as far as possible (less wages to pay), with the designated Commander occupying the Captain's seat as detailed in the relevant Flight Manual. It's therefore important to maintain your own standards, because you'll be on your own a lot.

You may think it a little over the top to see somebody with large amounts of gold braid emerging from a small aircraft and be wondering on what occasions you're able to call yourself Captain. As far as I can make out, it used to be a convention that if you either had 5000 hours, an ATPL of some description or a TRE/IRE qualification, you were entitled to do so. The trouble was that as smaller airlines became popular they did not have people so qualified and passengers were wary of flying with pilots who didn't have the requisite amount of the shiny stuff on their sleeves. Thus the various rank gradings have become blurred and you're now called a Commander if you're actually in charge of any aircraft (similarly, people in charge of smaller sea-going vessels are called Ship's Masters).

As an **Aircraft Commander**, you are first and foremost subject to the ANO, Part 5, Articles 35, 36 and 37 (plus a couple of others). Inside the Company, you are responsible to just about everybody else (but especially the Chief Pilot) for ensuring that aircraft are flown with prime consideration for the safety of passengers and persons on the ground; not negligently or wilfully causing an aircraft to endanger persons or property while ensuring that it is operated in accordance with performance requirements, Flight Manuals, checklists, CAA (and other State authority) regulations, the Operations Manual, Air Traffic Regulations, the UK Air Pilot, Aeronautical Information Circulars and Notams.

Seems a bit much, doesn't it? Hang on . . .

It's also up to you to keep your licences and personal flying logbooks up to date and to ensure that you are medically fit to complete your duties.

You must keep charterers and the Company informed of any accidents, incidents and alterations to charters caused by bad weather or other reasons.

Yours is the **final** responsibility for supervising the loading, checking and refuelling of Company aircraft and making sure that all passengers are briefed on Emergency Exits and the use of safety equipment (see also Chapter 6). You must check that the aircraft is serviceable (including radio and safety equipment) with a current Certificate of Release to Service in force and with previously reported defects notified in the Technical Log as being rectified or transferred to the Deferred Defects lists by a person so qualified. When it comes to loading, you must ensure that this is done in accordance with Company procedures and requirements, e.g. that no weight limitation is exceeded and that the C of G will remain inside the envelope at all times during flight.

You must leave a duplicate copy of the Loadsheet and Technical Log with a responsible person prior to each flight and ensure that all flight documents are correctly completed and returned to Operations at the end.

Although it's part of Ops' job to get a met forecast that covers the routes to be flown (including destination and alternate airfields), it's actually your responsibility, so you may as well do it yourself.

Your behaviour and representation of the Company in front of actual and potential clients must be exemplary.

The First Officer
It is possible that for legal, safety, weather or duty reasons a second pilot may be scheduled to occupy the other seat, in which case they will be performing the duties detailed below. Although two-crew operations are meant to be based on teamwork, sometimes the flight will continue to be operated on a single crew basis, despite the First Officer's presence. Whether this happens or not depends on Company policy, and you may actually find the equivalent of a pilot's assistant in the other seat (see below).

Much of any pilot's job consists of cross-checking and monitoring, and this is even more important in a two-crew operation where the aircraft is quite complex.

To minimize the risks of any errors, set procedures will be laid down whenever multiple crews are used.

First Officers will more than likely find themselves preparing the Navigation Flight Plans and maintaining the navigation and fuel log in flight, because they should be fully aware of the intended route, weather etc, that may affect it (constant briefings from the Commander on this and other points are essential, as the First Officer naturally must know the game plan if he is going to take over at any stage. This even extends to the crew agreeing between themselves over the routes to be flown, minimum safety altitudes, overshoot action, and so on).

They also supervise the loading and refuelling of the aircraft and prepare the loadsheets for the Commander's signature before each flight if it's not already done, by a handling agent. When it's raining, they're first in line to do the pre-flight check.

In addition, they carry out the checks (the Commander reads them, or vice versa), make radio calls, cross-check altimeters and other instruments and monitor each flight continuously.

They are supposed to advise you of any apparently serious deviations from the correct flight path (such as specific warning if, on an instrument approach, the rate of descent exceeds 1000 feet per minute or the ILS indicator exceeds half-scale deflection) or of any instrument reading which indicates abnormal functioning. In addition, they carry out secondary checks on engine power after the throttles have been set).

If, for any reason, you become incapacitated they should be prepared to assume command of the aircraft. Again, there is a set procedure here, as well. If you notice your Commander not performing up to scratch, you are meant to challenge him twice in a positive manner, and then take over equally positively, clearly saying the words, 'I have control'. You will probably not be surprised to hear there is also a procedure for tuning and identifying radios (mentioned above) — 'Lima India Charlie identified' is correct, not 'That sounds like it!'

The Pilot's Assistant
Some companies may make use of an extra crew member to ease your workload. They will not necessarily be pilots, but nevertheless are, somewhat misleadingly called 'safety

pilots'. Naturally, what they are allowed to get up to depends on their experience, but unless in dire emergency, if they do not hold an appropriate Professional Pilot's Licence (having passed all the relevant checks — see Chapter 2), they are **not** allowed any part in the physical controlling of any aircraft flying for the purpose of Public Transport, especially if they are not a member of the Operator's Flying Staff.

In the light of this, their duties should be clearly spelt out in the Ops Manual, possibly more than anybody else. For example, those with an R/T licence may carry out radio calls at certain less critical points in the flight, under the Commander's supervision.

The Cabin Attendant
Cabin Attendants are responsible to the Aircraft Commander for ensuring that catering is ordered for flights to which they are allocated and that such stores are correctly used by extending proper cabin service to the passengers.

It's their job to make sure that all passengers are briefed before take-off on the items detailed in the Passenger Briefing Card, which includes being properly seated with safety belts fastened for take-off and landing or any other times in flight as and when instructed. They must also ensure that doors and emergency exits are kept clear of obstructions during take-off and landing.

There may well be other staff around, such as the Flight Despatcher, Ramp Officer, Senior Steward(ess) etc, who are not catered for here, but it shouldn't be hard to deduce what they get up to, given the above examples.

Public Relations and Press Enquiries

As mentioned in the Introduction, how a Company is perceived by its customers depends on its image, which in turn depends on its employees. How you conduct yourself with respect to potential clients (including on the telephone, see Chapter 10) all adds to it.

Very often, whether a Company gets work or not isn't based on price or service (because these are very similar between outfits) but whether it has a good image. Advertising, for instance, is not geared to making you buy a particular product directly, but indirectly by enhancing your view of that product. So it is with your Company, and you are one of its least expensive and most important ways of advertising — it's not a good idea to be seen too often in the local bar in uniform.

Having said that, no formal statements should be made to the Press or other sections of the media without Management instructions.

Flying Staff Instructions and Crew Notices

From time to time it will be found necessary to change methods of operations etc, these either being temporary or too minor to warrant altering the Ops Manual at that time. These changes are brought to everybody's attention by means of Flying Staff Instructions (FSIs) or Crew Notices. They are among the list of items to be checked before each flight and will usually be found on the Ops Room notice board and in the back of the Ops Manual (with a copy being sent to the CAA). FSIs and Crew Notices are displayed for a period of six months (while a few build up) after which time they will either be destroyed or incorporated in the Ops Manual.

Expenses

It's important to note at the outset that Aviation is an expensive business, even for the person who ordinarily wouldn't be expected to invest in it. The effects filter down quite markedly. It's common practice for pilots to pay landing fees and suchlike as the trip progresses (indeed, some airfields will not let you depart until fees are paid) and the subsequent shock to your bank account may be quite damaging unless you've been given a float which is replenished weekly. Expect an amount of about £200-£300 and try and get it repaid as often as possible. There's no reason why you should subsidize the Company (you may be lucky and get a Company cheque book).

The taxman also allows Companies to pay a subsistence allowance which currently is anywhere between 95p and £1.50 per duty hour before it becomes taxable — some Companies may pay meal allowances instead.

These are to cover for missed meals and the fact that you wouldn't necessarily choose to eat at such expensive places as airport cafeterias, which unfortunately are usually the only places available when things are busy. Also, you will find that your life insurance gets loaded once you go professional, and this will help to offset the cost.

Sometimes the taxman allows pilots an allowance purely because of the job — check with BALPA for the up-to-date information (because they negotiated it), but you may find it's for airline pilots only.

Chapter 2
Training and Testing

Licences

As you know, an aircraft cannot fly unless it carries a properly licensed and type-rated flight crew of the numbers and descriptions required by law. Licensing and training requirements are covered by the ANO Part IV, Articles 19 and 20, together with Schedules 8 and 10. CAP 54 gives a detailed look at what's required for the grant of a Professional Pilot's Licence, but a brief summary is given below.

Most people who start flying as a career do so for other reasons than money; they see themselves as being permanently engaged on their favourite hobby and being paid for the privilege. However, professional flying is not like that, as those same people rapidly find out.

You must realise from the beginning that a professional attitude is required in terms of your financial rewards as well as your flying. In many cases (except when there's a shortage), you could probably get just as much satisfaction and much more money in your pocket at the end of the day from working in another field and flying for sport.

Think about it this way: to gain a CPL/IR at current rates on a full-time approved residential course costs around £65,000 (1990) — of **your** money (or, at least, somebody else's that you have to pay back in some way), assuming you do it in the minimum time. That gives you a licence that makes you employable only by an Air Taxi Company without having extensive continuation training that may consist of anything up to thirty-five hours, depending on how good you are. An airline will require you to do a Jet Orientation Course (JetOC) on top of your CPL, which just about takes you on-line as a co-pilot. Even in a simulator where you don't actually have to fly the aeroplane to get your type rating, that will cost at least £20,000 more.

To all that must be added the year's salary you don't earn while you're training, which means that you have to ensure a high enough salary that will give enough return to pay back this 'loan' of, say, £75,000 (assuming you would earn £10,000 as an eighteen-year-old). That's as big as a mortgage, so you would need the cash flow to be able to pay yourself back around £750 per month for twenty-five years — and that's before you start eating! (Mind you, it could be tax-deductible.) If I had that sort of disposable cash, I'd probably think twice about working as a pilot, especially now that the requirement to hold a BCPL is in existence. Even if you went up the ladder the traditional way as a flying instructor or got your experience in a non-approved way, I don't think the economics would be all that different. Worse, if anything, because it takes so much longer.

However, as I said, flying is the sort of profession where economics tend to take a back seat, so you will need to know that there are three grades of licence that entitle you to earn money as a pilot, the **Basic Commercial Pilot's Licence** (BCPL), the **Commercial Pilot's Licence** (CPL) and the **Airline Transport Pilot's Licence** (ATPL).

The BCPL is intended to be midway between the PPL and CPL and covers the legal situation of people such as flying instructors, who are in situations where money is paid for the performance of services with an aircraft, even though no 'passengers' are carried. In addition, aerial photography, banner-towing, parachute dropping and suchlike may be undertaken, being activities which may contain a 'substantial commercial element'. You need 200 hours total (including 100 P1) before you can hold the licence (400 if you want to do limited Public Transport, such as Pleasure Flying), together with an IMC rating. The approved course requirements for this licence are so close to the those of the CPL that it's uneconomic to take one. It is possible to count some of the flying instructor training towards BCPL requirements, but only if the timings are right.

Even if you do get 400 hours and your BCPL, you will still only be employed on local pleasure flying duties, since you will have to land back at the aerodrome of your departure on non-scheduled runs not further than twenty-five miles away from it. You will also be restricted to aircraft of less than 2300 kg all-up weight as a Commander.

For what people would normally think of as **Public Transport** purposes (that is, circumstances where passengers or cargo are carried for money), the CPL covers you for command of aircraft up to 5700 kg in weight and the rank of First Officer for anything else (though I don't think you will find too many CPL holders in the right hand seat of a 747). You can't have a CPL until you are eighteen, but you can take the exams beforehand — some of them up to twelve months in advance.

Neither can you have an ATPL until you reach twenty-one years of age, get 1500 hours under your belt and pass some more exams; though not necessarily in that order. The ATPL covers you for command on anything, subject to the need to get type rated (the CAA is unusual within ICAO in allowing you to hold an ATPL without a type rating on the high-performance type of aircraft that usually requires it).

Although the ATPL includes an Instrument Rating as part of its structure, the CPL may be issued without one. This makes the CPL a useful first step, but you're generally unemployable without an IR (the ATPL for helicopters doesn't need an IR).

If you have an ATPL, but allow any of the requirements that makes it valid lapse (such as a six monthly medical or an IR), then it reverts to a CPL.

Training in General

The importance of pilot training cannot be over-emphasised and you should be encouraged to take every opportunity to carry out asymmetric, flapless and engine-off landings, together with various approaches when on positioning flights.

When the opportunity allows, the Chief Pilot or Training Captain may carry out check flights for the purpose of ensuring that the highest possible standards are maintained, the intention being to maintain a 100% safety factor within the Company. This ultimately can only be achieved by strict adherence to all rules and mandatory regulations, common sense and the cooperation of all concerned.

Every Company must have a Training Policy and a Manual that codifies it. It's meant to be a separate volume, but in fact is usually included as a section of the Ops Manual if there's room. One copy of the Training Manual may need to be lodged at CAFU for reference purposes.

The instructions and recommendations in the Training Manual are intended for the use and guidance of everyone engaged in the training, conversion and periodic checking of all pilots employed by the Company and the requirements apply to all types of aircraft that may be operated.

Minimum crew requirements may also be found in the aircraft's Flight Manual, but they're likely to be further modified (on the safe side) by Company policy.

The ANO requires that training flights should take place at licensed aerodromes, and that weather minima should not be less than that required for Public Transport operations, although you are allowed to make one or two more instrument approaches in one session than you would normally be allowed to.

Checks Required

Your training doesn't stop once you've passed all those exams. You will come across continuation training for the rest of your career, if only to maintain your licences. Of course, it's possible that there may be training to increase your qualifications in the offing, but that is outside the scope of this book. If your Company is like any other, then they will try to recruit already qualified crews — they're cheaper; but once in a while they may have to take on somebody who needs a top-up as far as licences are concerned. If that is the case, then they will have to submit proper training syllabuses and include them in the Manual if they do it regularly. If they don't intend to do type conversions, then they should say so.

There are two things to note about checks before we go any further; there is an increasing bias towards a written element, and if you take a renewal and fail it before your previous check expires, then the first one expires as well!

As far as keeping your licences current is concerned, you will find yourself subject to the following checks in addition to those needed for normal licence upkeep, which you should already know about:

Emergency and Lifesaving Equipment Check

This is the one you do before everything else, but otherwise is carried out every thirteen months at the same time as the line and area checks (see below). It requires knowledge of the use and location of all emergency equipment, and must contain a written element. Usually, for small aircraft, a simple plan of the aircraft with boxes to put the location of any emergency equipment in will do, but increasingly two pages of multi-choice questions are in order.

Emergency training is usually organized by the Flight Safety Officer and should cover a range of subjects from First Aid (appropriate to the aircraft) to fire and smoke drills and water survival training. Instructions for the use of First Aid kits should be incorporated in the kits themselves but, if not, included in the Ops Manual. At the very least, verbal tuition should be given that covers practical methods of dealing with wounds, fractures, burns, care of the unconscious, skin contamination, shock, heart attacks, artificial respiration, hypoxia and hyperventilation, poisoning, use of oxygen and anything else he may think of.

Practical experience is necessary, and evacuation drills will need to be covered, as well as real dinghy drills and fire and smoke training. Wet dinghy drills need only be undertaken once in your career and should consist of inflation and boarding while wearing full clothing and an inflated life-jacket. Fire and smoke training will consist of about half a day annually (but it could stretch to three yearly) at the airport fire station, learning about their procedures and the actual use, as well as the theory, of fire extinguishers. You will also need to find out about the effects of smoke in confined areas and the use of goggles.

If you can provide documentary evidence of all the above having been done at a previous company, then that should be sufficient.

Type Rating Renewal Check

Required every six months by the ANO, in which it's referred to as a Certificate of Test (but only for CAA licensing purposes) in order to maintain currency, but you may have two in thirteen months, provided there is more than four months between them. However, the first test following an initial rating must be within six months or less. As a Schedule 10 check, it must be carried out by an authorised Type Rating Examiner (of Schedule 10 variety, who must be sponsored by a company —see later this chapter).

Biennial Competence or 'Base' Check

A check on your ability to carry out emergency manoeuvres at your normal flight station. It has the same frequency as the Type Rating Renewal Check (above), and for convenience is carried out at the same time, though this particular check legally need not be carried out by a TRE.

A Base Check is required to be carried out on each aircraft flown and although the statutory requirement is to assure your continued competence, it's usually also used as an opportunity for training, as it is a good time for practising drills and procedures that rarely arise in normal operations.

Some of the items included in a Base Check will be covered by touch drills (which are normally best attended to on the ground), as well as by a general discussion of operating procedures, emergencies, recognition and diagnosis of aircraft system faults, pre-flight briefing, etc. Additional precautions may be considered if you operate in extreme weather conditions. The complete list should be covered over two checks.

Occasionally, if two aircraft are very similar, Base Checks may be carried out alternately on each type. On multi-engined aircraft they will also be expected to be carried out alternately at night. Some companies may have separate VFR and IFR base checks.

The Base Check must contain the 'boxed items' contained in the 1179 check form.

It is possible that a pilot who has been Base Checked by another company may be acceptable for use by yours, but this will be by arrangement with your Flight Ops Inspector. In any case, the two companies must have similar content and procedures in their checks and the arrangements must have been agreed before the test date (see also Chapter 6, **Freelance Pilots**). However, this will not be valid in the case of a company just setting up because they have no AOC and therefore no legal status with which to set up agreements.

As the Base Check is concerned with the checking of your competence with regard to emergency manoeuvres, it's not good practice to carry passengers who are not directly concerned with the flight; actually, if such a passenger is not part of the organization you are working for, you could find yourself performing a Public Transport flight (see also Chapter 9).

The Instrument Approach Proficiency Check

This is a test of your skill in using typical instrument approach systems that may be in use at aerodromes of intended landing, but most companies will just certify you on all of them for convenience. As it has the same frequency as the Base Check, it's normally conducted as part of one, and will form part of the IFR Base Check if they are split. Only really relevant if you hold an Instrument Rating (see below).

An Instrument Rating

This is completed at thirteen-month intervals by an Instrument Rating Examiner and may be completed as part of a Base Check or at least tagged on the end. If such is the case, then the IRE should also be a TRE (both of these appointments, by the way, should be held through a company, otherwise your check will be invalid).

The IR's purpose is to establish whether you are maintaining the standards necessary for safe operations in controlled airspace under IMC.

A helicopter IR is only valid on type, whereas an aeroplane one is transferable within certain limits — if you later convert to a dissimilar type, then you'll probably have to renew it as well. You won't need it if you're only doing VFR work, such as pleasure flying.

Area Competence Check

The company must ensure that *en route* and destination facilities are such that a safe operation is run.

Part of this is achieved by the Area Competence Check which is carried out once every thirteen months, unless you have flown over the route(s) concerned in that time.

It is done with the line check for convenience and tests your knowledge of specific route(s) or particular areas of operations. See also **Airfield Categorization** in Chapter 5 which deals with difficulties of operation at particular airfields.

Recent experience

To be considered current as a Commander, you must have completed:

1) Day
   Three take-offs and landings on the relevant type within the preceding three months, including one performed in the preceding twenty-eight days (this is a CAP 360 requirement).
2) Night
   In addition to the above, the ANO also lays down that night currency requires at least five take-offs, circuits and landings at night (for fixed wing) and five flights which consist of a take-off run, a climb to at least 500 feet and a landing (for helicopters) within the previous thirteen months unless a valid Instrument Rating is held for the particular type of aircraft.

In addition, some companies may require you to have made a specified number of approaches or to have done some real Instrument Flying within a certain period.

Some may even require recency on type and will have special procedures should you be absent from the Company for more than twenty-eight days.

Unless your company only operates simple types of aircraft (refer to your FOI), it's rare for anyone to be current on more than three types of aircraft at once.

Not only is this sensible, but **multi-type currency** causes all sorts of other problems — training costs could get out of hand, and it will be quite difficult to keep up normal twenty-eight-day currency as well.

Mixing things always causes complications. Aeroplane or helicopter pilots may generally be permitted to fly two types (fixed or rotary wing) at the Company's minimum experience levels. If you have the licence coverage and not less than 500 hours P1 on fixed and rotary wing (i.e. you're ambidextrous), you may be able to stretch that to two of each type.

If you want more than that, you will need about 3000 hours P1 in order to be current on something else.

Line Check

This is required every thirteen months. It's a test of your performance of normal duties at your crew station, so will be done on a standard commercial flight (this is for final line checks only as initial ones only give you the status of 1st pilot under supervision. Lapsed line checks don't qualify, either).

It covers an entire line operation from pre-flight preparations to completion of post-flight duties and normally must be carried out on each type of aircraft flown, although it may be done alternately where types are similar.

It is not supposed to represent a particular route, but it must be an adequate representation of the Company's work. Line Checks may be carried out by fully qualified Line Captains.

Although the stipulated frequency is once every thirteen months, you might find a Training Captain hopping in on an empty seat once in a while before that. This is nothing personal — it's just better than leaving things to the last minute and risking a pilot being off-line because a check hasn't been done in time.

Alternative Seat Position Check

This is needed if you expect to fly in any seat other than your normal one, such as if you become a Line or Training Captain, where you need to be able to fly the thing home or get it on the ground if your examinee fails *en route* for any reason.

Sometimes in a helicopter you may have to do a compass swing from this position so that the engineer can conveniently make his adjustments, or you may be a Commander who occasionally needs to be a co-pilot.

If the latter is the case, provided you have completed a full Commander's Base Check which is still valid, the check may be abbreviated at the discretion of the Training Captain, but not below a minimum of an engine failure after take-off, an asymmetric go-around from DH and an asymmetric landing. For whatever reason, if done, it will normally coincide with a Base Check.

No training, checking or emergencies should be undertaken on Public Transport flights except those required for final or routine Line Checks — in other words, training is done on non-revenue trips, provided that you still have valid checks in force (if you take a friend on a check flight, it could be regarded as being Public Transport — see also Chapter 9).

As soon as all items of any check have been completed, the person conducting the test signs all applicable licences, amends the training records and informs Operations of the results so that they can amend their own records and boards. In addition, someone of higher authority (the Managing Director or Chief Pilot) must sign check forms on behalf of the Company before they become valid (the Chief Pilot shouldn't sign his own).

In the event of your failing a test, the circumstances are reported and arrangements are made for repeating it. A certain amount of training may be done after consultation with a suitably appointed Training Captain, who will make the necessary recommendations.

It will be usual for any Examiner to be a fully qualified Commander so that passengers can be taken home legally should a test be failed anywhere *en route*.

Pilot Qualifications

You must have some or you wouldn't have got the job! All companies have a minimum requirement (usually what you see when they advertise for pilots) which is sometimes dictated by their insurance company. You will obviously need to have the relevant professional licence for the type you propose to fly, together with performance and a certain minimum number of hours, which will vary according to the supply and demand of pilots.

The Chief Pilot will have discretion to use pilots with all sorts of variations, provided that a suitable training programme is established.

If you join, say, an Air Taxi Company already type rated and with about 250 hours charter experience, your training will be as little as possible and take the format of the Company Base Check. It will include a technical exam relating to the aircraft type.

As a result, you could find yourself just completing the following in order to get on-line (where a check is normally included within another, then that will be needed as well):

a) Emergency and Lifesaving Equipment Check
b) Base Check
c) Area Competency Check
d) Recent experience
e) Line Check

Don't forget, you need the Emergency one first (or at least the paperwork needs to be dated that way). If you require type rating as well, you will also need to complete a Type Technical Examination and 1179 Check (a proper training syllabus will have to be laid down for this, and will consist of a number of hours of ground and air training, typically twenty-five and five respectively), together with a minimum of two observed sectors (or two–three hours, whichever is the greater) before a final Line Check. If your Company expects to train and convert pilots regularly, then they will need to include the training syllabus as part of the Ops Manual. If it's a one-off occasion, then a Flying Staff Instruction should cover it.

Unless the aircraft you are converting to is very similar to one you already have endorsed on your licence, you will probably also have to renew your Instrument Rating on type.

If you're unlucky and not only require type rating but also have less than 250 hours charter experience, you may find yourself doing an initial Line Check with at least six observed sectors (which must consist of a minimum total of about ten hours) before your final Line Check!

The observed sectors are not part of basic training, but are to allow you to settle down and to help check on the adequacy of training procedures. All of the above is variable, however, and will change between companies.

The Training Captain is responsible for ensuring that full ground and air training is carried out, which is noted on the Record of Training and Testing.

Basic flying training is carried out by a qualified Instructor, as is initial training for Instrument Ratings or first twins. Other training may be carried out by any appointed Training Captain, who ought to be a TRE as well.

Specialized training for specific tasks (such as sling work, etc) should be given by a Training Captain experienced in the particular type of work.

Company Training Captains

Qualifications for this position are naturally more stringent due to the responsibility involved. The Training Captain will have the normal requirements for Company Pilot with the addition of more total experience on the relevant types and more total flying hours. Training Captains must have a TRE qualification in order to carry out Type Rating Checks, but otherwise it isn't necessary.

Nor does a TRE need instructor qualifications (unless giving instruction for first multi-engine conversions), therefore he may not have received formal instruction in the teaching and demonstration of engine failure actions. This is why he has to do a check ride with CAFU before being given the appointment.

There are two types of TRE — those able to do checks for Schedule 8 (initial type ratings and PPL renewals) and those for Schedule 10 (commercial renewals as well). The latter type must operate through a nominated Company, as must IREs.

If the Company is not large enough to have a separate Training Captain, the appointment may also be covered by another office holder. A list of the tests that may be carried out will be shown (possibly like that below), but external pilots should not normally do Company Line Checks:

	Type Rating	Base Check	Line Check	Area Comp	E/S Check
Fred Bloggs	X	X	X	X	X

Guidance to Training Captains

See also AIC 47/88 (Pink 106).

Because of the circumstances of a TRE's appointment (see previously), and the continuing requirement of in-flight training and testing (despite simulators), there will need to be some statement of policy as to how Training Captains should react under certain circumstances, such as how to reconfigure the aircraft before each take-off when practising manoeuvres like touch and goes, or other manoeuvres which demand a high degree of co-ordination between crew members in order to be done properly.

In these sort of situations, especially in bigger aircraft, there's quite a flurry of arms and legs as flaps are taken in, hands are changed on control columns to take charge of the nosewheel steering, the airspeed indicator is rebugged, etc., so definite procedures will need to be laid down in order to prevent accidents (however, a lot of guidance can simply be gleaned from reading the Ops Manual itself).

Immediately before any action takes place, the Training Captain should position himself in order to stop you applying the flying controls the wrong way and he should monitor the airspeed and other indications for abnormal conditions.

Engine failures (real or otherwise) should only be practised on briefed training flights or air tests (in fact, a thorough briefing for everybody is always essential, covering such things as heights and speeds to be flown, methods of simulating whatever emergencies you're practising, etc). For those after take-off and on single-engine approaches, the reported weather conditions at the aerodrome concerned should not be less than those required for visual manoeuvring.

The requirements of CAP 360 are really geared to Performance A aircraft, so if you're in something like Group C, power failure should not be simulated after take-off below Vxse (which will give the best angle of climb) or Vyse (the best rate), unless you have a clever (or brave) Training Captain.

Otherwise, during take-off the speed should always be below V1 or VToss with the crosswind component not exceeding fifteen knots or the aircraft maximum, whichever is the smaller. After the simulated engine failure, the take-off should be abandoned, unless your machine's performance is up to scratch.

Engine shutdowns should not occur below 3,000 feet agl (or higher), or in any weather other than VMC, otherwise you may cause the very accident the training is designed to prevent if the other engine stops! (Talking of which, if you do shut down an engine on any otherwise normal flight for whatever reason in a twin-engined aircraft, only in exceptional circumstances should you not land at the nearest suitable aerodrome. You are allowed a little more flexibility if you have more than one engine left operating, of course.)

Below the recommended minimum heights, **simulated engine failure** should be initiated by the Training or Air Test Captain closing the throttle sufficiently to cause a significant loss of power (unless there is a requirement for a complete closing down of the engine, in which case you should climb anyway). If you're in a helicopter, just lower the collective lever. However, problems may arise with propeller-driven aircraft where below a certain RPM (1,000 or so), feathering cannot take place, and you would actually get better single-engined aircraft response from a failed engine with feathered propeller blades!

The area underneath the aircraft should be suitable for the exercise (over an airfield preferably, in case of a forced landing being necessary) and the call 'practice engine failure' should be made at the time.

There should be some provision in the Ops Manual to cover double engine failure under IF conditions, and the time taken to restart engine(s), having shut them down.

Entries into autorotation or the glide should be made above 1,000 feet agl and (unless sure of landing correctly on a properly authorized engine-off landing area) full recovery should take place before 250 feet agl.

When practising touch and go procedures (in aeroplanes), twice the normal TODR should be available. Before initiating the go-around, the Training Captain should ensure that landing flap has been converted to take-off and that in all other respects the aircraft if fit to get airborne again. The aircraft should be positively climbing before being fully cleaned up.

Stop and go procedures require that the aircraft be at a standstill before reconfiguration takes place. The Training Captain should ensure the aircraft is actually reconfigured before giving further instructions.

For depressurization training purposes, a slow method of cabin pressure reduction should be used and aircraft should not be depressurized at an altitude greater than 15,000 feet (neither should an aircraft be depressurized when undergoing emergency descent).

Simulated Flight Conditions

If your Company is lucky enough to own one, a Flight Simulator may be used for Instrument Rating renewals and Instrument Approach Proficiency Checks provided that it has been approved for that purpose by the CAA. Simulators and procedure trainers may be used at other times for training purposes.

Simulation of IF conditions in VMC for training and testing purposes will need screens or other approved apparatus. Visors are acceptable, provided that the lower windows are whited out. A competent observer with a full field of vision must also be carried. Don't forget to tell ATC what's going on.

Chapter 3
Flight Time and Duty Limitations

General

Your personal performance diminishes as you get tired — but you don't need me to tell you that! Nor do you need to be told that, on average, at least seven hours sleep is needed per night where peak performance requires about nine. However, scientists are also beginning to think that it's not so much the amount of sleep you get, but when you get it, that counts. Therefore, fatigue is more likely to result from badly planned sequences of work and rest rather than the actual duration of duty.

The problem with fatigue is that it is so subjective and therefore difficult to legislate for. Not only that, your performance can start to fall off well before you actually feel tired. Variations while crossing time zones, for instance, can be anywhere between eight and seventy per cent. Some people can cope with vastly disrupted work patterns — most of us can't.

A surprising number (over 300, I'm told) of bodily functions depend on the alternation of day and night. You naturally feel best when all of your functions are operating in concert, but the slippery slope starts when they all begin to get out of synchronization.

The best known form of desynchronization is jet lag, but it also happens when you try to work nights and sleep during the day. When both of these happen at once, then personality differences begin to matter as well. If you're a placid type, you're likely to be affected least, but if you're of a nervous disposition, you could have problems.

One day for each time zone crossed is required before your sleep and waking cycles get in tune with the new location. Total internal synchronization takes longer (your kidneys may need up to twenty-five days to correct themselves).

Even the type of time zone change can have an effect — six hours flying westward means that most people will require about four days to adjust. Going the other way will need up to seven! This eastward flying compresses the body's rhythm and therefore does more damage than the expanded days found going West (North-South travel appears to do no harm).

Symptoms of jet lag are, naturally, tiredness, faulty judgement, decreased motivation and recent memory loss. They're aggravated by alcohol, smoking, high-altitude flight, overeating and depression (a normal pilot's lifestyle, in other words!). Adjusting your internal clock to coincide with destination time before departure and staying on home time throughout the trip could help, but this could cause problems if you intend to work or rest on destination timings.

In view of the dangers of fatigue, when working in Public Transport (or for an air transport undertaking, for that matter), there's a maximum working day laid down by law intended to ensure that you are rested enough to fly properly. It's a similar system to truck drivers' hours, except that there's no tachograph; Companies and pilots are trusted to stick to the Ops Manual and the CAA reserves the right to spot check the paperwork at regular intervals, mainly looking to see that flights are **planned** within the Company's scheme (if you don't see a Flight Ops Inspector for long periods at a time, then you can assume that your Company is well regarded in this respect).

These regulations do not apply elsewhere, so Corporate pilots (or unpaid instructors) have no legal protection in this area, apart from the basics laid down in the ANO. Consequently you could find yourself in a continuing battle with outrageous demands of Company executives who want to fly without regard to fatigue limitations. Working twenty-eight twelve-hour days non-stop is **not** uncommon!

In fairness, there are difficulties introducing Duty Hours schemes into a Corporate environment. The schedule often changes so much that you would need a lot of extra staff to cope with it. I suppose you could point out that if the aircraft is not flown in accordance with the ANO, the insurance becomes invalid . . . .

All aircrew and companies engaged in Public Transport flying are required to observe the Flight Time and Duty Hours schemes as laid down by the CAA. Depending on the size of the company, the schemes will be written in consultation with various interested parties such as Staff Unions, but a lot of them merely insert the relevant CAA document (CAP 371) as it stands into their Ops Manual, as (while recognising differences between companies) there's actually very little latitude allowed in what goes into this section, despite the fact that the requirements were originally written 'in basic form with reasonable freedom to apply them with common sense'.

Since the second edition of CAP 371 was published, several things have changed (due to the opening up of Third World countries, night freight and increased pilot mobility, amongst others) and flight up to maximum limits and beyond are now the norm. There is, therefore, a third edition of CAP 371 on its way (effective about April 1990) which will reflect the new working practices and have many anomalies removed, while trying to keep the same basic structure of the document. It's unlikely that the General Aviation pilot (or any in a non-scheduled environment) will notice much difference, though, as GA rarely changes. Most of this chapter is based on the scheme proposed for outfits in the sole-use charter business, where the number of passenger seats available is nineteen or less, thus is has to cater for a wide variety of aircraft and circumstances. Mainly, though, it assumes that Company operations are confined to an area within which the local time doesn't vary by more than two hours, and the use of in-flight relief to extend duty hours is not taken advantage of.

Unfortunately, the whole subject is very specialized and difficult to understand on first reading — what follows is an attempt at an English translation, so please don't quote me in court, especially in view of the proposed changes! All comments assume Public Transport on UK registered aircraft and may vary due to local arrangements with the relevant Authorities (it's important to note the frequent use of the word 'consecutive').

Put simply, there is a basic working day which generally is ten hours. This may be longer or shorter depending on the time of start and the number of crew involved. The earlier you start, the less you're allowed, but this could be offset by carrying extra crew. This basic day may be extended under certain circumstances, and within the resulting Duty Period there may be a maximum number of flying hours which cannot be varied, such as seven hours' helicopter flying within twelve hours on duty. If you have a special job which requires an exceptionally long working day, it is possible to apply for an exemption to cover it.

Cabin staff also have duty hours — they can be rostered for FDPs up to an hour longer than those allowed for aircrew (because they have to prepare the aircraft for passengers). However, they are subject to all other restrictions.

Your Responsibilities

These stem from various provisions of the ANO and CAP 371. Firstly, you may have to inform the Company of all your flying (including Aerial Work, which in turn includes paid, or remunerated, flying instruction), except private flying in aircraft that do not exceed 1600 kg Maximum All-Up Weight.

It's also up to you to make the best use of the opportunities and facilities for rest provided by the Company, and to plan and use your rest periods properly — you are obliged to inform Operations if you have difficulty achieving pre-flight sleep. They should respond by arranging for you to see a specialist.

Then there's the Aircraft Crew and Licensing part of the ANO which says that you're not entitled to act as a member of a flight crew if you know or suspect that your physical or mental condition renders you temporarily unfit to do so.

All this means that you should not act as a crew member (and should not be expected to) if you believe you are suffering (or are likely to suffer) from fatigue which may endanger the safety of the aircraft or its occupants.

Company Responsibilities

Duties must be scheduled within the limits of the Company's approved scheme. Pressure will be brought to bear by the CAA to ensure that companies give adequate guidance to sheduling and rostering staff on this point. Work patterns must be realistic with the intention of avoiding, as far as possible, over-running limits. As a result, the Company will need to have work patterns which avoid such nasties as alternating day and night duties (see Early Starts and Late Finishes) and positioning that disrupts your rest.

Unless you are in an airline or on the North Sea, it's obviously difficult to schedule too much in advance, but companies must undertake to advise you of work details as far ahead as they can (though not less than seven days), so you can make arrangements for adequate and, within reason, uninterrupted pre-flight rest.

Away from base, it's normally the Company's job to provide rest facilities (the legal definition is 'satisfactory in respect of noise, temperature, light and ventilation'). However, they may lumber you with finding them, as you're the man on the spot — they are allowed to claim that short notice precludes them doing it!

All this being said, it must be pointed out before we go on that very, very few companies below a certain level are actually honest about their duty hours. The reason is fairly simple in most cases — if you kept to the letter of the law you would duty-hour yourself out of business, especially when there's not a lot of staff around. In other cases, the companies simply have no respect for the law or their employees.

Discretion on this point is the better part of valour, but falsifying duty hours is but a short step removed from doing it to other documents, such as Technical Logs, and that would never do. It's difficult to give advice on this subject, save to point out that being pedantic is often counter-productive. I leave it up to you!

Maximum Permissible Flying Duty Period (FDP)

A **Duty Period** is any continuous period through which you work for the Company, including any FDP (see below), positioning, ground training, ground duties and standby duty.

A **Flying Duty Period** (FDP), on the other hand, is any duty period during which you fly in an aircraft as a member of its crew. It includes positioning immediately before or after a flight (say in a taxi or light aircraft) and pre/after- flight duties, so the start will generally be not less than thirty minutes or so before the first **scheduled** departure time and the end not earlier than fifteen minutes after last chocks on or rotors last stopped time, though these times may vary between companies (see also **Pre-and Post-Flight Activity** and **Positioning**).

If a Flying Duty Period immediately follows a period of ground or other duty, the FDP commences from the start of the other duty (FDPs come inside Duty Periods). In the case of **split duties** (see below), the intervening time on the ground is also included in the FDP.

The maximum rostered FDPs are found in tables included in the Ops Manual which in turn are taken from CAP 371 (The Guide to Requirements on the Avoidance of Excessive Fatigue in Aircrews). These tables (two of which are reproduced below) give limits dependent on acclimatization (or not) to the local time zone. You are considered to be acclimatized if you have had three consecutive local nights free of duty within a local time zone band of two hours (for a definition of 'local night' see under **Duty Cycles** or the **Glossary**).

TABLE C

Maximum FDP — Fixed Wing
Single pilot crews

Sectors	Up to 4	5	6	7	8+
0600–0759	10	9.25	8.5	8	8
0800–1259	11	10.25	9.5	8.75	8
1300–1759	10	9.25	8.5	8	8
1800–2159	9	8.25	8	8	8
2200–0559	8	8	8	8	8

TABLE D

Maximum FDP — Helicopters
Single pilot crews

Loc time of start	Maximum length FDP	Maximum flying
0600–0659	9 hours	6 hours
0700–0759	10 hours	7 hours
0800–1359	10 hours	7 hours
1400–2159	9 hours	6 hours
2200–0559	8 hours	5 hours

FDPs for fixed wing aircraft are usually more flexible than those for helicopters, because helicoptering frequently consists of relatively short flights during which several sectors are flown without stopping rotors — the high pilot workload involved makes you more tired. In fact, as you can see, in a helicopter, there's also a maximum number of hours you can fly within any FDP, in view of the fact that there are no sector limits.

Helicopter pilots engaged on repetitive short sectors at an average rate of ten or more landings per hour should have a break of at least thirty minutes away from the aircraft within any continuous period of three hours.

Aftre three hours' offshore shuttle operations in conditions other than day VMC, you should get a thirty-minute rest free of all duty.

As the objective of having these restrictions is to ensure that you're adequately rested at the **beginning** of each Flying Duty Period, it follows that if you need flexibility, it should be applied at the end. All FDP limits can be stretched by means of **Split Duties, In-flight Relief** or **Extensions** (see later). The only odd-one-out is the extension; use of split duties or in-flight relief must be planned, but extensions can be used on the day at the Commander's discretion, to cater for unforeseen delays, etc.

By the way, your passengers will need to be positively told about duty hours limitations, in writing if possible — they will take full advantage of you, otherwise!

Discretion to Extend a Flying Duty Period

There are always delays in aviation, due to anything from technical to weather reasons, and to cater for such occasions a Flying Duty Period may be extended beyond the maximum normally permitted if you think you can make the flight safely and have consulted the other members of the operating crew about their fitness, but the normal maximum is based on the **original** reporting time and calculated on what **actually** happens, not what was planned to happen. Sometimes, for example, you may have to exercise it if a lower per- formance aircraft is substituted on a route that usually uses a larger one, and consequently takes longer to get round the route.

This discretion is yours (as the Aircraft Commander) alone, but some Companies will try and make the decision for you before the first flight of the day, which is not usually when it should be used. In these circumstances, you may only extend the FDP by about 1.5 hours, saving the remainder of the three normally permitted for later.

Extensions of up to three hours are regarded as the absolute limit except in cases of emergency. Such emergencies consist of situations which, in your judgement, present serious risks to health and safety, such as Air Ambulance flights (see Glossary) where the patient may be put at risk by the delay caused by a rest-period. In such cases, the figures in the tables may be extended by up to four hours, provided that no in-flight relief has been allowed for and the previous rest period has been taken in full.

There must be at least forty-eight hours between extended Air Ambulance FDPs, and a spare (qualified) commander must be carried if it's planned to extend by more than the permitted four. The need for the trip itself must also be certified by a competent medical authority, and no passengers (other than next-of-kin of the patient) must be carried. Once the patient has been de-planed, you can't use any further discretion over the permitted four hours to get you home. You can only do three of these flights in any consecutive twenty-eight days.

In all cases where discretion is exercised, the circumstances should be reported to Operations on the Discretion Report form (see CAP 371). If the Duty Period is extended for more than two hours then the report should also be forwarded to the CAA within fourteen days.

Minimum Rest Periods

As well as having a maximum number of hours on duty, there's also a minimum rest time between duty periods.

A **Rest Period** is time preceding a Flying Duty Period which is intended to ensure that you're adequately rested **before** a flight. It does not include excessive Travelling Time (over ninety minutes or so) or Positioning.

You should have your rest periods (see also Duty Cycles) rostered far enough in advance so you can get proper rest. Minimum Rest Periods should be at least as long as the preceding Duty Period and not less than twelve hours, except when accommodation is provided by the Company, in which case the minimum may be eleven, subject to any exemptions that may be granted. Rest starts from the end of the Duty Period and not the Flying Duty Period (see earlier for the differences). A Rest Period must include a Local Night if it follows a Duty Period longer than eighteen hours.

Discretion to Reduce a Rest Period

You can reduce Rest Periods to below the minimum, but like extending Duty Time, it's at your discretion, and can only be done after taking due note of the circumstances and fitness of the other members of the operating crew. In any event, you must be able to get at least ten hours at the accommodation where you take your rest, subject to the requirements of Travelling Time.

Use of discretion for reducing rest is considered exceptional and shouldn't be done to successive Rest Periods (it's very much frowned upon). In general, you're better off extending an FDP than reducing a Rest Period if at all possible. Also, a Rest Period should not be reduced if it immediately follows an extended Duty Period, or vice versa (this is even more frowned upon, although it is allowed in exceptional circumstances, for example, allowing you to have a subsequent FDP no longer than the reduced rest period).

Your discretion to reduce a rest period (following an FDP that hasn't been extended) should not be for longer than one hour.

Split Duties

You can extend a duty day by other means than discretion, and provision is made for it to be done on duties with a long time gap between flights. Technically, a **Split Duty** is a **Flying Duty Period** which consists of two or more sectors separated by less than a minimum Rest Period, typically being a situation where you deliver somebody to a place and wait for him to come back. In other words, you can claim some of the period spent hanging around in the middle as 'rest' and tack it on to the end of the basic working day. What's more, you can plan to do this from the start, extending the FDP by half of the 'rest' taken if it's between three and ten hours (inclusive, providing the hours are consecutive).

The Company should make arrangements for a quiet and comfortable place (not open to the public, which should not mean the aircraft) to be available for the rest to be taken. If your rest is longer than six consecutive hours, then they should provide satisfactory accommodation (refer back to Company responsibilities).

The intervening rest period doesn't include any time required for immediate post- and pre-flight duties, typically fifteen minutes for each (see **Pre- and Post-Flight Activity**).

If the rest period gets to be longer than ten hours, then just start a new FDP (but see also **Minimum Rest Periods**). Also, there's nothing to stop you having two split duties within one FDP — the only proviso is that the different sectors (and their duty periods) should be separated by more than three hours in order to claim the extra.

In-Flight Relief

Although small operators don't require it (because their aircraft don't generally have the endurance), just in case you're wondering, this works in a similar way to Split Duties, in that you can extend the working day by using a proportion of 'rest' taken within it, but you must be away from both Flight Deck and passengers, and it is subject to certain limitations outside the scope of this book. The relieving crew member must also hold proper qualifications for the post he is relieving.

If you've been relieved and have no further duties on the flight, then the remainder of the FDP is treated as positioning.

Positioning

Positioning is the practice of transferring crews from place to place as passengers in surface or air transport, usually before or after a FDP, but also at any time as required by the Company (this shouldn't be confused with normal travel from home to work — see **Travelling Time** below). Many airlines use taxis for this, but you may be lucky and get a comfortable bus or a light aeroplane.

All time spent on positioning is classed as Duty, and when it comes immediately before a **Flying** Duty Period is included in it. Positioning is not normally counted as a sector, and if you're wondering what a sector is, it's the time between an aircraft first moving under its own power until it next comes to rest after landing (there are no sector limits on helicopter flying).

Travelling Time

Travelling time (that is, not Positioning but normal travel from place of rest to normal operating base) is not classed as duty, and therefore not included in duty hours totals. However, it becomes an important factor if long distances are involved.

Should your journey from home exceed 'a lengthy period' (about ninety minutes), it's up to you to make arrangements to rest nearer to work. When you are away from base and travelling times between the aerodrome and the sleeping accommodation provided exceed thirty minutes each way, the resulting rest period should be increased by the excess (that is, over an hour) enough to give you a minimum of ten hours (nine for cabin crews) at the sleeping accommodation.

If you are required to travel from your home to an aerodrome other than your normal one, the extra travelling time over and above your normal time is regarded as Positioning (for example, your normal trip to A is twenty minutes, but it takes ten to get to B from A, so there is ten minutes' extra Positioning to add to the FDP).

Standby Duty

Aside from aircrew actually flying, resting or taking time off in accordance with the Flight Time schemes, some crew members are needed to be available in case of emergencies, like sickness or extra flights.

Standby Duty is time where the Company requires you to be on call for duty and able to report within a specified period, say ninety minutes (this doesn't apply where you need merely to be contactable for notification of a duty that starts ten or more hours ahead).

The allowable FDP depends on the time standby starts, especially if you are held in immediate readiness at the airport.

Should you get called out before six hours on standby, then the total duty period consists of the standby time plus any allowable duty period.

If called out after six hours, the FDP mentioned above is reduced by the extra.

Cumulative Limits

Your average weekly total of Duty Hours should not exceed sixty, averaged over four consecutive weeks.

The number of early starts and late finishes should not exceed three consecutively or four in any seven consecutive days (officially, Early Starts and Late Finishes arise from any duty periods that impinge on the period between 0001–0659 local acclimatized time. With regard to this, sometimes you have to ring your customer within the time period 2300–0700 hours before you propose to fly and inform him as to whether you can go or not because of weather. If this go/no go time is earlier than one hour before the proposed departure from your place of rest, the time between the disturbance and the departure (minus one hour) counts as part of the FDP.

Your total flight hours during the preceding twenty-eight consecutive days should not exceed 200 **at the beginning of any flight**, but the expiry of the twenty-eight days is at the end of the day the flight begins, so a bit of bad drafting makes things confusing, because you don't know what you're going to fly that day.

Additionally, a helicopter pilot shouldn't do more than eighteen hours in three days, thirty in seven and 240 in eighty-four (3 x 28).

You shouldn't do over 900 hours in any twelve consecutive calendar months (and Article 60 refers).

Duty Cycles

Days off are periods available for leisure and relaxation free from all duties. A single Day Off includes two local nights and is to be at least thirty-four hours long. Subsequent days off will include a further local night for each additional one. A day off may include a Rest Period.

A **Local Night** is a period of eight hours falling between 2200 and 0800 local time.

If the Company can't manage to schedule flights much in advance (although they must make the effort), the days off must be rostered at least seven days ahead and may only be given up with your permission, assuming that rostering limits are not exceeded. If you lose a day off you must have one off in lieu to make up for it within the next twenty-eight days (days off are intended to be sacrosanct).

You should not work more than seven consecutive days between days off and must have two consecutive days off in any fourteen. You should also have a minimum of seven days off in any consecutive four weeks and have an average of at least eight days off in each consecutive four week period, averaged over three such periods.

Helicopter pilots (as always, a special case) should also have two consecutive days off following seven consecutive days on duty, and at least three days off in any consecutive fourteen (a single day off for helicopter crews may only follow up to a maximum of six days duty).

Records to be Maintained

Operations are responsible for completing your Record of Flying and Duty Hours from the information that you give them at the end of each flight. Sometimes you will be asked to maintain them on their behalf, but try and resist this, because if somebody is fiddling the hours then it's not you that gets it in the neck first. These records must contain information concerning the beginning, end and duration of each FDP (and the function performed during that period); the duration of each duty period (whether or not it includes a FDP); the duration of each rest period prior to a FDP or standby duty period; the dates of days off and weekly totals of duty. These must be preserved for twelve calendar months from the date of last entry, while discretion reports are kept for a minimum of six months. Non-regular pilots are responsible for providing details of their previous twenty-eight-day totals before under-taking a flying duty.

Pre- and Post-flight Activity

Pre-flight activity (that used for flight planning, etc) for the purposes of Duty Hours is a period of about thirty minutes before the first departure and Post-flight activity is about fifteen minutes after last chocks on/rotors last stopped time. In the case of a Split Duty, post and pre-flight activities between duties are about fifteen minutes each. All these may be shorter if the flight is **despatched** (that is, the planning is done by handlers, as opposed to the normal way, i.e. by you).

Delayed Reporting Time

If you're informed of a delay of less than four hours to your reporting time before leaving your place of rest, the FDP will be based on the original reporting time.

Pleasure Flying

Briefly (because it's dealt with more fully in Chapter 7), pleasure flying involves short flights which take off and land at the same aerodrome (not including photography). Presumably, therefore, this includes load slinging from helicopters as well. Under these circumstances (if you do only pleasure flying), a single FDP shouldn't exceed ten hours, except that you can stretch this to twelve if you're positioning to and from base.

Within that FDP, you should not spend more than a total of seven hours at the controls, except for up to an additional two when positioning only (in any case, you should not be at the controls **continuously** for more than three hours). Also, you should have breaks of not less than thirty minutes' duration each according to the following scale:

FDP up to 6 hours   at least 1 hour
FDP 6-8 hours   at least 1.5 hours
FDP over 8 hours   at least 2 hours

Split Duties do not apply, but normal rest periods do.

Mixed Flying

If you mix your types of flying, e.g. **Pleasure Flying, Air Ambulance** and normal **Public Transport**, then the most restrictive conditions apply.

Definitions

A couple of stray definitions that I couldn't fit in earlier:

A **week** is a period of seven consecutive days starting at any set local time on any set day of the week, as determined by the Company (the set day must be specified in the Manual, so why not say Monday?). A rostering period normally comprises four consecutive weeks, and **Rostered, Scheduled or Planned duties** are single or a series of duty days notified to you in advance.

Chapter 4
Weather Minima

General
Airways Manuals
Take-off Conditions
Weather — Arrival Action
Landing Conditions
Determination of Runway Visual Range
Calculation of Decision Height/Minimum Descent
    Height
Circling Minima
Basic Minima
Aerodromes without Approach Aids
VFR Flights
    Over water in helicopters

General

There are weather conditions under which you're not allowed
to land, attempt to land or take off. A minimum cloud-base and
visibility (known as **Runway Visual Range**) will be laid down by
the Company for each airfield it intends to use (in accordance
with State legislation), taking into account the navigation
aids available, terrain, obstacles, type of aircraft and crew
experience (it's mainly based on Performance Groups —
however, unclassified aircraft will need looking at individually).
The Company doesn't have to do all the hard work; they can
buy Airway Manuals in which all the calculations are done for
them, of which more later.

Most of this Chapter refers to IFR work, with a small reference to VFR at the back. As far as Public Transport is concerned, foreign airfields are also subject to UK minima, and those which apply to you will be the highest of:

a) The minima established by the State in which you are flying
b) UK minima as shown in the Airway Manual
c) Basic minima established by your Company

Remember that foreign airfields tend to close down automatically when the weather gets too bad, whereas an airport authority in UK may only close down on their own initiative in the case of snow or a blocked runway, which amounts to the same thing.

While you're not allowed to reduce the limits given, you are actively encouraged to increase them if you think it's necessary to do so. As they're calculated for fog conditions with little or no wind, you should make due allowance for rain and/or crosswinds. Naturally, minima specified are not valid if any factors affecting their calculation have been changed through Notams, or as instructed by ATC (for instance an ILS may have its categorization changed from Cat II/III to Cat I if work is in progress near the runway).

When further restrictions are necessary due to performance considerations (for example due to the need to visually avoid obstacles in the event of an engine failure on take-off), you will find details in the Airfield Categorization File kept in Operations.

Airfields not listed in the Airways Manual or Route Guide used by your Company are subject to separate assessment by yourself and Operations using Basic and/or State minima. The relevant figures for Basic Minima (see later) will be found in the Ops Manual. One copy of your calculations must be retained in Operations and another carried on board. Airfields used regularly in this way should have their details permanently included in the Manual, and it's the Company's responsibility to self-check these (see CAP 359 for further guidance).

There are moves afoot to make the rules in this chapter apply to flights other than Public Transport as well.

Bear in mind that although a CPL includes IMC Rating privileges, you will naturally find weather conditions more restricting if you have no Instrument Rating.

Airways Manuals

You need a route guide so you can get around the airways without messing things up for anybody else.

The ultimate Airways Manual is, of course, the UK Air Pilot, it being the source from which all others get their information. If you ever end up in court, the UKAP will be the one introduced in evidence, but that's not to say that the others are no good. They are all potted versions of it to varying degrees, and are much better presented. A Company is allowed to produce its own, which is more economical when there are only one or two routes being catered for.

The commercially available ones are really as good as each other, whichever one you get started on probably becoming your favourite. In addition to the best known ones, Jeppesen and Aerad, the RAF do a profitable sideline in selling their own and these are well worth a look (it's worth pointing out, though, that it's more difficult to gauge obstacle heights on Jeppesen charts. On the other hand, Aerad are only amended once a month and have several different styles of chart, making it difficult to get round the manuals. They do, however, cost less than Jeppesen).

All of them may contain some let-down procedures that have not actually been approved by the CAA, so inclusion of a procedure in a Flight Guide (other than the UKAP) doesn't necessarily mean it can be used for Public Transport flights.

The above guides are intended for IFR work. For VFR you'll need to carry your trusty Pooley's or Bottlang's, but Bottlang's doesn't carry helipad information.

Take-off Conditions

It goes without saying, I hope, that you shouldn't depart unless weather conditions around the planned route are better than the minima specified in the Manual. This isn't only for safety grounds; it also saves the customer money and inconvenience.

Speaking from experience, if you find the departure time creeping back because of weather, after about two hours' delay advise the customer to go twenty-four hours later. He's still going to take the same time at his destination — after all, he has a job to do which is the whole point of him going.

If you don't do this, you will find the day getting unacceptably long and the Company will probably still clock you on thirty minutes before take-off, regardless of the time you came in.

Some companies will try and pressure you into going just to get the customer's money, knowing full well they won't get anywhere. In this case, leave the choice up to the client. Offer no guarantees, but point out that he will still be charged if the whole exercise is a waste of time. Thus you pass the ball quite neatly into his court, and there's every chance you will be appreciated for not wasting his time, which must be expensive otherwise he wouldn't be flying.

In any case, you are responsible for ensuring that **before take-off** you have got details of the weather minima for the relevant times at every destination runway and at least one suitable alternative you can divert to if your intended destination becomes unsuitable for any reason. These must be noted on the Nav Log if you intend to use them. The figures for Met Visibility and Cloud Ceiling should be used (reported or forecast, and normally without modification) to determine whether conditions are suitable. Use RVR, though, in preference to Met Vis if you can get it.

Landing Distance requirements for wherever you land must be satisfied on both the most suitable runway for landing in still air conditions, and any runway that may be required due to forecast wind conditions (this last for Group E only).

You must also nominate a suitable alternate (also on the Nav Log) to return to when weather conditions at the aerodrome you're departing from are below those required for landing, regardless of how good they may be for take-off (just in case you have to return in a hurry for any reason). Favourable landing conditions at this alternate must be reported and forecast (possibly plus 100 feet on DH and 200 m on RVR) and it must be within a certain time at one-engine-out speed, typically thirty minutes for a twin piston and sixty for a turbine (the terrain and weather conditions *en route* must permit this, e.g. your single-engined climb performance may not allow you to get over obstacles in the way).

If no suitable diversion is available, then the flight should be postponed until one is or the weather at your departure point improves sufficiently. Before take-off, you should therefore have information on at least four airfields.

Weather — Arrival Action

Despite all the care you take about weather *en route*, should it deteriorate below acceptable limits you must consider diversion.

If conditions are subsequently known to be improving, you may request holding at the optimum available level for a maximum of one half of your holding allowance before going somewhere else, but if you eat into this, you would be well advised to have two alternates available, and to have enough fuel to be able to reach one of them (a minimum of sixty nautical miles away) with forty-five minutes' holding fuel on board on arrival.

There is something called 'Island Holding' which may be used in place of alternate fuel, but this is not permitted in Europe. Essentially, it's for use where a destination has no suitable alternate and you are then obliged to carry significantly more fuel than normal, that is, about two hours' worth as opposed to forty-five minutes. The amount of the reserve is related to statistical information about local weather conditions.

Landing Conditions

You must not descend below the *en route* Minimum Safety Altitude until your position relative to whatever aerodrome you hope to use has been positively identified (this is in IMC or VMC). You should also have a copy of the let-down plate available, with all required ground and airborne aids being serviceable.

When in IMC, you should not descend below the sector safe altitude (as shown on the chart) until established in the approach or hold procedure. The safe altitude is based on correct entry procedures and will therefore cover a certain area of ground, so if you're given something non-standard, such as a very long downwind leg that takes you off the chart, beware!

The **Decision Height** (or Minimum Descent Height, depending on the sort of approach) is the height at which you must overshoot if you can't see anything vaguely resembling a runway.

If the Cloud Ceiling is lower than this, you may (unless prohibited by national regulations) carry out one approach to check if you can see anything (known in the trade as 'assessing the visual reference available'), but Missed Approach action must be taken at **Decision Height** on a **precision approach** if you can't (see the Glossary for a definition of visual reference).

On **non-precision approaches**, if visual reference has not been established by the time you reach **Minimum Descent Height**, you may fly level at that height provided the aircraft heading is within fifteen degrees of the runway QDM. You may go down further if you can see where you're going, provided you can land at normal touchdown speed. If you can't see anything by your estimated time of reaching the landing threshold, you must go around.

A precision approach is an ILS or PAR, and will no doubt include Microwave Landing Systems when the time comes. A non-precision approach basically is anything else, such as VOR or ADF, which has only azimuth guidance (that's only left or right to you and me).

Before landing, you should really record the minima on the Nav Log. If you're fully visual, then just write 'VFR' in lieu.

After two successive overshoots you are allowed no more attempts until a significant improvement in the weather is reported — the meaning of 'significant' is left to common sense, but you can have a third go if you have previously used an autopilot (all this changes for purely training purposes).

You may abandon an instrument approach in favour of a visual one provided you have the aerodrome continuously in sight, the aircraft is below all cloud and conditions are equal to or better than those specified for circling (bear in mind, though, that minima apply to visual approaches as well. There will also be a minimum RVR value for these, generally 800m. This is to guard against shallow fog reducing the visibility in the final stages).

A visual approach must be authorized by ATC.

It's a good idea in a commercial environment always to have something up your sleeve, by which I mean — what do you do if the ILS goes off half way down an approach? In training, you would probably have gone around, but that's expensive and the commercial department will love you if you keep adding odd ten minute sectors to each flight. Nearly every ILS uses an NDB as an outer marker, so why not be prepared to convert to an ADF approach if need be? Or a VOR (or whatever)?

Determination of Runway Visual Range

Runway Visual Range is the maximum distance you can see in the direction of take-off or landing as determined by a certain procedure. The distance given to you by ATC is taken as the RVR for the time being, i.e. it's only valid for a short time. Where RVR is not available, reported Met Visibility may be converted to RVR by using the following table:

Lighting Available	Reported Met Vis multiplied by	
	Day	Night
Hi intensity App and Rwy ltg	1.5	2.0
Other lighting	1.0	1.5
No lighting	1.0	

Note: This table should not be used in the following European countries: Belgium, Bulgaria, France, Greece, Israel, Luxembourg, Spain, Tunisia, Switzerland, USSR and Yugoslavia.

If your Airway Manual does not contain the information, **Minimum RVR** can be obtained from a table given in the Operations Manual, which will in turn have been extracted from CAP 360 (like the one below). This will give you the minimum acceptable RVR relative to the type of lighting and Decision Height; for instance, if there's no lighting available and the DH is 200 feet you can expect a minimum RVR of 1000m.

DH or MDH (in ft)	Approach Lighting Length (meters)				
	High Intensity		Low Intensity		None
	>450	<450	>450	<450	
200 — 225	600	650	800	900	1000
226 — 275	600	700	800	900	1100
276 — 325	650	750	900	1000	1200
326 — 375	700	800	900	1000	1300
376 — 425	750	900	1000	1100	1400
426 — 475	800	1000	1100	1200	1500
476 — 525	900	1100	1200	1300	1600
526 — 575	1000	1200	1300	1400	1700
576 — 650	1100	1300	1400	1500	1700
651 — 750	1200	1400	1500	1600	1700
751 — 850	1300	1500	1600	1700	1800
851 — 950	1400	1600	1700	1800	1900
951 — 1050	1500	1700	1800	1900	1900
1051 — 1150	1600	1700	1800	2000	2000
1151 +	1700	1800	1900	2000	2000

If the reported RVR is below the figures given, then you're not allowed to even start an approach (or at least descend below 1000 feet above the aerodrome elevation) even if you have established visual reference above that height. As they say in the trade, there is an approach ban (see the Glossary for a full, boring definition).

You may get an RVR report with three figures, covering the touch-down, middle and stop end of the runway respectively. Where these **Multiple RVR reports** are given, the one associated with the touch-down point must be equal to (or greater than) landing minima, but reports for further down the runway merely need to be sufficient to enable you to stop safely. They should not, however, be less than take-off minima.

The RVR for landing from a visual circuit is 800 m, or the lowest Cat 1 RVR for the intended runway, whichever is the less, regardless of approach lighting, time of day or type of aircraft. As mentioned before, this covers you for shallow fog conditions, where you may see the airport completely from height, but lose sight of it as you descend on the approach.

It is proposed to change the above tables in order to make more specific allowances for precision and non-precision approaches which must have something like a three-degree glideslope. The tables apply to all aircraft categories and are reproduced below — they all refer to high intensity lighting except for the last column:

DH	720m+	400–719m	–399m	Other lighting
200–250	600*	700	800	900
251–300	650	800	900	1000
301–350	700	900	1000	1100
351–400	750	1000	1100	1200
401–450	800	1100	1200	1300
451–500	900	1200	1300	1400
501–550	1000	1300	1400	1500
551–600	1100	1400	1500	1500
601–650	1200	1500	1500	1500
651–700	1300	1500	1500	1500
700+	1500	1500	1500	1500

* If centreline, touchdown and threshold lighting is installed, 550 m is permitted when DH is 200 feet.

MDH

200–250	650	800	900	1000
251–300	700	900	1000	1100
301–350	800	1000	1100	1200
351–400	900	1100	1200	1300
401–450	1000	1200	1300	1400
451–500	1100	1300	1400	1500
501–550	1200	1400	1500	1600
551–600	1300	1500	1500	1500
601–650	1400	1500	1500	1500
651–700	1500	1500	1500	1500
700+	1500	1500	1500	1500

Calculation of Decision Height/Miniumum Descent Height

The starting point for the calculation of Decision Height is the Obstacle Clearance Height for the intended landing aid. If an OCH is not available, then use Circling Minima.

The DH for precision approaches (ILS/PAR) is obtained by adding ten feet (sink allowance) to that, after the Pressure Error Correction for the type, which will be found in the Flight Manual, thus DH = OCH + PEC + 10 feet. If the ILS has an offset localizer, the DH must not be less than the height at which the localizer intercepts the runway heading.

The OCH for non-precision approaches include a fudge factor for sink and PEC, therefore OCH may be read directly as the Minimum Descent Height (MDH for non-precision approaches being more or less equivalent to DH for precision approaches), or MDH = OCH.

The MDH for a 'break-cloud' approach should never be less than the visual manoeuvring height for the airfield.

Circling Height should be regarded as MDH/DH for any instrument approach followed by circling.

If you're a new boy, that is, you have less than fifty hours P1 on the relevant type, expect to increase your DH or MDH by 100 feet.

Circling Minima

Circling is the process of visually manoeuvring to a runway after an Instrument Approach to another one, and minima laid down for this procedure will give the necessary obstacle clearance within a prescribed area. Circling height will be published in the Airway Manual, pre-calculated to a standard formula.

Where this information is not available, just add 300 feet to the highest obstacle within four nautical miles of the airfield (provided the result is not less than 500 feet agl).

You can get a reasonably accurate assessment of the appropriate circling visibility required in metres by multiplying the aircraft's circuit speed in knots by a factor of twenty, e.g. if speed = 120 kts, then visibility must equal 2,400 m.

Where mountainous terrain exists, Circling Height clearance will take account of the height of it and its effect on turbulence.

During a circling procedure you should not initiate descent below minima until aligned with the runway to be used, except that you may descend to 500 feet agl on base leg at your discretion if you have the whole of the runway continuously in sight.

Circling procedure must be employed if the final heading of the authorized let-down procedure diverges by more than thirty degrees from the heading of the runway on which landing is intended (to cover offset localizers). Since there is a minimum RVR of 800 m for a visual approach, there is an approach ban if the RVR is below this.

Basic Minima

Each regularly used runway should have minima allocated for it. In exceptional circumstances (where you come across a new one), you must be able to calculate your own — the Ops Manual will have tables for take-off and landing which cater for this. These will have been extracted from CAP 360, so are fairly standard stuff. However, they're higher than anything pre-calculated because they won't have been given the same detailed consideration. Also, they're blanket figures which allow for the fact that anything outside Performance Group A needs to visually avoid obstacles if an engine fails on take-off. Cloud Ceiling figures will therefore vary according to where you can start to construct your Net Flight path data, so if that happens at 300 feet (that is, your engines are assumed to be working up till then), expect an appropriate Cloud Ceiling (of course, it could be reduced as well, to 100 feet if your Inspector agrees).

The same principle goes for RVR figures, which are related to the time required to see and avoid obstacles — if you're going at 90 knots, 1,500 m RVR will give you thirty seconds between seeing and missing.

Take-off

Take-off minima are dependent on many factors, including the Performance Group of the aircraft, availability of markings, lighting, runway surface and width, distances available and the experience of the operating crew (inexperienced crews should add 100 feet and 200 m to these figures). Any minima used other than that laid down must be retained with the flight documentation for three months.

CC figures are in feet and RVR in metres. The figures given for Performance Groups C, E and F assume you have enough room to re-land (at least twice the TODR).

Perf Groups	B and C CC/RVR	E and F CC/RVR	CC/RVR
High intensity Centreline lighting	0/150	200/500*	300/500**
High intensity edge lighting and rwy centreline marking	0/200	200/500*	300/500**
Low intensity edge lighting and no rwy centreline marking (night)	0/300	200/600	300/800
Rwy centreline marking with or without low intensity edge lighting	0/350	200/600	300/800
No lighting or marking (day), low intensity edge lighting and no rwy centreline marking	0/500	200/1000	300/1000

There must be adequate visual reference to stay over the runway in the initial stages of take-off.

* This may be reduced to 100/300 if EDA is more than twice TODR
** This may be reduced to 200/400 in similar circumstances

Landing

TYPE OF AID	DAY HI LIGHTS		NIGHT HI LIGHTS	
	DH(ft)	RVR(m)	DH (ft)	RVR (m)
ILS	200	600	200	600
ILS Nil GS	250	600	250	600
PAR	200	600	200	600
NDB	300	650	350	650
VDF	300	650	350	650
VOR	300	650	300	650
SRA .5 nm	250	600	250	600
SRA 1 nm	300	650	300	650
SRA 2 nm	350	700	350	700

Use your discretion for airfields without lighting.

For example, taking off with high intensity centreline guidance may allow you to have a Cloud Ceiling as low as 100 feet and visibility of 200 m if your aircraft is in the correct performance bracket. If you're landing with an ILS by day, then DH is typically 200 feet with an RVR of 600 m. Flying to those limits is hard work — there's no sense in making them lower.

Remember the minimum visual approach visibility is 800 m. Autopilot unserviceability may increase any limits.

Aerodromes without Approach Aids

If your destination does not have the aids required for any reason (due to unserviceability, perhaps), you can **either** fly to your destination entirely in VMC **or** fly under IFR to a selected aerodrome where you can carry out an Instrument Approach, then continue under VFR to your original destination.

In the latter case, permission must be obtained from ATC at the selected aerodrome, which should have an authorized let-down procedure, and be within twenty-five miles of the destination (it also helps if the forecast weather between the two aerodromes is better than 1000 feet cloud-base agl and three nautical miles visibility).

VFR Flights

Quite straightforward, this bit.

On land, helicopters should have a minimum cloud-base of 600 feet agl (1500 feet at night) and 1000m visibility (3 km at night), whereas aeroplanes will require 1000 feet cloud-base agl (1500 feet over water or at night) and 3 km visibility at all times.

When flying outside IFR in reduced visibility it's advisable to adjust your airspeed so as to maintain a one minute visual reference ahead, e.g. at 120 knots, the inflight visibility should be at least two nautical miles. However, you should give serious thought to diversion prior to deterioration below this.

Flying in VMC on top of cloud is not allowed in single-engined aircraft, but in twins it may be undertaken by non-Instrument Rated pilots if the cloud cover within ten nautical miles of the destination is forecast to be less than ⅝ at 1000 feet with a minimum visibility of 1000m. The forecast should be valid from take-off until two hours after ETA. Don't forget you may also need a certain minimum amount of navigation equipment.

When crossing estuaries, it's a good idea to be able to see the other side before leaving the side you're on. Thus, you get as little of the goldfish-bowl effect as possible.

Over Water in Helicopters

For extended trips over water in helicopters (North Sea, mainly) what's required depends on the range of the flight, whether long, short or very short (see the Glossary for definitions).

For **long range flights** by day, the conditions over the entire over-water part of the route should be a 600-foot cloud-base (above the surface) with 6 km visibility by day (the cloud-base doubles by night). You can take off, however, with visibility in the first thirty nautical miles down to 4 and 5 km by day and night, respectively.

Temporary reductions may be accepted down to 500 feet and 3 km for up to fifteen minutes, whereupon normal IFR conditions will apply (this can be extended to thirty minutes if you've got an autopilot with a coupled radio altimeter).

For **short range flights** by day, the conditions are a 500-foot cloud-base with 3 km visibility, and by night 1200-foot and 5 km. Again, if the weather gets worse, you can continue for fifteen minutes under the conditions above.

Very short range flights allow you to fly below and clear of any cloud at 250 feet above the surface with a visibility of 3 km if you're by yourself, or two if you're two-crew. By night, the cloud-base is 500 feet and the visibility 8 km for single pilot, or 5 km otherwise.

Chapter 5
Flight Planning

General

Proper Planning Prevents Poor Performance (that's the clean version). It's also true. In just the same way as setting yourself up properly on finals produces a good landing, setting yourself up properly before going flying in the first place produces a good trip.

As we're not strictly talking about drawing lines on maps (which you should know about anyway), I've combined the operational planning which technically is up to you with the procedure for setting up a charter, since they are both part and parcel of the same thing. With any luck, Ops will have done their part for you, but there will always be some overlap which will have to be sorted out amongst yourselves.

Procedure for Charter Queries

It may happen that you're the only one in the office one day, and a customer calls wanting to go somewhere. How do you quote for a job? There's no real substitute for experience in what is really the function of Ops or Sales, but the following is based on sound practice and most circumstances are catered for.

All quotes given for work (including sub-charters) should have a record kept of them. There will usually be a quotes book or file somewhere, and what you quote must be entered under the appropriate headings, including full details of commissions offered, etc. At the initial stages, the important information required is:

a) Customer's Name
b) Contact telephone no
c) Date of trip
d) Route details
e) Load details
f) Timings
g) Alternative action if diverted

The last one is quite important, as you quite often will have to make that decision on behalf of the client and the more information you can get prior to the actual task, the better you will look if things go wrong.

This information (and more) is catered for on the Flight Brief, a document that every company is obliged to have, which is what you get before you take off telling you what the job is going to involve. The only problem is that some companies treat the above information as Top Secret — you go away and do a job, and you're told what you did when you come back!

Invoicing is on a flight time basis, so every effort must be made to provide the most efficient service while keeping costs down to a minimum — this is as much for the customer's benefit as the Company's.

The charterer shouldn't be expecting any service that's illegal or unsafe — most common is landing without permission ('It's all right, he's a friend of mine') and flying overweight ('We got it all in last week'), not to mention bad weather at the destination ('I can see the end of the garden'). It's too easy to get a reputation as a cowboy company while trying to give a service that shouldn't really be provided. You'll get no thanks for it anyway, so why bother?

When quoting, be careful and polite and give the impression that you know exactly what you're talking about. Try to give all the information wanted on the phone, then they will be less likely to go elsewhere. If you have to call back, then do so within, say, fifteen minutes. At all costs ring back when you say you will, even if it's just to say you haven't got the information requested yet. It's all salesmanship!

All quotes should be valid at the time given, say for about seven days — things can change over a three month period.

Normally, you just take the hourly rate and multiply it by the flying time. The aircraft speed for flight planning purposes should be found in the Flight Planning or the Technical section of the Ops Manual, and hourly rates should be shown on a chart somewhere in the office. Some companies have pre-calculated quotes for the more frequent destinations.

You will then need to take account of everything else that costs money, namely landing fees, handling charges, Customs/Special Branch etc, not to mention the dreaded VAT, except for foreign trips and those in aircraft with more than twelve seats, which are exempt (see later in this Chapter for further details on going overseas).

Company Policy should be to accept payment in advance, rather like buying a rail ticket; British Rail don't let you on their trains without seeing the colour of your money. Some approved customers may be invoiced afterwards, but even then a written (Aircraft Booking Acceptance Form) or telexed (for short notice flights) confirmation of the booking and a willingness to pay within seven days of invoice receipt is required. This next bit is **very** important: the more the client is in a hurry to depart, the greater must be your insistence on payment first!

If he is a new customer and you don't insist (politely) on payment in advance, you could find yourselves giving a free service, as it is extremely difficult extracting money for a one-off service from an unknown person in retrospect, especially when the panic's over.

If they plead inability to pay in advance (no credit cards, cheque book at home, whatever) then it is better to refer them somewhere else. You won't make a terribly good impression if you become responsible for a bad debt. The Company should accept all major credit cards anyway, so the problem should not arise.

There is a good general point on this subject that doesn't really apply here, but should be made all the same. If any Ops or Sales people are reading this, here is a tip: some customers imply that they are going to put a lot of work your way and want a discount as a result. OK, there is nothing wrong with that, it's all good business, but don't give the discount immediately, otherwise you'll probably find they have only one or two trips and then disappear, effectively getting cheap flying. The best way to deal with anyone who may be half-serious is to give a retrospective discount, such as every thirteenth hour free, or a cheque for ten per cent of the money spent every fortnight. If he's any sort of businessman, your customer will understand. If he doesn't, then he's likely to cause other sorts of trouble as well, like arguing about the bill.

There may or may not be a minimum charge for your Company's services, but if it's busy or there is a likelihood of more lucrative work, charge one hour per half day as the machine is effectively prevented from being used. If business is slack, compromise a little, but remember that passengers are rarely on time, so don't do too much tight scheduling (refuelling at some airports can take up to an hour-and-a-half).

Having got the basics in your mind, the other considerations include:

h) **Is the load acceptable** for the aircraft? Is it dangerous cargo? (If it is, see Chapter 6).

i) **Aircraft and crew availability**. How many hours to the next scheduled maintenance and are there enough to do the proposed flying? When is it next scheduled? Are the crew numbers sufficient and are they cleared to operate into that airfield (check the Airfield Categorization file — see later this chapter).

j) **Crew duty hours are acceptable**, i.e. the totals aren't too near weekly or monthly limits. When did the crew last come off duty and when does their rest period end?

k) **Departure and destination** points are open when required. All prices quoted should assume normal opening hours, so early or late movements will incur extension fees. These can be pretty hefty as they usually charge a minimum fee (using Heathrow can cost different amounts, depending on all sorts of variables ranging from the time of day you fly to the direction you approach the airfield from). Think about getting an indemnity for out-of-hours use if the aircraft is small enough (below 2730 kg, therefore not needing a licensed airfield) and you use it often enough.

l) **Prior permission must be obtained** for landing at the departure and destination — you must get the owner's consent to use any landing site, especially in a helicopter (this consent is assumed if using a licensed airfield — it's part of the terms under which a licence is granted). Speak to the landowner himself or his representative, but if you have to ask somebody else, get a name that you can use as a reference later so you can cover yourself. This is a good time to mention that in Aviation a lot of the extra work you get involved in is not because it's necessary, but more to cover your (or more likely somebody else's) rear against things going wrong later. The bigger the organization, the more this is true — always protect yourself. See also Chapter 6 — **Helicopter Landing Sites**.

m) **Handling** for departure point and destination available and booked.

Handling charges are really only applicable at Gatwick and Heathrow in UK when meeting, inter-lining or departing passengers on to domestic or foreign flights. Self-handling is permitted at Heathrow, but not at Gatwick (even for refuelling) where you have to nominate a handling agent. Handling Agents available include airlines as well as private companies, so try those if you get stuck. Handling is actually a sore point amongst many operators (as are Eurocharges), so be careful before you incur them. Self-handling is a real pain to the pilot, but some customers (and companies) won't pay for what is essentially an expensive taxi ride, despite the inconvenience which the use of a Handling Agent avoids.

Always expect to incur handling charges when abroad (see **International Operations** later this chapter).

n) **Eurocharges**. Use of the Airways costs money and the larger the aircraft, the more it will cost, but below a certain weight (not really significant), it's free. Naturally, if you go VFR you don't get charged, but even if you only cross an airway *en route* the civil servants will have their hands out. There may be pressure to fly VFR everywhere in order to escape these charges, even to the extent of flying at 1000 feet through Amsterdam in cloud claiming to be visual (true!).

o) **Fuel availability** (and booked if on a tight schedule or opening hours extension). With a full load, you will have limited endurance, so you may have to allow for a refuelling stop somewhere along the line. You should offer the customer a choice of refuelling *en route*, which is usually cheaper, or flying away to refuel whilst he is on business, which is more convenient. Don't forget the extra flying and landing fees.

p) **Site/performance characteristics**. Check the runway length! (Airfield Categorization file again.) When quoting for a helicopter trip, unless there is clear access don't quote for landings in built up areas. Hotels are always a good bet with golf clubs a reasonable second. Farms are also worth trying. If you're stuck, the local police station may know somebody who has had a helicopter land before where they've been involved.

q) **Grid references correct**. Remember that passengers don't want to tramp through muddy fields, so pick a landing site with good transport access. Use the gazetteer in the back of the road atlas to locate small villages and then go on to the Ordnance Survey sheets so that a six-figure grid reference is obtained for the landing site. A description of the site is useful, as is getting it marked somehow.

r) Check that any CAA **exemptions or dispensations** required are valid and that the conditions therein can be complied with.

s) **Police and other services should be notified** as a courtesy — this is a legal requirement where the public has access to sites.

t) For flights to Ireland, the Channel Islands and the Isle of Man you have to go through a Special Branch security check through a **designated airfield** (you'll find the list in the UKAP).

u) **Correct seating and bar** fitted — see Engineers.

v) **Paperwork correct** (for a full list see Carriage of Documents and Navigation Equipment later in this chapter):

Captain's briefing sheet

Navigation Log
Trimsheets/Loadsheets
Terrorism Cards
WX ordered on telex or fax
OS maps as required
Customs documentation

All the above (as required) should be placed in a large envelope for whoever is going to do the job.

You should only get involved in **sub-charter flights** when approached directly by the customer. If a broker or another operator calls for a machine that you haven't got, then say there's no availability and he will go elsewhere. It's better not to get entangled with two lots of commission and other arrangements, as it gets rather complicated and too many intermediaries leads to confusion and a dissatisfied customer. Incidentally, if you do have to turn down work, plead full commitment rather than unavailability — it gives a better impression.

If you do get involved in sub-chartering, the normal trade discount is seven-and-a-half per cent on the flying — you just invoice the commission to whoever does the job. Sometimes you will get a net quote, which is the minimum that they want; add what you want on top, using the following guidelines which will ensure a reasonable commission if you add them on before passing on a quote to the customer:

Small piston-engined fixed wing quotes, i.e. Aztecs, Navajos, etc. — add on enough to bring in a minimum of £75.00 per day, but always round up to the nearest £5.00.

Large piston-engined fixed wing, i.e. Chieftains, Titans, etc — add on to bring in £85.00 per day.

Jets and Turbo-Props; add on to bring in £100-£150 a day on short runs and £200-£250 per day on longer ones.

On those few occasions when you know you're dealing with someone to whom money is no object, and whose need is immediate, have no hesitation about adding on anything from £500-£1000 for those exotic flights to the Middle East, etc. Don't forget about payment in advance, though!

When dealing with Hall Porters, etc, not only add on as described above, but again to make his commission about seven-and-a-half per cent or about £100.

For helicopter sub-charters, add £50 per day for single-engined machines and £100 per day for twins.

You might get away with waiting time as well.

Computing Fuel and Oil Requirements

Fuel and oil consumption rates and weights for flight planning purposes should be found wherever Technical or Flight Planning information is kept. It is usual to keep a regular check on the fuel contents during flight to see if things are going according to plan, thus keeping a check on the fuel consumption. This is actually written down on the Flight Progress Log (PLOG) every hour or so on long trips.

Helicopters have special capabilities of landing away from aerodromes which are reflected in the minimum fuel figures allowed. These assume VFR flight over hospitable terrain (which usually means that fuel is readily available), but flight over inhospitable terrain should be treated the same as for aeroplanes (see below, but when doing extended sectors over water, contingency reserves should not be below ten per cent of destination fuel plus alternate. Also, an additional thirty minutes of loiter fuel should be carried). Special conditions will apply when the flight is conducted under IFR (needless to say, you shouldn't think of going IMC on fuel reserves planned for VMC).

Alternate landing sites should also meet single-engined landing requirements.

Otherwise, enough fuel should be carried for the estimated time of flight to the next refuelling point (based on forecast meteorological conditions), plus five per cent of that together with holding fuel for twenty minutes. Allowance should also be made for a start up and run allowance and minimum inflight contents (or unuseable fuel).

This effectively means that each flight ends with about thirty minutes' fuel on board. For flights beginning and ending from the same aerodrome (pleasure flying), or those with an average landing rate of ten or more an hour (external loads or shuttling) where fuel is available on site, the holding allowance may be reduced in order to allow flexibility for natural breaks in the movement of loads, but check this with your Flight Ops Inspector (see also Chapter 7, **Pleasure Flying**, for further thoughts on fuel reserves).

The aim with **Fixed Wing** flights should be to plan to arrive over the destination in a position to make an approach, overshoot and fly to an alternate and carry enough fuel to hold for forty-five minutes (or thirty if a turbo jet) at the alternate. Then you must still be able to carry out an approach and landing.

Therefore, you should carry enough fuel for the estimated time of flight to destination and alternate, plus five per cent on top for contingencies, plus holding fuel, which may be a set minimum amount. Contingency fuel is to cater for errors in forecast winds or navigation and any ATC restrictions that may be encountered. There are circumstances under which it can be ignored, but this will have to be agreed with your FOI (for instance, block or tabulated figures may be used for fuel consumption that already take into account a fudge factor for headwinds, etc).

Don't forget the start up and unusable fuel allowances for type.

When it comes to **IFR** however, journeys can be split more into specific phases. Fixed Wing and Helicopters should carry fuel for start, checks, taxi, approach and landing (one phase), take-off and climb (another), cruise and descent (yet another) plus ten per cent plus diversion to the alternate, which will include allowances for climb and approach, as well as realistic routings.

Then fuel for forty-five minutes holding (at the alternate) at the most economical speed and unusable fuel allowances for type should be added. By arrangement, block figures can also be used for all these phases which ignore the take-off and climb.

Fuel flow will have to be adjusted if you plan to use any specialized equipment in flight, such as heaters, or not use anything essential, such as an engine (single-engined fuel flows should be found in the technical section).

Further discussions about Critical Points and Points of No Return with relevance to 'wet footprints' will be found later in this chapter under **International Operations**.

Oil consumption rates should be published and common sense applies here, i.e. that contents should be checked before take-off and not fall below minimum contents, being replenished as necessary.

Navigation Log

A Navigation Log and Fuel Flight Plan (sometimes known as a Progress Log) is used for all IFR flights in the suggested style overleaf (this one has been used in anger several times, but you may have other ideas. It does at least have the minimum requirements as specified by CAP 360). There are occasions when a reusable one may legally be used, such as certain schedules and trips under 100 nautical miles, but it's easier just to use a new one all the time. It's intended to contain all necessary information in an easily readable form to ensure the safe navigation of the aircraft along its intended route, therefore all possible columns should be completed before flight.

Completing it is easy enough, but the following points should be remembered when planning and keeping up the form in flight:

a) In the LVL (level) column, the actual height should be entered on each leg — check that it's not below the MSA! If it is, then 'V' (for VFR) should follow the level entered, which you would be if you've any sense.

b) The fuel requirements for each sector should be entered in the spaces provided. For flights more than one hour long, the actual fuel contents should be recorded roughly every hour, but use discretion where a natural sector break occurs before or after this time by five to ten minutes or so.

c) The nominated alternate should be shown immediately after the destination airfield workings, leaving one line blank. It's normally sufficient to enter the straight track distance between the destination and alternate, the MSA, track and calculated flight time, a five minute let down allowance and the leg fuel calculation.

However, although straight line diversions are often adequate, they should be realistic and include SIDs, STARs and the like, where they make the trip protracted.

d) If you've got room, leave a blank line between each sector to help deal with re-routings and direct clearances.

e) There is a requirement to record pre and inflight weather for the destination and alternates. The weather minima must be calculated and entered prior to departure if less than twice the minima is forecast (weather obtained for flight planning purposes should be carried on the flight and included in the voyage report).

f) When given changes in heading, altitude, squawk or radio frequency, write them down and cross the old one out. It's too easy to forget when things are busy.

Carriage of Documents and Navigation Equipment

Documents and Navigational Equipment as listed below should be carried on all Public Transport flights (if you're going abroad, you also need to read International Operations later in this chapter). It's quite an exhaustive list, which after a time becomes automatic, but it does save embarrassment when you get ramp checked!

a) Aircraft Radio Station Licences (inc W/T) and Radio Installation Certificate.
b) Certificates of Airworthiness, Registration and Insurance
c) Certificates of Maintenance Review and Release to Service
d) Technical Log
e) Crew Licences
f) Current Deferred Defect list
g) Operations Manual (all relevant volumes)
h) Flight Manual
i) Topographical coverage of the area to be flown with danger areas marked — you don't actually need to carry an OS map (except for the London Helicopter Routes — see Chapter 6)
j) Current Flight Guide and/or Airway Manual
k) Checklist
l) Passenger briefing cards
m) Exemptions and Permissions (when required)
n) Loadsheets/Weight distribution information (if required)
o) Torch (if night flying)
p) Computer
q) Captain's flight brief
r) Prevention of Terrorism cards
s) Noise certificate (if relevant)

Minimum Altitudes

You should already be familiar with the low flying rules, but an Ops Manual will still have to state them just to tighten things up legally.

Just to make things awkward, foreign States may have other ideas which must take precedence if you are flying over their territory.

In addition to the normal limitations imposed by the ANO, the minimum height for **helicopters** must be such that in the event of engine failure a landing can be made without danger to persons or property on the surface. This is very loosely worded, but it does mean you should consider the auto-rotational characteristics of your aircraft when low level, especially when downwind.

Helicopters should normally be flown above 1,200 feet or so agl (try for a bit more at night) unless operating under instructions from an Air Traffic Control agency or on a specialist task such as filming (with suitable exemptions, of course!). See Chapter 6 for Special VFR considerations.

For each sector of the track to be flown by **any** aircraft (that is, each intended track from one reporting point to the next), there will be a Minimum Safe Altitude, sometimes known as Sector Safe Altitude.

For flight in controlled airspace that is well defined by two separate navigation aids, it's 1,500 feet above the highest terrain or obstacle within ten nautical miles of intended track. This distance increases to twenty nautical miles outside controlled airspace or for general application. Within twenty-five nautical miles of the departure or landing aerodrome (and if you're under radar control), it's 1,000 feet above the highest terrain or obstacle within five nautical miles of intended track.

Where the track crosses mountainous country over 2,000 feet in elevation, the following heights should be added:-

	Windspeed in knots			
Elevation of terrain	0-30	31-50	51-70	over 70
2000-8000 feet	500 feet	1000 feet	1500 feet	2000 feet
Above 8000 feet	1000 feet	1500 feet	2000 feet	2500 feet

These are to safeguard against the effects of turbulence and standing waves, but if you've got a wind around fifty knots, consider going somewhere else anyway.

In the event of an engine failure during any point of the flight, you must be able to continue to a suitable landing point maintaining at least the minimum safe altitude with a positive gradient of climb at 1,500 feet above it.

Naturally, some aircraft are not able to maintain much height with one engine out (some are pushed with two), and there will be charts in the Flight Manual that will indicate your expected rate of descent with respect to weight and temperature, etc should an engine failure happen. **Drift Down** is discussed further under Performance in Chapter 8.

You must enter the final MSA figures in the Navigation Log. When in IMC *en route* you should not fly below those figures until you have established your position on an approved let down procedure; thereafter you must stick to the minimum altitude specified.

Maximum Altitudes

Unless you operate pressurized aircraft, all operations are restricted to 10,000 feet, or within limits imposed in the Flight Manual, whichever is the lower, unless oxygen is available.

See also **Use of Oxygen** in Chapter 6.

Airfield Categorization

Each airfield you may be called upon to use is graded as to its suitability for use by the average Joe Pilot, depending on the surrounding terrain and severity of local weather, amongst other things. Proper grounds for classification into one area or another, however, include lack of details in the normal flight guides, performance restrictions due to runway conditions or obstructions in the vicinity, complex departure procedures and political restrictions.

Airfields are colour coded as to their suitability (but with respect to operational characteristics only) and the pilots' self-briefing file on airfields is kept in the Operations office, being reviewed quarterly by Ops based on advice from the Chief Pilot and feedback from crews. On return from a flight it will be your responsibility to check that the information concerning the airfield is correct. Where changes have occurred, you should inform Operations, who will recategorize the airfield as necessary. Temporary changes will be recorded in the file, while those of a more permanent nature will take the form of an amendment to the Operations Manual. Anything not mentioned should be checked out with the Chief Pilot.

a) Category A — GREEN

Airfields that present no undue difficulty and, where applicable, have a published let-down procedure. You may operate into these airfields at any time provided you're signed up as current on your Route Competency Certificate. No prior briefing is required and this category is unrestricted.

b) Category B — YELLOW

Those airfields have some degree of difficulty such as non-standard approach patterns, proximity of high ground, or other peculiarities. You may operate into them provided you're specifically briefed (by a little something in your flight brief) and certified as competent into each named airfield on your Route Competency Certificate. Where an airfield would be in the A list were it not for runway length, it will be sufficient to record satisfactory performance data before you go.

c) Category C — RED

Especially difficult airfields for pilots without recent familiarity, either in terrain, meteorological conditions or non-standard approach procedures. You may fly into them only if you (or an accompanying pilot) have done so in the last thirteen months. The certification itself is valid for thirteen months and must be signed up on the Route Competency Certificate.

The complete airfield categorization list used to be by AOC region, but now it's world-wide, so it's quite big. Also, it changes every week as the CAA HS-125 goes off and checks everything, but the following list is reasonably up-to-date. I've only included the most common destinations for reasons of space (trying to bridge the gap between giving a sample of what's required and being useful to the pilot without an Ops Manual). Note that going to Berlin is not allowed without special briefing and clearances from the Foreign Office. If you really want to go there, check out AIC 27/89 (Pink 116).

Airfield	A	B	C	Remarks
Aalborg	X			
Aberdeen	X			
Albecete	X			
Alesund		X		high ground
Alexandria	X			
Algiers	X			
Amsterdam	X			
Ankara		X		high ground elevation
Athens		X		high ground procedure
Barcelona	X			
Bardufoss		X		high ground procedure
Basle		X		high ground
Bedford	X			
Beirut		X		high ground politics
Belfast (both)	X			
Bembridge		X		runway length no aid
Benbecula	X			
Benson	X			
Bentwaters	X			
Bergen	X			
Berlin (all)			X	politics
Bern		X		high ground
Biarritz	X			
Biggin Hill	X			
Bilbao		X		high ground
Billund	X			
Binbrook	X			
Birmingham	X			
Blackbushe		X		no aid
Blackpool	X			
Bordeaux	X			
Bournemouth	X			
Bremen	X			
Brest	X			
Bristol (both)	X			
Brize Norton	X			

Brough		X	runway length
Brussels	X		
Caen	X		
Cairo		X	high ground
Calais	X		
Cambridge	X		
Cardiff	X		
Carlisle	X		
Casablanca	X		
Castlebar		X	runway length
Cherbourg	X		
Chivenor	X		
Church Fenton	X		
Clermont Ferrant		X	high ground
Cologne/Bonn	X		
Coltishall	X		
Coningsby	X		
Copenhagen (all)	X		
Cork	X		
Coventry	X		
Cranfield	X		
Cranwell	X		
Culdrose	X		
Damascus			X politics
Deauville	X		
Denham		X	runway length no aid
Dieppe		X	runway length
Dijon	X		
Dinard	X		
Dishforth		X	no aid
Dounreay		X	high ground procedure
Dublin	X		
Dundee		X	runway length
Dusseldorf	X		
East Midlands	X		
Edinburgh	X		
Eindhoven	X		
Elstree		X	runway length no aid

Exeter	X		
Fairoaks		X	runway length no aid
Finningley	X		
Frankfurt	X		
Gamston		X	runway length no aid
Geneva		X	high ground
Genoa		X	high ground
Ghent		X	runway length no aid
Gerona		X	high ground
Gibraltar		X	politics
Glasgow	X		
Gloucester/Cheltenham	X		
Goodwood		X	grass runway
Guernsey	X		
Gutersloh	X		
Halfpenny Green		X	runway length
Hamburg	X		
Hanover	X		
Hatfield	X		
Hawarden	X		
Humberside	X		
Ibiza	X		
Ingoldstat	X		
Inverness	X		
Ipswich		X	grass runway
Islay	X		
Isle of Man	X		
Isle of Skye		X	runway length
Jersey	X		
Jerusalem			X	politics
Kilkenny		X	runway length no aid
Kinloss	X		
Kirkwall	X		
Koksijde	X		

Laarbruch	X		
Lakenheath	X		
Lampedusa	X		
Leavesden		X	runway length
Leeds/Bradford	X		
Leeming	X		
Le Havre	X		
Leicester	X		
Le Touquet	X		
Leuchars	X		
Linton-on-Ouse	X		
Lisbon	X		
Liverpool	X		
London (Gatwick)	X		
London (Heathrow)		X	high density
London (Stansted)	X		
Londonderry		X	runway length
Luton	X		
Luxembourg	X		
Lydd	X		
Lyneham	X		
Maastricht	X		
Machrihanish	X		
Malaga		X	high ground
Malta	X		
Manchester	X		
Manston	X		
Marham	X		
Marseille	X		
Middle Wallop		X	grass runway
Mildenhall	X		
Mönchen Gladbach		X	runway length no aid
Naples		X	high ground
Newcastle	X		
Northampton		X	runway length
Northolt		X	high density
Norwich	X		
Nottingham		X	runway length no aid
Odiham	X		

Airport	1	2	3	Notes
Oslo		X		high ground
Ostend	X			
Oxford		X		runway length
Perpignan		X		high ground
Perth		X		runway length
Peterborough		X		runway length / no aid
Plymouth	X			
Poitiers	X			
Prestwick	X			
Rome (all)	X			
Ronchi de Legionari	X			
Rotterdam	X			
Scatsta		X		high ground / no aid
Scunthorpe	X			
Shannon	X			
Shawbury	X			
Shobdon		X		runway length / no aid
Shoreham		X		runway length
Silverstone		X		runway length / no aid
Sligo		X		runway length / no aid
Southampton	X			
Southend	X			
Stapleford		X		grass runway
Stavanger	X			
Stockholm (all)	X			
Stornoway	X			
Sumburgh		X		high ground
Swansea	X			
Teesside	X			
Tel Aviv			X	politics
Thruxton		X		runway length / no aid
Tiree		X		high ground / procedure

Location				
Toussous-le-Noble		X		runway length
Tripoli			X	politics
Trondheim		X		high ground
Upper Heyford	X			
Valley	X			
Venice	X			
Waddington	X			
Warton	X			
Waterford		X		runway length no aid
Wattisham	X			
West Freugh	X			
White Waltham		X		grass runway
Wick	X			
Wildenrath	X			
Wittering	X			
Woodbridge	X			
Woodford	X			no aid
Woodvale		X		runway length no aid
Wycombe Air Park		X		runway length no aid
Wyton	X			
Yeovil		X		grass runway
Yeovilton	X			
Zagreb		X		
Zurich		X		high ground

Others

In addition to the above categorizations, airports are allocated a three-letter code by IATA. This is used for commercial purposes, such as reservations, ticketing and baggage labelling. It's also used on signals sent on the Aeronautical Fixed Telecommunications Network (AFTN), Air Transport's own Telex system.

In the same way, ICAO issues a four-letter one (you will already be familiar with the EG — codes on flight plans; see also Chapter 9 for an explanation of the differences between IATA and ICAO). As you will have gathered, the first two letters stand for the country and the last two the particular airport. There may be another two added for a specific address within the airport.

International Operations

On the face of it, going abroad should be no harder than internal flying, except that you have longer stage lengths and sometimes nothing but water underneath (even single-engined aircraft go regularly across the Atlantic, albeit indirectly). The basic principles of navigation, accurate flying and fuel management are just the same and you could be forgiven for thinking there was nothing to it.

At one level this would be correct, especially when pottering around Europe, but real international operations require deeper planning and knowledge than you think. For instance, do you know to what accuracy your instruments need to work? Do you know what instruments you need? Is your knowledge of the principles of radio you learnt for your exams up to date? Can you still calculate a Point of No Return? How would you get into Berlin? I'll bet you couldn't file a Flight Plan off the top of your head, or even know when you need to! (See Chapter 6 for that.)

Using the Northern (via Greenland) or Southern (the Azores) route across The Pond, or anything else equally complicated is OK once in a while, but if you have to do the trip regularly, there's no substitute for doing it the proper way, for which you need the right aircraft (see Chapter 10).

You certainly need the right avionics. If you intend to join the big boys and use the non-radar Organized Track System across the Atlantic, for instance, where separation is down to sixty nautical miles between aircraft (and distance from track of twenty-five nautical miles is known as a Gross Navigation Error), you will need approved long range navigational equipment (INS, Omega, with LORAN-C OK in certain places only) and communications equipment (HF). The mere fact that you've got this stuff on board doesn't mean you can file a flight plan and launch off, however — you may find that the aircraft itself has to be certified specifically with that equipment. It will be some time yet before satellite systems are fully in operation.

You also need equipment capable of establishing true Mach numbers, because speed control is another method of separation, which is naturally based on accurate position reporting (if your HF radio fails, there is a common VHF frequency, 131.8, which you can use to ask other aircraft to relay for you). The OTS tracks themselves are established twice daily and there is a one-way day and night track structure according to winds and demand.

ICAO and the CAA jointly publish an operations manual for this particular area of operations, and you will find further details in that. Ask for the MNPS *Airspace Operations Manual*.

As far as general knowledge goes, knowing where to look is half the battle — it's the planning that's most important, the fine print especially. Jeppesen or Aerad will have details of the overflight and landing clearances you may need, together with entry requirements for you and your passengers.

You may not realize it, but you actually need permission to fly over any country. In most cases, this is taken for granted in the interests of commercial activity — after all, other countries have to fly to the UK. But a delay causing restrictions over a commonly used country may well cause you to go elsewhere, possibly a hostile country, which can't be bothered to trace you later if you don't pay the fees. This leaves you with two problems — getting the permission in the first place, and paying in advance.

A little reading of the newspapers will give you an idea of any political restrictions you may encounter. Some permissions make take thirty days or more to obtain — if you go without them, you'd better swot up on your Interception Signals as well!

Naturally, you will need passports (including visas) and licences (with all related certificates), but you may also want to take proof of immunization for cholera, smallpox, tetanus, typhoid, yellow fever and anything else nasty you can think of.

As well as the Public Transport documentation laid out in Carriage of Documents earlier in this chapter, the aircraft itself should carry any flight authorizations, permits for overflight or landing rights, insurance details, maintenance information, UK Customs form C42 (permit for temporary export/import), General Declarations (crew and passenger) and passenger/cargo manifests, tickets or waybills.

The C42 is required for every aircraft leaving the UK and intending to return. On it, you will need to list types and serial numbers of engines and other equipment, so have these to hand. If you go abroad a lot, you can have a six-monthly version. Remember (talking of Customs), that crews have very much smaller duty-free allowances than passengers.

You will have to pay your way, so don't forget credit cards or other financial instruments, particularly cash if you're going somewhere out of the way where you may need to bribe somebody to get what you need (the Mafia is alive and well in many places).

The flight plan system is very complex, so if you have pre-filed across several stages, it's worth asking at every stop-off point while taxying in whether the outboard plan is OK. If it isn't, and you're somewhere like Nice, you'll then have to walk a couple of miles round all the relevant offices (that's when you need a handling agent).

If you're going very far away, do you need a survival kit? Flying north of a certain latitude in Canada requires a comprehensive one to be carried. Depending on circumstances, you may need a Polar (or Tropical) survival kit. If in doubt, check out the ANO, Schedule 4.

Aircraft minimum equipment lists need to be checked — for instance, some countries may require LORAN or HF/sideband, as well as the normal ADF, VOR, etc (certainly near the Azores). You can rent, if you're only on a one-off trip. Don't forget to take a few spares, if possible.

There is an *Airports and Handling Agents Manual* (published by Jane's) which, together with the *Official Airline Guide*, contains information on bank schedules and normal daily life in the country of your destination (you don't want to arrive when there's half-day closing). In these circumstances, handling agents, while having limited usefulness in the UK because of their cost relative to the whole trip, can be worth their weight in gold when you're abroad. You can use their credit, for one thing, and they can do most of your work as you come down the ILS, because you will have contacted them by radio on the way in.

Although English is the language of Aviation, it's not always so, and some nationalist controllers may insist in speaking their own language (one helicopter pilot of my acquaintance got one out of this habit by reading back an imaginary clearance to proceed across Paris City Centre at 1,000 feet!).

GMT, of course, is now UTC (but a rose by any other name . . .).

Just in case you've forgotten, here are some formulae:

Time to PNR $\dfrac{E \times H}{O + H}$ where E = endurance, O = gspd out in kts and H = gspd home in kts

Time to CP $\dfrac{D \times H}{O + H}$ where D = total distance in hours

The CP can differ depending on the type of emergency. If it's a medical one, for instance, then your aircraft will have no change in performance characteristics and you won't lose any airspeed, but if you lose an engine, it will all change drastically, as you'll also find out if you lose pressurization and have to descend. As most aircraft keep similar fuel flows with less airspeed when you lose an engine, this means that your effective range will decrease by whatever percentage.

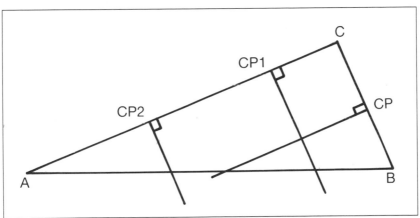

To find out whether you're better off using an alternate, calculate Critical Points for A to C and B to C. From these points drop perpendicular lines to see where they cross the original track. If they cross each other before crossing the original track, using the alternative is out. If they cross the track before each other, then use the alternate if you get a problem between the points where they cross the original track (A to B).

This is where carrying proper reserves becomes important, because that slower speed will eat into whatever you planned to have left over. What you need to do is calculate what fuel you estimate having left at the CP, and use the anticipated engine out airspeed against wind (you can obtain tables of statistical winds from Boeing) to obtain groundspeed, and divide it into miles to go. If your endurance is less than this, you will not get to where you want, and if you're over the

Atlantic, you will get your feet wet! (The shortfall in endurance divided by two gives you the time either side of the CP during which, if an engine fails, you are faced with such a situation, which is probably why it's called a wet footprint. In practice, you can gain a little extra by drifting down, but don't bank on it.)

Chapter 6
General Aircraft Operations

General

Visual Flight Rules — Special VFR

Flights On and Off Airways

Requirements for filing Flight Plans

Special Helicopter Zones

Freelance Pilots

Recording of Flight Times

Security of Information

Carriage of Authorized Persons

Carriage of Unauthorized Persons

Maintenance of Records

Performance

Operations from Contaminated Runways

Runway Braking Action

Helicopter Landing Sites

Checklists

Technical Logs

Deferred Defects

Check A Inspections

Altimeter Setting Procedures
 VFR operations
 IFR operations

VOR/RNAV

Radio Procedures
 Radio failure
 RT emergency procedures

Action in the event of an Accident
Action in the event of an Incident
Aircraft Overdue Action
Assistance to Others in Distress
Flights Over Water
Flights over Inhospitable Terrain
Ditching
Operations and Forced Landings in Remote Areas
Airmiss Reporting Procedure
Birdstrikes
Carriage of Munitions of War
Carriage of Livestock
Carriage of Freight Overseas
Carriage of Dangerous Goods
Smoking in Aircraft
Refuelling
Pilots to Remain at Controls
Flying in Manual Control
Passenger Control and Briefing
Fitness to Fly
Use of Oxygen
Incapacitation
Meteorological Hazards
    Thunderstorms
    Windshear
    Turbulence
    Wake vortices
    Standing waves
    Frost, ice or snow on aircraft
    Heavy icing
Use and Location of Emergency Equipment
Two Crew Operations

General

This chapter covers the sort of subjects which, in an Operations Manual, would concern aircraft operations in general, whereas special tasks and items specific to particular machines would be found elsewhere. For instance, while checklists and their methods of use would be mentioned here, what's actually in them would very probably be found in the Technical chapter relevant to the aircraft concerned. Safety matters are also included, but in a large Manual they would possibly have their own chapter — in practice it's difficult to separate them properly and in fact there are several things in this chapter that could arguably end up somewhere else. The following subject headings cover things that should be brought to the attention of Operating Staff and are by no means exhaustive — they may be added to or taken away as required.

Visual Flight Rules — Special VFR

It's important to realise the significance of Rule 23 of the Rules of the Air and Air Traffic Control Regulations 1976 and the definition of Special VFR.

It should not be used as a means of getting around the provisions of Rule 5, e.g. you can't use a clearance of 'not above 1,000 feet' as an excuse to fly low-level over Birmingham where you should be over 2,000. If you are so cleared, it's only from an Air Traffic point of view — they're assuming you know what you're doing and are making you an offer you **can** refuse!

Flights On and Off Airways

Public Transport flying, in aircraft that can take advantage of it, will normally take place under IFR, routing either via established airways or advisory routes. When outside these areas, a minimum of Radar Information Service should always be available.

There are four types of radar service you can get. The first is **Radar Advisory Service** (RAS), which gives information and advisory avoiding action from conflicting traffic. It can be requested at any time, but is usually used in IMC conditions. This can be time wasting, especially if it's a good VMC day and you're continually given vectors downwind that take ages to catch up on. You are not obliged to accept the avoiding action, but if you don't, you must inform the controllers, as you must if you change heading or altitude for any reason.

Radar Information Service merely provides information about conflicting traffic. How you avoid it is up to you.

Flight Information Service is just somebody to talk to. There's no radar and very limited information about other traffic as not everybody calls up. They can, however give you weather and Notam information, as they are usually not as busy as radar controllers.

Procedural Service gives separation between participating traffic but without the luxury of radar. It's mainly used on approach and advisory routes.

The controller will state the type of service provided (so it goes on tape and can be used at the subsequent Board of Inquiry), so even though you may have been identified, don't assume you have the service requested until told so.

Remember, in VMC, it's still your responsibility for collision avoidance, so you will need to maintain a good look-out.

Flying VFR where weather or other circumstances demand that you should be IFR (i.e. in order to avoid Eurocharges) should be avoided.

Requirements for filing Flight Plans

A flight plan **must** be filed on the following occasions:

a) For all flights across a UK FIR boundary
b) For all flights in controlled airspace notified for the purpose of Rule 21, whether VMC or IMC
c) For all flights within any controlled airspace in IMC or at night (unless under SVFR)
d) For all flights in any controlled airspace in VMC if the flight is conducted in accordance with IFR
e) For flights in certain SRA/SRZs irrespective of weather conditions (i.e. the Cross Channel SRA)
f) For all flights that use ADR facilities
g) For all flights made by aircraft with a Max All-Up Weight of more than 5700 kg and with a destination more than 40 km from the departure point
h) For all flights in the London or Scottish Upper Flight Information Regions
i) At any time at your discretion

In addition, a flight plan **should** be filed:

j)   For all flights over hostile terrain that may require the alerting of SAR, such as more than ten miles from the coast or over sparsely populated or mountainous areas. Don't forget to close it properly if required.

Special Helicopter Zones

The London Specified Area is where you can't fly so low in a helicopter that you're unable to land clear in the event of an engine failure. This means that no single engined helicopter can operate in it unless proceeding along the River Thames.

As you are over water, flotation equipment is required, together with approved life jackets which must be supplied for all occupants.

Specific routes for helicopters flying in the London Control Zone and through the Specified Area are shown in the *Air Pilot* and included in *Pooley's Guide*. They're also overprinted on a special OS map, a copy of which you must have with you.

Information on other zones which have special helicopter procedures, such as Glasgow, will also be found in the *Air Pilot*.

Freelance Pilots

Freelancing need not be as precarious a living as it sounds. Like a lot of other things in life, it depends very much on who you know as well as what you know. If you're known to be reliable, that is, get out of bed in the morning, turn up on time, don't crash and generally deliver passengers safely, you will always get work. Larger companies, including airlines, have been known to use freelancers from time to time.

If you do decide to make a living out of it (at least it gives an illusion of control over your life — you are in a position to say no, after all, especially to companies who are known to be less than enthusiastic about maintenance), the taxman will be watching to ensure that you are in fact working for more than one customer, but it doesn't do to be too dependent on one anyway. At some stage, though, you may want a regular job (they do have some benefits!) and it could be difficult to convince the average interviewer why you've gone your own way in the past. Just a point to bear in mind, but see also Chapter 12.

While their usefulness is now recognized in relieving short-term problems, especially in smaller companies, the use of freelancers used to be (and sometimes still is) frowned upon, as they are more difficult to keep control of (at least as far as Duty Hours and paperwork are concerned). They will be working for several other companies which have their own procedures (I'm sure the CAA gets fed up with the number of times they're told that a particular pilot isn't working for another company — by every company he works for!).

Now that aircraft are more complex, and it becomes increasingly difficult to hop from one machine to another with ease (especially regarding the policy on multi-type currency), all freelance pilots must be checked to the Company's standards. The operative phrase is 'by or on behalf of the Operator', which means that the Company must maintain strict control.

Provided that the Ops Manual says so, or a Flying Staff Instruction is issued to cover the occasion, there's no reason why other Companies' pilots and paperwork shouldn't be used, but their standards must be similar and a mutual exchange of paperwork must take place. However, the catch is that there must be a **pre-existing** arrangement for this to happen, which must be formally established in writing.

Despite the fact that everybody pinches everybody else's Ops Manual anyway, and the forms are therefore the same, it's a legal problem — as the checks must be performed 'by or on behalf of, etc', it could be argued that if the forms have been just backdated, this won't have been done. For instance, it would be difficult to claim that tests conducted by one Operator were done on behalf of another, unless there was an arrangement to that effect at the time and the other operator's requirements were taken care of.

As a result, all required checks should take place and be signed up at the same time as the testing Company's (for example, a TRE common to two companies should conduct a test and fill in the two sets of paperwork at the same time).

The other companies' Training Captains may also need to be listed in your Manual, which they must also have a copy of, otherwise they won't know to what standards you operate.

Recording of Flight Times

Flight times recorded in personal flying log-books are from first movement under power until rotor run-down for helicopters, and from first chocks away with the intention of taking off until final chocks on for fixed wing.

Flight times in Technical Logs, by contrast, are from take-off to landing only, sometimes entered in decimal hours. It's common practice, where several flights are made per hour without closing down (such as pleasure flying), to record the first take-off and last landing times and to note the actual airborne time in between.

There are many ways of doing this, the most accurate being with a stop-watch, but there is an unofficial and widely used practice (by arrangement with your local CAA surveyor), when pleasure flying, of using two thirds of the total time between first take-off and last landing. Accountants love it, but engineers don't, as they regard the wear and tear as still taking place.

Too much of this sort of paperwork will really play havoc with servicing schedules (and profit and loss figures) as parts will wear out a lot quicker than anticipated, despite the 'fudge factor' allowed by the CAA when setting up maintenance requirements.

Timings should be local, unless operating consistently in another time zone.

Security of Information

The nature of General Aviation frequently involves you being party to confidential information which shouldn't be discussed or relayed to third parties. When passengers freely discuss business, it's tactful to make use of the intercom cut-off switch. Documents, maps or written instructions should also be regarded as confidential.

Carriage of Authorized Persons

In addition to those listed in Art 106 (1) of the ANO, an Authorized Person (as far as the Company's concerned) is normally a fare paying passenger on a properly arranged trip or a non fare-paying passenger flying with the permission of Management or Operations — however, when going foreign, nobody is authorized until they have passed through Customs.

Under the terms of the ANO, you have discretion to refuse to carry anyone who seems unfit for any reason (see also *Fitness to Fly* later in this section).

All Flight Operations Inspectors will be designated in the Ops Manual as being Authorized Persons and will from time to time wish to fly in Company aircraft to check on operational procedures (that is, unless the Commander thinks the safety of the flight will be compromised). Arrangements for these flights will normally be made in advance, but the right is reserved for Inspectors to board aircraft without prior notice. Inspectors carry authority/identity cards which will be produced on request.

Carriage of Unauthorized Persons

No unauthorized persons should be carried as passengers on Company aircraft, if only for insurance purposes (well, not intentionally, anyway).

Although there are many attempts at security at every airport, it is still distressingly easy to walk up to an aircraft at several of them without being challenged once. Nowadays, no terrorist with any brain at all is going to try and take explosives through a passenger terminal — therefore it won't be long before they try and get to an aircraft from the tradesmens' entrance, which means it may be you that gets hijacked one day, even if you are in a little aircraft.

It would appear that Terrorists belong to three categories, but they all will have one common denominator, in that they have got to the desperate stage in order to be where they are.

The first is ideologically motivated.

He believes that the higher cause he represents is superior to anything else and thus is morally correct, even if it does mean killing. The only fear he will have is of failure and he is likely to belong to a well organized group, with others somewhere in the pipeline.

A loner, on the other hand, may either be craving attention or striking back at the organization that owns the aircraft. In other words, his motivation will be more personal. Such a person will be unpredictable as well as dangerous, but will also have no specific plan. Perhaps just pandering to his ego will help you.

Lastly, there is the psychopath who is actually sick and doesn't understand what's going on anyway (no, not part of the Management!). In addition to the previous characteristics, he will also be very volatile.

Of course, if your luck is anything like mine, you will get a combination of all three! However, the essential point is that each one must be treated individually — there can be no general plan of action to cater for every case.

Having said that, you **must** stay calm — you will be no good to anybody if you don't. Resistance is almost certain to provoke harm. If you can, try to make yourself as inconspicuous as possible. It may be difficult to grasp, but you must realize that (temporarily at least) you are no longer in control. Pilots by nature tend to have larger than average egos, but if there is a clash, you would be wise to subdue yours. You will have to wait for your opportunity to come later. If possible, tell ATC every small detail which may be helpful to someone storming the plane later, should it become necessary. You must also tell the truth and not try any funny stories. Terrorists have **no** sense of humour.

If you have a weapon at all, it's time, like the equivalent of 'working to rule' and abandoning the short cuts that normally make the wheels of aviation run smoothly. Any excuse will do; you need more maps, fuel, staff, servicing, oxygen or whatever — anything reasonable, in fact.

The idea is to keep the aircraft on the ground, as once you are flying rescue becomes very unlikely. Make him do a bit of work — it will help distract him. Also, don't make eye contact — nervous people become more so if you do. Don't resist; and don't volunteer, either. Try to remain invisible.

Talking of which, despite any scruples about 'Captain's responsibility', escape is also a good way of stopping things. If he hasn't got a crew he can't go anywhere!

Aside from the unusual type of authorized person mentioned above, there are certain types of passenger who are excluded from flying anyway, and these include people under the influence of drugs or alcohol, infected with a contagious disease, of unsound mind and a danger to the aircraft in general. They should only be carried with special safeguards and prior arrangements.

Maintenance of Records

Like anything to do with officialdom, there is a lot of paperwork which must be preserved. The following records should be kept for the times stated:

Certificates of Maintenance Review and Release to Service — two years after expiry

Aircraft, propeller and engine log books — two years from withdrawal

Certificate of Compliance — two years after expiry

Weight schedule — six months

Technical log sheets — two years

Pilot training records — two years after leaving

Duty records — one year from last entry

Discretion reports — six months

Flying log books — two years from last entry

Flight documentation — six months

Navigation Logs — three months

Loadsheets — six months

Performance

The take-off and landing phases of any flight are the most critical, demanding the highest skills from the crews and placing the most strain on the aircraft. Because of this, strict regulations are in force governing the information used for the calculation of take-off or landing performance. Of course, in the old days (say, during the war), as long as there were enough engines to lift the load, that was all that mattered. No real thought was given to reserves of power and the like.

Now it's different, and performance requirements will be found in the Air Navigation (General) Regulations with details being worked out before the issue of a Certificate of Airworthiness for any type.

They are subsequently incorporated in the Flight Manual, which actually forms part of the C of A.

In addition, Article 35 of the ANO requires you to ensure that your aircraft will have adequate performance for the proposed flight.

Aircraft are certified in one of several groups (A, A (Restricted), A2 or B for helicopters, or A, B, C, D, E or F for aeroplanes), the higher the performance of the aircraft, the lower the alphabetical letter (a 737 comes under Performance A, for instance, while anything up to nine seats that may require a forced landing after engine failure will come under F).

The group in which an aircraft operates depends on its certification, Maximum All-Up Weight and the number of passengers that it carries. Within these limits you may choose which group to operate in, then becoming liable to the appropriate weather and weight limitations (for example, it may be more acceptable commercially to operate in a lesser group if it enables you to take more payload, and thus make more money).

Individual aircraft of a given species will vary in performance due to such variables as the age of the airframe and engines, or the skill and experience of the crews. What you can do on one day under a given set of circumstances may well be impossible another time.

The original testing, of course, is done with a new aircraft and highly experienced pilots. The results of this testing are known as **unfactored**, and not all foreign aircraft performance data is actually verified by the CAA, though they do carry out spot checks occasionally. In fact, any quoted figures are a mixture of actual readings and calculated (or guesstimated) adjustments from them. The 'performance' of an aircraft is therefore a set of average values — particular machines may be better or worse.

There are certain fudge factors applied to these unfactored figures to ensure they comply with UK public transport requirements — data so factored is known as **net** performance (and as **gross** performance when it's not). Occasionally, performance data (as amended by the CAA) in a flight manual will already be factored, especially in Groups C and below. However, you will have to check the small print on the chart for this, just in case they try and surprise you.

Figures and graphs are based on Standard conditions which allow for fixed reductions in pressure and temperature with height. As we all know, the real world isn't always like that, so these assumptions may not always be true and due allowance must therefore be made for them (if your aircraft is performing sluggishly, you may find it's not the machine, but the conditions it has to work under that are at fault).

Performance A aircraft are required (with one engine out) to clear all obstacles under the departure track within a defined area by a specified margin — this doesn't rely on 'seeing and avoiding' such obstacles. All the relevant data will be in the graphs. Some groups have no information available at all in some areas. For instance, an aircraft in Performance Group C is assumed to have all engines working above 200 feet, under which there is no data for landing or take-off (that's why the take-off weather limits for this type of aircraft will rarely be below this, because you must be visual to avoid any obstacles you may meet should an engine fail). Lower groups, on the other hand, can have no specific provision for engine failure at all.

In order to function correctly, each group requires certain conditions to be met, either in standards of power available, environment or special procedures. For example, take-off, landing and reject areas need to be prepared surfaces for Group A helicopters, which also have to achieve certain net gradients at particular points in the climb. Groups A (restricted) and B are more relaxed, but still have limitations — you need somewhere to land in emergency, but for these you only need to avoid risk to third parties while meeting certain weather limits.

Keeping to the helicopter theme, Group A take-off procedures involve a vertical and backwards lift-off to a predetermined height before going forward. That point is known as the Critical Decision Point (or CDP), and it gives a choice of action if an emergency happens (actually, ICAO now call it the Take-off Decision Point, or TDP). Having moved backwards, you still have the take-off spot in sight and it's therefore available for landing. At CDP (or TDP), if you elect to carry on to forward flight, you should be able to clear the landing spot during the steep dive you have to make to achieve flying speed (that's why the CDP is about thirty or forty feet high). Things happen in reverse on landing. This procedure is not without its critics, since prolonged hovering at high engine power outputs is not good engine handling.

Anyhow, whatever you are flying, you will find the data needed to check your performance either in the Flight Manual (which will have a UK supplement if your aircraft is foreign made) or the owner's manual or pilot's handbook if this is not available. General principles concerning distances for take-off and landing are similar for aeroplanes and helicopters; for example, take-off distances for both will increase by ten per cent for each 1000 feet increase in Pressure Altitude. UK supplements override any information that may be in the standard manuals.

Some factors affecting aircraft performance include:

a) **Runway length**, details of which are declared by the Airport Authority. These are published in the *UK Air*

Pilot. This declared distance is the **Take-off Run Available** (TORA). Any areas at the end of the TORA which are unsuitable for an aircraft to run on, but which are nevertheless clear of obstacles, are called **Clearways**. These combined with the TORA form the **Take-off Distance Available** (TODA), which should not be more than 1.5 x TORA. It's a similar situation for landing.

However, getting the wheels off the runway is only part of the process of take-off. Performance assessments also require an aircraft to clear an imaginary screen (usually thirty-five feet, but fifty feet for piston aircraft) at the end of the TODA (TORA + Clearway, remember). The distance it takes to do this is the **Take-off Distance Required**. If a single runway distance is given, it must be used for both TODA and TORA. The Take-off Run Required (factored TODA) is 92% of the TODR.

Part of the Clearway may be able to support an aircraft while stopping, although not under take-off conditions. This may be declared as **Stopway** which may be added to the TORA to form the **Emergency Distance Available** (EDA). This is the ground run distance available for an aircraft to abort a take-off and come to rest safely. The essential point to note is that Stopway is ground-based. EDA is sometimes also referred to as the **Emergency Distance** or **Accelerate-Stop Distance**.

The greater the EDA, the higher the speed the aircraft can accelerate to before the point at which the decision to stop or go must be made in case of an engine failure.

Obviously, the TODR must not be more than the TODA. If not stated in the Flight Manual as having been done, the TODR must be factored by 1.33, **after** the corrections in the following sub-paragraphs have been multiplied together and applied (factoring means that the distances needed are multiplied by those figures to provide a safety margin).

The **Landing Distance Available** must similarly not be less than the **Landing Distance Required**. If there is a choice of runways, the LDR is the greater of that on the longest one in zero wind conditions or that on the runway used due to forecast winds (this last except for those in Group E — see also Chapter 4).

Don't forget the Landing Distance Required is from a height of fifty feet. Unless the Flight Manual states otherwise, the LDR must be factored by 1.43 (giving 70% of the distance available), again, after applying the following corrections.

b) **Airfield altitude and ambient temperature**. The higher they are, the less dense the air and the less the ability of the wings and the engines to 'bite' into it, thus requiring more power and longer take-off runs to get airborne. **Humidity** has a similar effect, but is usually allowed for in the graphs.

TODR will increase by 10% for each 1000 feet increase in aerodrome altitude and 10% per 10°C increase in temperature (factor by 1.1).

LDR will increase by 5% for each 1000 feet increase in pressure altitude and 10°C increase in temperature (factor by 1.05).

c) **Aircraft weight** — greater mass means slower acceleration/deceleration and longer distances. TODR will increase by 20% for each 10% increase in weight and LDR 10% per 10% increase in weight (factor by 1.2 and 1.1). Very few aircraft allow you to fill all the seats when you have full fuel.

Some manuals give take-off and landing weights that should not be exceeded at specific combinations of altitude and temperature, thus ensuring that climb performance is not compromised. These are known as **WAT limits** (Weight, Altitude and Temperature), and are mandatory for Public Transport flights.

Sometimes rates of climb are given instead of WAT limits, so you need to be aware that a Public Transport aeroplane must be able to maintain a rate of climb of 700 fpm if it has retractable landing gear, and 500 fpm otherwise.

In a multi, if you can't visually avoid obstacles during climb or descent, you must be able to climb at 150 fpm with one engine out at the relevant altitudes and temperatures (that's 500 feet in five miles!). This means **all** obstacles — you can't exclude frangible ones, so you may have to restrict take-off weight to meet these requirements (see also sub-para g, below).

d) **Runway slope** uphill in the direction of take-off will also delay acceleration, therefore increasing the distance required. The converse is true of downhill slopes and a rule of thumb is that TODR will increase 10% for each 2% of uphill slope. The same figures apply for landing with a downhill slope (factor both by 1.1). When landing, an uphill slope aids stopping, thereby giving a reduction in LDR (any gains from landing upslope or taking off downslope, though, should not be made use of but accepted as a bonus. That is, don't use them as part of your planning).

e) **Surface winds**. Headwinds will reduce the distances required and improve the flight path after take-off. Tailwinds have reverse effects and crosswinds may even exceed the ability of the tyres to grip the runway (crosswinds will not only cause a handling problem, but may also increase the TODR if braking is required for guidance purposes). Forecast winds must be factored by 50% for a headwind and 150% for a tailwind — this may already be allowed for in the charts.

   TODR and LDR will increase by 20% for each tailwind component of 10% of the lift-off and landing speed (factor by 1.2).

f) Performance information is based on a dry, hard surface. The **state of the runway** can affect directional and braking ability and is discussed more fully in **Operations from Contaminated Runways**, next.

   Meanwhile, for dry short grass (under five inches), the TODR (LDR) will increase by 20% (20%), a factor of 1.2. When it's wet, 25% (30%) — factors of 1.25 and 1.3. For dry, long grass (five to ten inches), TODR (LDR) will increase by 25% (30%), and 30% (40%) when wet (it's not recommended that you operate when the grass is over ten inches high).

   For other soft ground or snow, the increase will be in the order of 25% or more for take-off and landing.

g) Take-off requirements also need to consider obstacles which may exist further along the take-off path and cannot be avoided visually. The area to be considered is a funnel extending up to 1500 feet above the airfield elevation from the end of the TODR within seventy-five metres either side of track (this is with all engines operating). The **Net Flight Path** is made up of segments covering various stages of flight (such as when the undercarriage or flaps are raised) and is so called because NET performance data is used to assess it. The NFP commences from fifty feet above the end of the TODR, this being the imaginary screen that the aircraft must clear.

If an obstacle (including a frangible one) intrudes on the Net Flight Path, then take-off weight must be reduced until it's cleared by a margin of thirty-five (or whatever) feet, thus this factor may be a determining one in calculating **Restricted Take-off Weight** (see also **Loading** in Chapter 8).

It is permissible to make gentle turns to avoid obstacles and thus negate the need for fiddling with take-off weights, and there will be graphs in the Flight Manual allowing you to calculate radii and procedures to do this. However, you will need to be visual as well, so there will have to be a minimum cloudbase specified to cover for this.

If an engine fails in the climb out, normal practice would be to return to the point of departure, but if you can't do this for any reason (such as weather) then the NFP and the MSA must be examined at the flight planning stage. It may even be necessary to climb overhead the airfield in order to achieve the height required before departing for the return alternate.

You must use the one-engine inoperative net flight path data from the point at which full instrument flying commences, or is expected to commence.

h) Similar to Net Flight Path is the **Balked Approach Flight Path**, which commences at DH above the upwind end of the LDR.

i) You must be capable of continuing the flight from any point of engine failure at or above the MSA to 1500 feet above a suitable airfield (within WAT and runway limits), where you must be able to maintain a positive rate of climb.

Consideration must therefore be given to height loss, and the likely **drift down** rate with engine(s) out is established from the Flight Manual. The charts will indicate how quickly you can expect to descend, based on aircraft weight, temperature, altitude, etc.

If the MSA is quite high (say over the Alps at 14,000 feet), you are obviously going to be pushed to get there in some aircraft with two engines, let alone one. If you have to go that way and you suspect you may have performance problems, you could always work out your drift down with emergency turn procedures, information about which will also be found in the Flight Manual.

What you do is establish a point one side of which performance is OK and the other side of which, if you have an engine failure, you make an emergency turn to get yourself away from the area and (hopefully) out of trouble. Again, the charts will indicate the rate of descent in a turn and all you need do then is ensure that your MSA reduces at a greater rate than your altitude!

If you can't comply with any of this, you may have to reduce your weight until you can.

j) Peculiar to landing is **aircraft speed** — a higher one than specified naturally requires a longer distance.

k) **Power settings** are important. Some noise abatement procedures require the use of reduced thrust on take-off, but these obviously have the effect of tightening performance limits, which in turn will increase all your distances.

EPR gauges should not be used as a sole indication of engine power output, and should be cross-referenced with other instruments, especially when there is a chance of the probes icing up.

The relevance of this becomes more important in the case of an engine failure after V1, where some aircraft allow the use of full throttle without the possibility of exceeding performance limits (those with automatic controls, for instance). Other types need the levers to be set more accurately, and a likely idea of what the limits will be to be known before take-off.

l) Other miscellaneous problems which will increase distances required include low tyre pressures.

It's obviously not a good plan to operate simultaneously to the limit of all the above factors, as you would be if you arrive high and fast at a wet, downward sloping runway with a tailwind! AIC 52/85 (Pink 76) contains other useful information on performance considerations.

Operations from Contaminated Runways

A contaminated runway is one that has significant amounts of standing water, ice, slush, snow or even heavy frost along its surface. The most important factors concerning these are the loss of friction when decelerating and displacement of (and impingement drag when accelerating through) whatever garbage is on the runway. **Aquaplaning** is a real risk, which is a condition where the built-up pressure of liquid under the tyres at a certain critical speed will equal the weight of the aircraft.

Higher speeds than this will lift the tyres completely, leaving them in contact with fluid alone, with the consequent loss of traction. As a result of this, there may be a period during which, if one of your engines stops on take-off, you will be unable to either continue or stop within the remaining runway length, and go water-skiing merrily off the end! (Actually, you're more likely to go off at the side, so choosing a longer runway under these conditions won't necessarily help.)

The duration of this risk period is variable, but it will reduce or increase in proportion to variations in aircraft weight.

It is possible to determine a rough speed at which you can expect aquaplaning to occur, and this is equal to about nine times the square root of your tyre pressures, 100 lb per square inch therefore giving you approximately ninety knots as a probable speed to expect trouble. If this is higher than your expected take-off speed then naturally you are safer than if it were otherwise. The point to note is that if you start aquaplaning above the critical speed, for example, when landing, you can expect the process to continue below it; that is, you will slide around to well below the speed you would have expected it to start if you were taking off.

Most of the factors that will assist you under these circumstances are directly under your control, and it's even more important to arrive for a 'positive' landing at the required fifty feet above the threshold at the recommended speed on the recommended glideslope than for normal situations.

Having tyres that are under-inflated doesn't help, either — each two or three pounds below proper pressure will lower the aquaplaning speed by one knot, so be careful if you have descended rapidly from a colder altitude.

Aquaplaning aside, it's obviously a good idea to avoid using a contaminated runway, but if this isn't possible, there are techniques that may assist you to reach a speed at which you can continue the take-off in the event of engine failure, or stop in the shortest practicable distance, which will include not taking off with a tailwind component or carrying unnecessary fuel.

In addition, taxying techniques that avoid the collection of snow and slush by the airframe should be used, together with anti-icing measures. Don't taxi directly behind another aircraft and try to use maximum runway length and take-off power.

The recommended maximum depth of slush or water for **take-off** should not exceed 15 mm, and of dry snow 60 mm. Wet snow should be treated as slush.

The airfield must have either a paved runway with an Emergency Distance Available of not less than 1.5 x TODR (Performance Group C — say a PA23) or 2 x TODR (for something like an AA5 — Performance Group E) or 1500 feet, whichever is the greater; or a grass runway with an Emergency Distance Available of not less than 2 x TODR (PA23) or 2.66 x TODR (AA5) or 2,000 feet, whichever is the greater. The minimum cleared width should be seventy feet.

There should be provision for you to identify the point on the runway which is a distance of 40% of the EDA from the start of take-off as a check against acceleration. If .85 V2 has been achieved by this marker, then continue the take-off, rotating at .9 V2. V2 should be achieved by fifty feet. If you can't get that speed, then the take-off should be abandoned, keeping the nosewheel in contact with the runway, the throttles closed and maximum (safe) braking applied.

The maximum depth of slush or water for **landing** should not exceed 3 mm, with the limitations applied for snow being the same as for take-off. Don't forget to exercise great caution when landing on runways with a crosswind associated with snow or ice.

See also AIC 82/1986 (Pink 88).

Runway Braking Action

Critical fluid depths for aquaplaning can vary from approx .1 to .4 of an inch, depending on the surface. The presence of water or liquids on a runway that may affect braking action are described as follows:·

DAMP	Surface colour changed due to moisture
WET	Surface soaked, but no significant standing water visible.
WATER PATCHES	Significant standing water patches visible.
FLOODED	Extensive standing water patches visible.

Helicopter Landing Sites

Ideally, flights should be undertaken from licensed sites and official information regarding them is given in the *Air Pilot* — the details supplied in other flight guides, while extracted from it, should not be regarded as official.

Life being what it is, however, you will find that most places you land at will be unlicensed, as helicopters are more able to make use of unlicensed aerodromes for Public Transport purposes (aircraft below 2730 kg MAUW don't need a licensed aerodrome, provided the flights do not begin and end at the same place, take place at night, are not for training and cannot be regarded as regular services). Article 78 of the ANO requires licensed aerodromes to be used whenever scheduled services for the purposes of Public Transport take place.

The owner of any piece of land does not need special permission to use it as a Helicopter Landing Site, provided that certain conditions are met. Naturally, it must not be in a congested area otherwise you will come up against the ANO. It must also be only for his private or business use, that of his employees or anyone specifically visiting him for social or business purposes. Finally, no structure must be erected in connection with its use for helicopters aside from temporary ones (such as windsocks), otherwise the Planning Permission people will become interested. There is no need to notify them of anything unless the land is intended to be used as a helipad on more than twenty-eight days in any one year.

In addition to having permission to use the land, the local police should be informed where possible, as well as the other emergency services, especially where the public would normally have a right-of-way (such as a park).

If an unlicensed site is to be used for Public Transport operations, then a landing site card should be raised and kept in the Landing Site library, which is kept in Operations, possibly as part of the Airfield Categorization file. This may then be used in conjunction with the OS Map for others to self-brief before using it.

If you're performing shuttle flights at a special event, such as Epsom races, making more than five movements at a place (a movement is a take-off **or** a landing), this makes it a 'feeder site', and subject to stricter standards than Pleasure Flying (see also Chapter 7).

Depending on the Performance Group of the helicopter, sites should have physical characteristics that allow you to make emergency landings without danger to persons or property on the surface, or significant risk to the helicopter and its occupants. An alternate site for a twin-engined helicopter should meet single-engined requirements, which means Group B.

Group A helicopters need sufficient take-off space for the weight to be carried and take-off, landing and reject areas must be prepared surfaces.

In addition, a 3% net gradient of climb must be achievable in the first segment and 1.5% in the second if an engine fails. Group A (Restricted) requires that a 50 fpm climb must be maintainable at 1,000 feet above the take-off point (Group B types are regarded as being unable to do this). For the two latter groups, a prepared surface is not required, but there must be somewhere to land in the event of a reject that will cause no risk to third parties.

If the size of the site is insufficient, say, less than two-and-a-half times the rotor diameter, and has obstructions, the Performance Group may well be downgraded to something like B (this depends on what's in the performance graphs). It works the other way round, as well — a Group B could pretend to be a Group A if there's more room to manoeuvre, which means it could carry more payload.

The type of take-off will depend on the size of the area available. A Group A take-off technique should be used when the area is restricted. However, clear climb-out paths should still be available. Group A take-off techniques should also be used from elevated sites without obstructions in order to allow the helicopter to land back on the site in the event of the failure of a single engine before the Critical Decision Point has been reached.

Although an air or ground inspection is needed to cover for all this, it's not always possible to do so prior to flight. When this is the case, the charterer should be asked to supply a large scale map of the landing site and approaches. Heights and positions of local obstructions should be noted.

If on arrival you decide that the area is not suitable, then you shouldn't use it (easier said than done!). It is therefore most important that the charterer is fully aware of your Company's requirements and that he will be charged for an abortive flight should the landing site not meet the required standards.

How do you tell how suitable a site is from the air? Difficult, that. The easy answer is to suck it and see, but confined or congested areas (see below) don't meet Performance requirements for Public Transport, and you may be contravening the famous Rule 5 as well.

Your customer wants to land. You, on the other hand, have a licence to protect. If you're at all unsure, do a couple of flypasts and feel your way down. If it's a confined area, there will be a point beyond which you're committed, so don't go beyond that point until you are sure.

While you're looking, check through the Size, Shape, Surroundings, Surface and Slope as a guide. If the approach has to be steep, pick a point to aim for where you know your tail will be clear.

The following criteria should apply to all unlicensed landing sites. These are technical requirements which do not necessarily take account of anything like Rule 5. The ANO regards a congested area as one 'substantially used for recreational and residential purposes', etc. This therefore officially makes a golf course a congested area, though you would be forgiven for thinking otherwise. A rule of thumb is 60% buildings and trees, but specifics have not been tested in court yet.

There should be at least one approach and departure lane containing either no or only isolated obstacles — a downwind component is not acceptable. The lanes and the landing areas should be big enough to ensure that, according to published performance data, you can land, take off and reach a safe height that enables you to touch down into wind following an engine failure, whilst avoiding all obstacles by a safe margin.

Try to avoid marshland underneath the lanes because, while it may be soft, there is still a probability of skids nosing or wheels sinking in during an emergency landing. The terrain beneath the lanes must be suitable for emergency landings with respect to slope, softness, frangible obstructions, etc. Water is OK provided the Performance Group is suitable or you've got the usual lifejackets, floats, etc.

The landing pad itself ideally should be level, drained and have a grass or solid surface that does not blow up dust at the slightest provocation (in practice, it's OK as long as you can drive the average car over it). Its diameter should be at least twice the length of the largest helicopter to use it, including rotors. Watch out for anything that may snag the skids.

Some people like the touchdown area marked with an H, but provided the grid reference is accurate enough, it shouldn't be too hard to see a few people expectantly looking into the air as if they were waiting for the Second Coming!

If you're wanting to land where there's a gathering of 1,000 or more people at an organized event, remember that no landings at unlicensed sites should be undertaken within 3,000 feet of that assembly without written permission from the CAA and the event organizers (iaw Rule 5 (1) d (i) of the ANGR).

Pleasure Flying and Feeder sites are special cases and are considered in Chapter 7.

Checklists

They're funny things, checklists. You need them, and yet if you let passengers see you using them, they wonder if you know how to fly the aircraft properly! Psychologically, it may be a good idea to use them as discreetly as possible, or even from memory.

Checklists should be available for every crew member, and they will also be fully listed in the Operations Manual. They should be used on all relevant occasions, but on single-crew flights checks usually done in the air may be completed from memory. However, memorized drills must be strictly in accordance with Company checklists, and emergency drills must be verified as soon as possible.

It may be helpful to have the vital actions placarded somewhere — either on the back of a sun visor or printed on the Nav Log.

It's worth considering leaving the navigation or anti-collision lights (or engine-out warnings) on when you leave aircraft, despite what the checklist says about switching them off. It's very useful for informing you that you've left the Master switch on as you walk away!

Technical Logs

Each aircraft must have a Technical Log completed for each flight, just a small part of the mountain of paperwork that's generated every day. The types of Tech Log (as they're known) are many and varied, but fashion seems to dictate something with multi-sectors, a sample of which follows. Actually, some Tech Logs are hopeless, being badly designed and obviously concocted merely to satisfy legal requirements with no thought for the people who have to use them.

If you ever have to design one of your own, please restrict the temptation to include a loadsheet with it — try to keep that separate if you can. The main reason for Tech Logs being bad is that people try and cram too much information on them; if your aircraft are below a certain weight, loadsheets are not required anyway. The CAA Airworthiness Division issue a leaflet (which is an extract from BCARs) giving guidance on compiling Tech Logs. Some examples may also be found in CAP 450.

On the particular example included, a different page is used for each day, but successive flights by different pilots may be entered on the same one (this is because provision has been made to identify the pilot in each case).

It's your responsibility to ensure that the Check A slot is signed, preferably by the engineer/pilot conducting it (see later this Chapter for more about Check As). Talking of engineers, you must also check that previous defects entered have been rectified (or deferred — see later) by a person so qualified. In addition, check the validity of the Certificate of Maintenance Review and the Certificate of Release to Service before flight (these are both issued by your Maintenance Contractor). To assist in keeping track of servicing requirements, the next Maintenance Due date should be entered from the Certificate of Release to Service in box 1, being immediately comparable to the current date, which is in the box to the right, box 2.

The hours at which that maintenance is due are also entered in box 3. The aircraft hours brought forward (from box 7 to the previous page) are then entered in box 4 and the total of box 3 minus box 4 is then entered in box 5. This gives you an indication of the hours required to the next check, which should be compared against the proposed flying for the day. It's your responsibility to ensure that the aircraft has sufficient hours (and days) available to do what you want before the next maintenance check is due.

The aircraft fuel state and uplifts must be correct (and make sure they match with those on the Nav Log and the Load Sheet!).

The Acceptance Signature certifies that the foregoing have been checked, the loading is satisfactory and that the aircraft is accepted for flight.

CHECK A SIGNATURE	APS WEIGHT	DATCON START	TYPE	REG	NEXT CHECK	DATE	TECHNICAL LOG No.
					DUE DATE 1.	2.	

	OIL			FUEL		LOAD PLAN	DE-ICE		PILOT NAME	ACCEPTANCE SIGNATURE	FROM	TO	DEFECT REP No.	AFTERFLIGHT SIGNATURE	T/O TIME	LOG TIME	TOTAL TIME	ENG CYCLES
	UP	OPT	ARR	UP	OPT		START	FINISH										
1 L / R																		
2 L / R																		
3 L / R																		
4 L / R																		
5 L / R																		
6 L / R																		
7 L / R																		
8 L / R																		
9 L / R																		

THE PILOT'S ACCEPTANCE SIGNATURE ABOVE CERTIFIES THAT THE AIRCRAFT IS LOADED IN ACCORDANCE WITH COMPANY OPERATIONS MANUAL PROCEDURES, THAT THE APPLICABLE BEFORE FLIGHT INSPECTION HAS BEEN CARRIED OUT AND THE AIRCRAFT IS ACCEPTED AS BEING FIT FOR SERVICE.

THE WORK RECORDED BELOW HAS BEEN CARRIED OUT IN ACCORDANCE WITH THE REQUIREMENTS OF THE AIR NAVIGATION ORDER FOR THE TIME BEING IN FORCE AND IN THAT RESPECT THE AIRCRAFT/EQUIPMENT IS CONSIDERED FIT FOR RELEASE TO SERVICE

No	Defect	No	Action Taken	Signature	Authority	Date		
							Daily Total	6.
							Next Check Due	3.
							Aircraft hrs brought fwd	4.
							Hrs to next check	5.
							Total Aircraft Hrs	7.

Example of a Technical Log

Before take-off one copy of the Technical Log should be left behind at the point of departure. If this isn't possible, then the copy must be carried in an approved fireproof container together with the rest of the aircraft documents.

There is some controversy about fireproof containers. They're only really relevant in helicopter operations where sometimes it really is impractical to leave a copy behind, as passengers tend to board with the engine running and don't want to waste time while you close down and find a suitable stone to leave a copy of the paperwork under.

At the moment, trials are taking place with a bag made of that shiny stuff that airport firemen use as uniforms, but it only preserves documents if a sheet of cardboard is inserted either side of them! All the bag seems to do is ensure that everything burns up inside without harming anything outside (a bit like fireproof flying suits).

The dotted line on the form is a suggested place to put the perforations, otherwise you're continually undoing the whole book to extract a copy.

At the end of each flight, take-off and landing times and the duration of each flight should be entered.

Defects should be entered next and the aircraft is then grounded until they're either cleared or deferred in accordance with current regulations. If there are none, just write 'Nil Further Defects' or 'NFD' for short.

Whenever a defect is entered, a new page is commenced. If this isn't possible, for instance due to lack of sheets, then the defect description should include the sector number.

A new sector line should be commenced when either fuel is uplifted, a landing away is carried out, the engine has been shut down or a new pilot is used.

If there is no provision for determining the identity of the pilot on each sector, then a new page must be started every time the pilot changes. A new page must also be started (in addition to entering a defect) if a new Check A or de-icing procedure is performed.

At the end of the day's flying, the total hours are added to comprise box 6, and the totals of box 6 and box 4 are added to give a/c total hours which should be entered in box 7, and then transferred to box 4 of the next page. After that, a copy of the completed Log is transmitted to the Maintenance Contractor by whatever means your Company uses (you know, cleft stick, runner or similar).

Deferred Defects

A deferred defect is one which will not prejudice the safety of a flight, but which should be rectified as soon as practicable after its completion.

For instance, the minimum navigational equipment for **IFR** operations in most areas is 2 VOR + 1 ADF or 1 VOR + 2 ADF, ILS, DME, Transponder, Marker and 2 720 channel VHF Comms (below FL100 in Amsterdam you can get away with 1 VOR and 1 ADF, but watch out for Germany).

However, provisions are made in regulations for you to fly when not more than one item of the above list is unserviceable, if it isn't reasonably practical to effect any repairs or replacements prior to take-off, especially as the assistance of outside maintenance organizations should not be sought without the prior approval of your own Maintenance Contractor.

On the assumption that you, as the Aircraft Commander, are satisfied that the forecast weather conditions, latest route information and other relevant factors are such that your flight can safely be made in accordance with any other regulations that may be in force (with respect to the above items only), you are allowed to complete one flight to a place where repairs may be effected. The ANO (Article 11(1)) also allows you to fly to a place where a Certificate of Release to Service can be issued for any defect rectification when you are at a place where it is not reasonably practical to do so. In this case you will have to submit a report to the CAA (FOD 7) within ten days, so to cover yourself, the flight must have been made to the nearest place at which certification can be made, and the aircraft must have been suitably equipped for the route, as well as taking into account any hazards to the liberty or health of persons on board.

Except where otherwise indicated, deferred defects apply under all operating conditions, but this in no way absolves you from ensuring that your aircraft is safe for flight. Although other people may be involved, the final decision remains with you regarding the acceptance of an aircraft. At least 1 VHF communications radio should be serviceable at all times.

Defective equipment should be isolated from the remainder of the system to which it belongs by the removal of fuses, blanking of pipelines, locking of selectors or the taking of other actions that will promote safety. This will include the labelling of defective equipment as such (in the case of gauges, the label needs to be placed so that no readings can be taken).

As a general rule, a defect will only be allowed so that you may return to base. Only under exceptional circumstances should you depart from base with one. Normally (away from base), reference to the lists will be sufficient, but in the case of defects not listed, to do with cargo and safety equipment or caused by lightning strikes, severe turbulence or propeller damage, guidance must be sought from the maintenance contractor.

All defects when they occur should be entered in the relevant part of the Technical Log. The aircraft should not then fly until the defect is either cleared or deferred in accordance with current regulations. A new Technical Log page must then be started, but if, for any reason, the same page must be used, the defect(s) must be clearly identified by numbering.

In addition, details of deferred defects should also be recorded on the Deferred Defects Sheet, which is carried with the Tech Log.

When a deferred defect is finally cleared, the entries are made on the current Technical Log page, not the original, and DD Sheet noting the original DD Sheet number, the rectification action and the clearance certification.

For specific details of what is or isn't allowed, refer to the Technical Section of the relevant aircraft. Each company's list of Deferred Defects is submitted and approved by the CAA who refer to a master list kept for each aircraft on the Civil Register. Once your Company's list has been approved, there must be no deviation from it without their approval, so if you get a defect that is outside the list given, you will have to play it safe and ground the aircraft.

On top of the list being approved, the Company will also be issued with an exemption from the ANO allowing them to fly on Public Transport without the scales of equipment normally specified by it.

Check A Inspections

Each day, before the first flight of any aircraft, a Check A Inspection is carried out in accordance with the approved maintenance schedule. Although it's meant to be a specific maintenance inspection, as laid down in the Light Aircraft Maintenance Schedule (LAMS), it's sort of equivalent to a pilot's preflight inspection, which in turn is equivalent to the 'external walkround' detailed in the Flight Manual. If you've ever been in the Army, the Check A is similar to the status of the 'First Parade' given to every vehicle at the start of each day, where all the tyre pressures and oil levels are checked.

On smaller aircraft, it may be carried out by a Commander with the approval of the Chief Pilot, who will arrange for the necessary training with the Company Maintenance Organisation. In keeping with General Aviation practice, the Commander performing the first flight of the day normally performs the Check A. If so, he is responsible for signing the relevant box of the Tech Log. You are responsible (as Commander) for checking that it is signed by the person who did it.

The term 'Inspect' is interpreted to mean that all items are examined externally and *in situ* and that their condition when so inspected is sufficient to preserve continued airworthiness.

Throughout the Inspection, a thorough examination should be made of all surfaces and parts of the aircraft for signs of damage, corrosion, loose or missing rivets or bolts, distortion, cracking, dents, scores, chafing, kinking, leaks, excessive chipping of paintwork, overheating, fluid contamination and any other signs of structural or mechanical damage.

In addition, all parts should be checked for general security and cleanliness and a particular inspection should be made of each drain and vent hole to ensure that it is unblocked.

Altimeter Setting Procedures

The altimeter on the Commander's instrument panel is No 1, and the one on the co-pilot's is No 2. If two altimeters are on the Commander's panel, the one to the right of the artificial horizon in the standard T position is No 1. The following altimeter settings are suggested for each stage of flight:

	Single crew		Two crew	
	No 1	No 2	No 1	No 2
Taxi, T/O	Afd QNH*	Afd QNH	Afd QNH*	Afd QNH
Climb, cruise				
below TA	QNH	QNH	QNH	QNH a/reqd
above TA	1013.2	RQNH	1013.2	1013.2
Descent	Dest QNH	Dest QNH	Dest QNH	Dest QNH
Finals	QFE	QNH	QFE	QFE
Overshoot	QNH	QNH	QNH	QNH

* QFE for circuits

In flight, the altimeters should be specifically checked on levelling, prior to descent, on changing a setting and when completing initial approach checks. The difference between their readings should be plus or minus fifty feet.

Where a marked difference is apparent between altimeter readings in flight, the lower reading altimeter should be treated as the master during any descent.

VOR/RNAV

VOR ground stations are almost always at a focal point of airways systems. When using a VOR, care must naturally be taken not to enter controlled airspace unwittingly. Due to topographical and other considerations, a number of VOR ground stations have limited range and accuracy on certain radials, details of which may be found in the *Air Pilot*. As the RNAV uses VOR as the basis of its operation, it follows that readings could be misleading in those areas.

As they are Class 3 navaids, RNAV indications should always be supported by raw data, such as direct readings from a VOR or NDB. In other words, they should never be used as the sole reference for position reporting.

Radio Procedures

Despite the fact that you don't always have to (depending on where you fly), a radio listening watch should be kept at all times during flight as a matter of airmanship.

Radio checks and radio selection before departure should be covered in the relevant aircraft checklist.

There are one or two points that should be brought out at this stage that aren't often taught properly during training. The first is to wait a split second to speak after pressing the transmit button. This gives all the relays in the system a chance to switch over so that your message can get through in full, that is, not missing out the first bit.

Secondly, whenever you get a frequency change *en route*, not only should you write it down on your Nav Log, but change to the new frequency on the **other** box. Both these methods give you something to go back to if you can't get through on the new one for whatever reason (although it is appreciated that this could create difficulties where aircraft have two station boxes and you have to switch them both every time). Also, use the switches on the station box to silence radios, not the volume controls, otherwise you get endless embarrassing situations where you transmit, get no reply, wonder what-in-hell-is-happening and suddenly realize you turned the volume down and have been blocking everybody else out. That's when the Standard Air Traffic Voice tells you he's been calling you for the past five minutes . . . .

a) **Radio failure** (this will be more comprehensively covered in your Airway Manual)

i) **VFR/Special VFR in controlled airspace**
Where clearance has been obtained to the boundary on leaving or to the field on entering, proceed as planned. If any doubt exists about clearances obtained before radio failure, or if clearance was only given to hold at the next reporting point, you should clear the zone by the most direct route as quickly as possible, avoiding airfields.

ii) **VFR outside controlled airspace**
If the flight can be completed without entering controlled airspace, just carry on. Don't enter controlled airspace even if previous clearance has been obtained.

If you can't complete the flight without entering controlled airspace, divert to the nearest suitable landing point and telephone for permission.

The military have a system of flying a left or right-handed triangle pattern that is recognisable on radar, although it's usually only used if you're lost as well as having a duff radio. Use it as a last resort, though, because ATC have other things to look out for than possible triangles.

If they do recognize your problem, they will send up a shepherd aircraft to formate on you and bring you down, so remain VMC if you can, and as high as possible so that radar can see you better. Although it's a better way of getting noticed than just using the triangle, if you can squawk, then do so, because that will give a height read-out to assist the shepherd.

If you can only **receive** messages, fly in a **right** handed pattern for a minute (if your airspeed is under 300 knots, make it two). Fly at best endurance speed and make each 120 degree turn as tight as possible.

If you can't transmit either, then do the same, but to the left.

b) **RT Emergency Procedures**

You should always declare an Emergency, even if you have to downgrade it later.

The Distress call (or 'MAYDAY') is used when the aircraft is threatened by imminent danger and is in most urgent need of immediate assistance.

If and when the threat of danger has been overcome, the Distress Call must be cancelled by notification on all frequencies upon which the original message was sent.

The Urgency call (or 'PAN') is used to indicate that the aircaft has a very urgent message to transmit concerning the safety of a ship, aircraft or other vehicle, or of some person on board or in sight.

Action in the Event of an Accident

An accident has occurred if anyone (whether associated with an aircraft, or a third party) is killed or injured, or the aircraft itself sustains damage or structural failure requiring major repair or replacement of the affected parts.

That's a long-winded way of saying that if a person or aircraft gets damaged between chocks off and chocks on, you've had an accident!

'Injury' means anything that requires hospital or medical treatment and results in suspension of, or substantial restrictions in, a person's activities for a period of five days or more.

'Damage' does not include engine failure or damage, if it is limited to the engine, its cowling or accessories. Neither does it mean anything that is limited to propellers, wing tips, antennae, tyres, brakes, fairings, small dents or punctured holes in the aircraft skin.

When a notifiable accident (in accordance with the above definition) occurs, the pilot or senior survivor, the Company or the aerodrome authority (in that order, if at all possible) should take as much as possible of the following action after life-saving measures have been taken:

a) Fuel and battery OFF — disconnect the battery if there is no risk of a spark igniting fuel vapour.
b) Prevent any further tampering with the wreckage by **ANYBODY** except in order to save life.
c) Inform the Company by the quickest means of:

    1) Aircraft and Reg No
    2) Time and position of accident
    3) Details of survivors
    4) Nature of occurrence/other details.

d) Notify Police, Fire, Ambulance, ATC, Gas/Electricity.
e) Examine the aircraft for relevant abnormalities.
f) Record names and addresses of witnesses, with comments.
g) Take weather details.
h) Make sketches and take photographs.
i) Refer all media enquiries to the Company.
j) Complete a CAA Occurrence Report Form.

Aircrew involved in an accident should be medically examined and stopped from flying until cleared again by the Chief Pilot in consultation with the Medical Examiner. No comments should be made until either they feel fit to do so, or one night's rest has passed since the accident, whichever is the sooner.

The Operations Department is to:

k) Send an Immediate signal to the Air Accidents Investigation Branch, Dept of Transport (telephone 01 276 6000 and telex 858119), copying the same to the CAA Flight Operations Inspectorate at Aviation House, South Area, Gatwick Airport. The identifying abbreviation ACCID should be used and as much of the following information as is to hand should be included:

    1) Aircraft type, model, nationality and registration
    2) Names of owners, operators and hirers
    3) Name of Commander
    4) Date and time of accident (UTC)
    5) Last point of departure and next point of intended landing
    6) Location of accident.

7) Number of persons reported (this is a Fire Service phrase meaning people involved in an incident, i.e. those on board, killed, injured, etc)
8) Nature of the accident and any other information that may be necessary

l) Inform Chief Pilot, Engineering and Directors
m) Ensure that relevant documentation is available for inspection.

You can find more information if you need it from AIC 66/84 (Pink 63).

Action in the Event of an Incident

An incident is any happening other than an accident which hazards or, if not corrected, would hazard any aircraft, its occupants or anyone else. The definition could possibly include any happening that:

a) involves damage to an aircraft
b) involves injury to a person
c) involves the impairment, during flight, of the capacity of a crew member to undertake the functions to which his licence relates
d) involves the failure of an aircraft system or the equipment of an aircraft
e) involves the use in flight of any emergency procedures
f) arises from the control of an aircraft in flight by its flight crew
g) arises from the failure or inadequacy of ground facilities or services
h) arises from the loading or the carriage of passengers, cargo or fuel not covered by the above but which could endanger the safety of the aircraft, its occupants or any other person.
i) could be relevant to Flight Safety, whether or not the experience is first-hand.

You will probably find that all of that is covered in the Mandatory Occurrence Reporting Scheme, under which you're obliged to report potentially dangerous occurrences which may endanger an aircraft. The MORS is mandatory for all

Public Transport aircraft over 2300 kg, and voluntary for anything else.

If involved in an incident, you should complete form CA 1673 within ninety-six hours of the occurrence, the completed form being forwarded to the Flight Safety Officer and subsequently to the CAA by Operations in accordance with the MORS.

The ANO Article 94 refers, as does CAP 382, 'Occurrence reporting' and AIC 23/89 (Pink 53). Try also (0293) 567171 if you need further help.

Aircraft Overdue Action

An aircraft is overdue thirty minutes after its last known ETA. If an overdue aircraft or accident is suspected, the last known point of departure and next planned destination should be contacted as well as the *en route* ATC.

If there is no success, contact the ATCC and initiate SAR and accident procedures. Naturally, should the aircraft subsequently be found, the above action should be cancelled.

Assistance to Others in Distress

You should, at your discretion and with due regard for the safety of your own aircraft, render any assistance that is practical and possible for the saving of life in any event demanding such assistance.

The prime function of a non-SAR equipped aircraft on arrival at a scene of distress is to act as a communications relay for properly equipped rescue units, assuming that they are coming. If not, then rendering first aid assistance becomes the primary function (provided you can land).

If you are first on the scene:

A   ssess nature of emergency and survivor details
B   roadcast position and details
C   alculate endurance and alternates
D   irect other aircraft and hand over to rescue commander
E   nsure constant visual contact
F   loat life-raft to survivors (helicopter)
G   ive survivors a wide berth to avoid downwash (helicopter)
H   over high — fifty feet or so (helicopter)

If you are not first on the scene, inform the controlling aircraft of your endurance and what assistance you can give. If you are not required, clear the area.

Whilst it is appreciated that the media require information about disasters, etc, no aircraft should operate at such an event to the detriment of rescue services and aircraft that may be present.

Flights Over Water

In a helicopter, for any flight beyond autorotational distance from shore, or when flying along the Thames in the London Control Zone, approved life-jackets for each person on board should be carried.

In addition to life-jackets, flotation gear should be fitted and working.

For flights involving more than three minutes over water, the following conditions should apply:

a) A dinghy and SARBE must be carried.
b) No night flying (single-engined only).
c) Two way radio communication must be maintained with position reporting every ten minutes.
d) Flight plan to be filed.
e) SAR to be notified.
f) Immersion suits to be worn when practical.
g) A radio altimeter must be fitted and working in accordance with Scale EE of Schedule 4 of the ANO (it must also have a voice warning).
h) Passengers must be given a full briefing on the use of all emergency equipment.

In an aeroplane, when flying over water for a distance greater than ninety minutes flying time at the recommended over water speed (whatever that is), an approved life-jacket for each person on board must be carried, in addition to life-rafts sufficient to accommodate all persons on board the aircraft. If over thirty minutes, a practical demonstration needs to be given.

Also, when beyond gliding distance from shore, the life-jackets need to be carried whenever it is reasonably possible that a landing may have to be made on water in case of emergencies during take-off or landing — this is to cover for coastal airfields.

If you're in a single-engined aircraft, and going beyond gliding distance from land, then make the passengers wear their life-jackets from the start, and ensure they know how to use them. In a twin, it is sufficient just to point out their location and the instructions on the briefing card. However, if one of the engines stops, you then become single-engined, so get your passengers to don them immediately.

Flights Over Inhospitable Terrain

Inhospitable terrain is, regarding endurance, where fuel reserves are scarce. Otherwise, it's where SAR facilities are not exactly plentiful, either. If you need to operate north of Latitude 61°N, you ought to carry something like the following, which of course should be checked before take-off:

  a) Duplicate ADF for flights over Central and Northern Sweden
  b) Topographical Maps
  c) Between 1 Nov to 31 March inclusive:
    1) SARBE
    2) 4 marine flares
    3) 5 SAMS survival bags
    4) Solid fuel stove
    5) Waterproof matches
    6) Survival booklet
    7) Clothing, i.e. parka, contact gloves, etc

Tropical areas also need consideration — see also **Operations and Forced Landings in Remote Areas** and Schedule 4 of the ANO.

Ditching

A successful ditching depends on sea conditions, wind, type of aircraft and your skill. It's also a good idea to have a basic knowledge of sea evaluation, as a proper selection of the ditching heading may well determine the difference between survival and disaster.

Whereas waves occur because of local winds, swells (which relate to larger bodies of water), rely on more distant and substantial disturbances. They move primarily up and down, and only give the illusion of movement, as the sea does not, in fact, move much horizontally.

This effective movement is more dominant than anything caused by the wind, and therefore doesn't depend on wind direction, although secondary swells may well do. It's extremely dangerous to land into wind without regard to sea conditions; the swell must be taken into consideration.

The vast majority of swells are lower than twelve to fifteen feet, and the swell face is the side facing you, whereas the backside is the side away from you. Oddly enough, this applies regardless of the direction of swell movement.

You will need to transmit all your MAYDAY calls and squawks (7700) while still airborne. If time permits, warn the passengers to don their lifejackets (without inflating them, or the liferafts) and tighten seat belts, remove any headsets, stow any loose items (dentures, etc) and pair off for mutual support, being ready to operate any emergency equipment that may be to hand (they should have been briefed on this before departure).

One passenger should be made the 'dinghy monitor', that is be responsible for the liferaft. If it's dark, turn on the cabin lights and ensure everybody braces before impact (the brace position helps to reduce the flailing of limbs, etc, as you hit the water; there are different onces for forward and aft facing seats).

If only one swell system exists, the problem is relatively simple — even if it's a high, fast one. Unfortunately, most cases involve two or more systems running in different directions, giving the sea a confused appearance.

Always land either on the top, or on the backside of a swell in a trough (after the passage of a crest) as near as possible to any shipping — this means that you get neither the water suddenly falling away from you, nor the cabin being swamped with water, and help is near at hand.

If the wind is strong, consider landing across the swell if it helps minimize ground speed (although in most cases drift caused by crosswind can be ignored, being only a secondary consideration to the forces contacted on touch-down).

Thus, if the swell is formidable, it's advisable to accept more cross wind in order to avoid landing directly into it. The simplest method of estimating wind characteristics is to examine the wind streaks on the water which appear as long white streaks up- and down-wind. Whichever way the foam appears to be sliding backwards is the wind direction (in other words, it's the opposite of what you think), and the relative speed is determined from the activity of the streaks themselves.

Shadows and whitecaps are signs of large seas, and if they're close together, the sea will be short and rough. Avoid these areas as far as possible — you only need about 500 feet or so to play with.

The behaviour of the aircraft on making contact with the water will vary according to the state of the sea; the more confused and heavy the swell, the greater the deceleration forces and risks of breaking up.

In an aeroplane, you should aim to have as high a nose-up attitude as possible consistent with safe handling, as there will be little control once you're on the water. Trim for the sea surface rather than the horizon. You will need a lot of power (if your engines are working) at this stage. Reduce thrust a little earlier than you would on a normal landing as this will help to lessen the chance of overshooting what may be the only clear area for miles. It will also help to stop you skipping over the water several times. The use of power is so important that it's best to ditch before your fuel is exhausted (assuming your engine's working), especially at night.

If you have less than full power, or none at all, use a higher than normal approach speed, which will give you more inertia in hand at the flare-out. This will give you more ability to feel for the surface and avoid the possibilities of stalling high or hitting the water unexpectedly.

Landing is less hazardous in a helicopter due to the capability of minimizing forward speed. Once in the water, hold the aircraft upright and level using all the cyclic control there is. Use the rotor brake (if you've got one) to stop the blades. Otherwise, be prepared to roll over to stop them.

Whatever you're in, instruct passengers not to leave until everything has quietened down. When you do, take the flotation and survival gear, but keep everyone together (remember that even seat cushions float). Attach the raft to the aircraft until you need to inflate it as it will sail away downwind at the least provocation.

If your aircraft (whatever it is) is floating comfortably on the water and with no danger of fire, consider remaining on board. Don't be tempted to leave a relatively safe vessel, but have liferafts ready for a quick exit if need be. This way, you will be more conspicuous, and warmer.

Make safe everything you can, then try and retransmit the MAYDAY call.

Don't assume rescuers can see you. Splash, use flares or mirrors to attract attention, but let them come to you. Don't leave the security of the raft or aircraft unless you are actually being rescued as the downwash or wind will blow them away from you.

Apart from drowning, the real threat is hypothermia, so once in the water, keep moving. Don't attempt to swim unless land is less than a mile or so away. Cold makes people give up, so make every effort to keep a positive mental attitude. Except in mid-ocean, SAR will be operational very soon after the distress call is made, so switch on the SARBE or ELT as soon as convenient. This will also assist a SAR satellite to refine its fix on you as it goes through subsequent orbits. Try not to point the aerial directly at rescue aircraft as this may put them into a null zone and cancel the signal.

If a speech facility is provided, this should only be used as a last resort. Not only will it wear your batteries down quicker, but it will also take priority over the homing signal used to fix your position by SAR.

At night (or at any time for that matter), don't be disturbed if the rescue helicopter disappears for ten minutes after first finding you. It will be making an automatic let-down to your exact position after having located your overhead at height. This is where the temptation to use speech is very strong, but it should be resisted all the more because this is the part where the homing signal from the SARBE is most needed. If you feel the need to do something, fire off a few mini-flares instead.

On the question of ELTs, not all military helicopters monitor 121.5, as it's primarily a civilian emergency channel, so get one with 243 Mhz as well, because this is where they mainly listen out.

When finally in the winch strop, don't grasp the winch hook, because of the possibility of shocks from static electricity.

Operations and Forced Landings in Remote Areas

Because of the difficulties of communication in remote areas, it is most important that Operations are fully aware of your intended routings, destinations and sensible timings. If you have to make a forced landing, you must ensure that the Company is notified, together with the appropriate ATC, so that overdue action is not set in motion unnecessarily.

When operating a helicopter in remote or inaccessible areas, take into consideration the problems associated with recovery should the engines fail to start after a shut-down. If you have to, position your aircraft as close as possible to a track or road to save trouble later (engineers also prefer you to be as near as possible to a pub, if you can manage it).

If you're forced down, the same principles of passenger preparation for landing apply as for ditching (see above). Having arrived on the ground, the first task (if necessary) is to assist survivors and apply first aid, and the second to provide shelter (the absence of food and water will not become a problem for some time). Consider using the aircraft for shelter if it hasn't burned away. Don't wander too far away from it, and ensure that everybody stays within sight of each other at all times. Use any remaining aircraft fuel for light and heat as necessary.

Maintain a positive mental attitude. Wait before operating the SARBE or ELT until it is likely that SAR services are in your area, thus conserving batteries. Otherwise, follow the instructions given in **Ditching**, previously. Unlike ditching, you will be better able to try and maintain a constant position.

You can communicate with SAR aircraft visually by making the following signals on the ground, which are only a selection of the full range available (see the *UKAP*). They should be at least eight feet high with as large a contrast as possible being obtained between the materials used and the background.

Require assistance	V
Negative	N
Require medical assistance	X
Affirmative	Y
Proceeding this direction	->

Rocking of the rescue aircraft's wings during daylight and flashing of the landing or navigation lights twice at night indicates that your signals are understood.

Airmiss Reporting Procedure

An **Airmiss Report** should be made whenever you think your aircraft may have been endangered during flight by the closeness of another aircraft to the extent that a risk of collision existed.

An initial report should be made on the frequency in use at the time, as it could be difficult tracing the other aircraft later. Prefix your call with the words 'AIRMISS'. If you can't do this, the report should be made by telephone immediately after landing on Freefone 2230 (which belongs to West Drayton).

The completed form CA 1094 (which is for confirmation only) should be forwarded to the Joint Airmiss Section within seven days. See also the *UKAP* (RAC 3-1-13 para 9) and AIC 24/89 (Pink 115).

Birdstrikes

Prevention is better than cure, and it may be better to try to avoid birds as much as possible, although some stroppy pheasants have even been known to attack aircraft lining up on the runway! Notification of permanent or seasonal concentrations of birds are sometimes issued in Notams.

Otherwise, keep away from bird sanctuaries or other areas where they may be expected, such as along shorelines or rivers in autumn or spring — migrating birds use line features for navigation as well, but they don't necessarily keep 300 m to the right!

Noticeably fewer birdstrikes occur at height, so try to fly as high as possible. Avoid high speed descent and approach — half the speed means a quarter of the impact energy. A short delay on the approach could mean the clearance of a group of birds, as they do move in waves. Groups of birds will usually break away downwards from anything hazardous, so try to fly over them if possible — beware of stalling or spinning, though. You could try and use landing lights to make yourself more visible.

A hot windshield is more pliable and therefore less susceptible to shattering if it gets hit. Some aircraft require these to be on for take-off and landing, but if there is no indication in the flight manual about the optimum warm-up time, use fifteen minutes. Overheating is just as bad as underheating, so be wary if your aircraft has been left in the sun a long time. See also AIC 54/83 (Pink 45). If a birdstrike does occur, stop and inspect the damage immediately. If you can't do this and have to carry on, make sure you have as much controllability as possible before trying to land again — fly the aircraft first.

A (yellow) Bird Strike Report should be submitted even if there is no damage. If the damage to the aircraft warrants a Mandatory Occurrence Report, then a Birdstrike Report may be submitted instead, provided nothing else has occurred to change this.

You will be asked what the species is (or was), and if unsure, you're invited to parcel up the remains and send them to the Aviation Bird Unit, but what the Post Office think of that idea, I don't know. The Bird Unit can be found on (0483) 232581.

Further details may also be found in AIC 13/89 (Pink 112).

Carriage of Munitions of War

Munitions of War should not be carried, provided that a weapon not classed as such may be carried as passengers' baggage if it's stowed in an inaccessible part of the aircraft and not primed or loaded. A full definition of what these are is given in CAP 360 Part 1 (see the Alphabetical Index to Civil Aviation Publication at the end of this book).

Ammunition to do with a sporting weapon may be carried, however, provided that the total consignment weighs no more than 5 kg and it's kept separate from the weapon itself. Munitions of War may also be Dangerous Goods (in the case of ammunition), so there may be a separate procedure.

If you ever need it, permission to carry munitions of war may be provided through the usual channels, which basically commence with an application to your Flight Ops Inspector at least ten days before the permission is required, who will then contact the Home Office. Then you will be visited by a gentleman in a trilby hat. If the journey also involves going abroad, the Foreign Office will also become interested, making diplomatic moves, etc, on your behalf. Actually, the whole process has the potential for being rather messy and is best left alone anyway.

Carriage of Livestock

If you ever get lumbered with this problem in a small aircraft, you can carry guide dogs or police dogs on special operations only, if they're restrained with a leash, but be very careful with wet ones; not only will the extra moisture mist up the windscreen, but the first thing they will want to do is shake themselves dry once inside the cabin, thus soaking everyone in sight!

Otherwise, carriage of animals is forbidden unless they're in a suitable carrying case and accompanied by a responsible person, preferably their owners. The carriage of livestock is covered by the Transit of Animals (General) Order 1973, but

IATA also have Live Animals Regulations which should tell you all you need to know about labelling, hygiene, feeding, etc.

You may also need to carry animal first aid and emergency kits, with any drugs and humane killers being kept under lock and key by you, the Commander. Any attendants must also have been trained in their use.

Horses are something of a special case, perhaps needing a groom to stand by them on take-off and landing (you will need a special exemption for this, together with a large aircraft).

Don't forget that there are stringent regulations regarding the carriage of animals across International boundaries.

Fuller details will be found in CAP 360, Part 1, Section 3, paragraphs 5 and 6.

Carriage of Freight Overseas

Freight is easier to carry than passengers in the UK (mainly because it doesn't answer back!), but considerably more complex when doing it overseas (actually, having said that, as long as the paperwork is **properly** done, moving freight can be surprisingly speedy).

And that's the problem: the paperwork. The best advice I can give you is **never** self-handle freight if you can possibly help it — always employ an agent. However, for one box it can seem over the top — even assuming you find the right forms, they all require special computer codes which describe the goods, but the book on these alone is thicker than a telephone directory and has no intelligible index. Don't expect help from Customs, either — you might get it, but being fair, filling in your forms is not part of their job, as they will no doubt gleefully tell you.

Usually, therefore, all you will be asked to do is simply transport the stuff from airfield to airfield with the formalities being taken care of by the client.

However, it is difficult to claim that you are only a carrier if anything goes wrong, as the vehicle used for conveyance is liable to forfeiture as well as the goods concerned, so you need to know a bit of what goes on to cover yourself.

First of all, you should impress upon the client that you are not a properly qualified freight agent, and that you reserve the right to use such people at both ends of the journey. Naturally, he will have to pay for this.

However, circumstances may lumber you with a parcel on your hands one day, so if you must do things yourself, try and do it through a major airport, even at the expense of greater landing fees. A part-time Customs officer at a small one who is waiting to go home will be no help at all!

Each carton must have a label with the consignor's and consignee's name and address on it. It must be covered by a **cargo manifest** which should have each item in it listed separately, numbered and described. There will also need to be an **air waybill**, which is the freight equivalent of a passenger ticket.

If you can, try and get sight of what's inside the boxes and check that it doesn't tick! Be especially careful of people asking you to take wrapped 'presents' for others at your destination.

Carriage of Dangerous Goods

Many goods, due to their magnetic or chemical properties, may be a hazard to an aircraft or its crew. The whole of the following is abridged from the standard insert as issued by the CAA, which must be adhered to; therefore, it's very boring and should only be read out of dire necessity!

The legislation on the Carriage of Dangerous Goods by Air is set out in the Air Navigation (Dangerous Goods) Regulations 1985 made pursuant to Article 47 of the ANO, in which it is stated that dangerous goods must not be carried unless a Permission has been granted by the CAA.

These are amplified by the ICAO Technical Instructions for the Safe Transport of Dangerous Goods by Air.

The conditions contained in such a Permission must be complied with at all times and this will mean that such goods must be in total compliance with the provisions of the ICAO Technical Instructions for the Safe Transport of Dangerous Goods by Air (DOC 9284-AN/905).

Dangerous Goods as defined by ICAO are divided into nine classes as follows (with examples as given):

1) Explosives (fireworks, ammunition)
2) Gases, compressed, liquefied or dissolved under pressure (aerosols, gas lighter refills)
3) Flammable liquids (paint, thinners)
4) Flammable solids (non-safety matches), substances liable to spontaneous combustion or emission of flammable gases on contact with water (barium or sodium)

5) Oxidizing substances (bleaching powders) and organic peroxides (glass fibre repair kits)
6) Poisonous substances (insecticides, drugs) and infectious materials (bacterial agents)
7) Radioactive materials
8) Corrosives (mercury, acids)
9) Miscellaneous (magnetized material)

The provisions of the ICAO Technical Instructions do not apply to the following:

a) aircraft parts, equipment and supplies (other than fuel) carried by the Company if authorized by the CAA Airworthiness Division or required aboard the aircraft for its operation including:
   1) Fire extinguishers
   2) Cylinders containing compressed gases
   3) Aerosol dispensers
   4) Distilled spirits
   5) Hydraulic accumulators
   6) Non-spillable batteries
   7) First-aid kits
   8) Signalling devices
   9) Items of replacement thereof, except that batteries, aerosol dispensers and signalling devices must be packed in strong packaging and not more than one aircraft survival kit or inflatable life-raft may be loaded in any inaccessible cargo compartment.
   10) Alcoholic beverages, perfumes and colognes carried on board the aircraft for use or sale during flight(s).

b) The following items carried by passengers or crew:
   1) Alcoholic beverages, perfumes and colognes, provided that the net quantity in each receptacle does not exceed half a litre and that the total net quantity of perfumes or colognes does not exceed two litres.
   2) Medicinal or toilet articles which are necessary or appropriate for a journey, where the total net quantity of same per person does not exceed two kilograms or two litres and the net quantity of each single article does not exceed half a kilo or half a litre.

3) Small gaseous oxygen or air cylinders required for medicinal use.
4) Small carbon dioxide gas cylinders worn by passengers for the operation of mechanical limbs, also spare cylinders of a similar size may be carried if required to ensure an adequate supply for the duration of the journey.
5) Securely boxed cartridges for sporting purposes in Division 1.4S, in quantities not exceeding five kilograms gross mass per passenger for personal use, excluding ammunition with explosive or incendiary projectiles.
6) Dry ice intended for use in food and beverage service aboard the aircraft and dry ice in quantities not exceeding two kilograms per passenger when used to pack perishables in carry-on baggage.
7) Personal smoking materials intended for use by an individual when carried on his person. However, lighter fuel and refills and lighters containing unabsorbed liquid fuel are not permitted.
8) Cardiac pacemakers containing radioactive material (such as plutonium batteries) when surgically implanted.
9) Wheelchairs with non-spillable batteries (see Packing Instructions 800 in the ICAO/IATA regulations) as checked baggage, provided that the battery is disconnected, the battery terminals are insulated to prevent accidental short circuits and the battery is securely attached to the wheelchair. If such a wheelchair has spillable batteries, the battery must also be removed from the wheelchair and carried in strong rigid packaging as follows:
    i) The packaging must be leaktight, impervious to battery fluid and be protected against upset using any appropriate means of securement (other than by bracing against freight or baggage).
    ii) the batteries must be protected against short circuits, secured upright and surrounded by compatible absorbent materiel sufficient to absorb their total liquid contents, and:
    iii) The packaging must be marked with an orientation label (i.e. 'This way up'), be marked 'Battery, wet, with wheelchair' and be labelled

with a 'corrosive label' (examples to be found in ICAO regulations).
The Commander must be informed of the location of a wheelchair with an installed battery or the location of a packed battery.

10) Catalytic hair curlers (i.e. the Braun hair curler) which contain hydrocarbon gas. No more than one is permitted per passenger or crew member when contained in baggage, provided that the safety cover is securely fitted over the heating element. Gas refills for such curlers are not permitted.

Mercury instruments or containers must be regarded as if they were lead-acid batteries and similar precautions with their carriage must be taken (see paragraph 9, above). Although such instruments or apparatus are not classified as dangerous goods by regulations, you should nevertheless be aware of the consequences of mercury contamination.

Aerosol cans left in cockpits in hot weather are prone to overheating and subsequent explosion if the temperature gets sufficiently hot to melt the solder securing the can and increase the pressure inside it.

Few companies hold a general permission to carry dangerous goods. If the requirement arises, then permission will be required under regulation 3(1)(a) of the Air Navigation (Dangerous Goods) Regulations 1985. Further information or advice can be sought from your Flight Ops Inspector, or the Dangerous Goods Section, telephone (0293) 573800; telex 878573.

Smoking in Aircraft

Smoking should take place only in accordance with the Flight Manual and even then only with your permission. In any case, there should be no use of smoking materials during run-up, taxi, take-off, landing, shut-down or within fifty metres of any aircraft whilst on the ground.

Refuelling

Jet and piston fuels are different with regard to the way that contaminants (particularly water) mix with them, due to variations in their specific gravities. The s.g. of water compared to Avtur, for instance, is so close that it may take up to four hours for it to settle out, whereas the same process may take as little as half an hour with Avgas.

As a result, there is always some water in suspension in jet fuel, which must be kept within strict limits — that's why Avtur requires two filtration stages, one for solids and one for water (the presence of water also implies that of certain bacteria which have a habit of eating through fuel tank linings. Check that additives to kill the bacteria are included in the fuel).

The ANO Article 87 lays down the requirements to be met for aviation fuel installations, while CAP 434 expands on these, providing guidelines and procedures to be followed.

Wherever possible, aircraft parked overnight should have their fuel tanks completely filled to prevent condensation. Half filled fuel drums left overnight should not be used for the same reasons.

Scrupulous cleanliness is essential — whenever any openings or connections have to be left open, they should be protected with blanks or covers. If this isn't possible, openings should be left facing downwards.

Drain plugs, valves, filter bowls, sumps and meshes of all filters should be checked regularly for sediment, slime or corrosion. These checks should be carried out and signed for daily.

Each day before flying, and when the fuel is settled, a water check should be carried out both in aircraft and containers (but see sub-paragraph c, below, for drums). Samples should be collected in a transparent container and should show no sediment, free water or cloudiness. If there is only one liquid present, ensure that it is not all water. The instructions for the use of water detectors are displayed on the containers.

All fuel (and oil) uplift should be entered in the Technical Log in the relevant spaces for each sector.

Aircraft should normally be refuelled with engines stopped, but some airfields provide facilities for running refuels in helicopters, which may be taken advantage of if no passengers are on board and you consider the operation safe to perform.

Otherwise, everybody not involved in the actual process of fuelling should keep clear — at least fifty metres away, but for exceptions see later.

Naturally, only competent and authorized personnel should operate fuelling equipment, who must also be fully briefed by their Company. In practice, of course, refuellers usually know very well what they are doing, but you should still be in full communication with them.

During any refuelling operation the following precautions should be taken:

a) The correct grade of fuel is used. The quality should also be checked (say, by viewing that day's test fuel sample record, or even viewing it yourself), and this is particularly important at unlicensed aerodromes.

b) Fire extinguishing equipment must be available and crews must be familiar with its use.

c) Barrels, when used, must be undamaged and be in date (give-aways for this include faded labels). When checking a drum, have it standing for as long as possible, but at least half an hour. Then draw a sample from as far down as possible through a water detector. If you suspect contamination, be prepared not to use the last third of the barrel's contents.

d) Run fuel for a minute or so to clear pipes.

c) A clear exit path must be maintained to allow quick removal of fuelling equipment in emergency.

f) The aircraft, fuelling vehicle, hose nozzle, filters or anything else through which fuel passes should be electrically bonded throughout.

g) Aircraft should not be refuelled within 100 feet of radar equipment that is operating. Only essential switches should be operated, with radio silence being observed when fuelling is taking place.

h) Fuelling should be avoided during electrical storms and bulbs or electronic flash equipment should not be used within the fuelling zone. Non-essential vehicle engines should not be run.

i) All brakes should be applied.

j) At the end of operations, fuel caps must be refitted and all leads, pipes, etc detached from the aircraft. All drains should be checked, particularly after fuelling from drums.

k) In the event of spilling anything, either use a neutralising agent, move the aircraft or wait for it to evaporate before starting engines again. Skin contamination by fuel can produce serious burns, particularly if soaked clothing is left on. Any treatment should include removal of affected clothing and washing.

Passengers should not normally remain on board during refuelling, but in certain circumstances (i.e. casevac) it may be permitted, provided that the following conditions are met in addition to the above:

l) Passengers are warned that refuelling will take place and that they must not produce ignition of any substance by any means (including operating electrical switches).

m) **NO SMOKING** signs are on, together with sufficient interior lighting to identify emergency exits.

n) A responsible person is at each main door which should be open and free from obstacles.

o) The fuelling crew is notified if fuel vapour is detected in the cabin.

p) Ground activities do not create hazards.

q) The Fire Authority is informed.

r) Fire extinguishers are close at hand.

Pilots to Remain at Controls

At least one pilot should be at the controls of any aircraft at all times between start-up and shut-down. They must also wear a safety harness at all times when seated at their station, with the shoulder harness being fastened for take-offs and landings.

It is only mentioned here because there may be a situation where a passenger is about to walk into a running tail rotor or propeller (or otherwise be out of control) and there's nobody else to assist you if you are by yourself. In the same way that it's illegal to drive a fire engine across red lights in an emergency, you can't legally leave your seat and the aircraft unattended, but it is justifiable afterwards if something dangerous is about to happen.

Flying in Manual Control

Aircraft equipped with servo controls should not be placed in manual control unless you are accompanied by a pilot or engineer qualified on type. There should be no passengers on board and dual controls should also be fitted. A clear system of verbal orders should be established prior to flight for the switching in and out of the hydraulic system, because of the kick that occurs when it happens.

Passenger Control and Briefing

How to handle passengers in general is very much a matter of Company policy. Some passengers like to be spoken to, some don't, but there are some small areas of attention you can give without being obtrusive. Just going round checking seat belts and doors helps (never trust a passenger to shut doors properly), as does a look over your shoulder before take-off and occasionally during the flight.

People new to flying are fairly obvious, and they may not appreciate such commonplace occurrences (to you, anyway) as noise, turbulence, pressure changes, strange noises from the front (stall warnings, gear coming up and down, etc), nor the lack of toilets.

However, the Air Navigation Order imposes on **you** the responsibility for the safety and well-being of your passengers. Check out Articles 36 and 37, and in there you will find that you're supposed to brief them before every flight, or at least take all reasonable steps to do so (this is covered later).

Ideally, all engines should be stopped when embarking or disembarking passengers, but occasionally it may happen that circumstances demand otherwise, though it should not be done at the expense of safety.

Nobody should enter the area of ground covered by the main rotor disc of a **helicopter** without your permission (indicated by 'thumbs up' during the day, or a flash of the landing light by night).

Movement in and out of this area should be to the front or at forty-five degrees to the longitudinal axis of the aircraft, ensuring that all movement is within your field of vision. Additionally, no movement should be allowed during start-up or run-down (due to the dangers of blade sailing) and nobody should approach the rear of a helicopter AT ANY TIME (unless it's a Chinook). You can help by landing in such a way that passengers have no choice but to go forward.

If the flight entails a running disembarkation (other than pleasure flying — see Chapter 7), one passenger should be briefed to operate the baggage door and do the unloading. Everyone else must leave the rotor disc area. Similar action must be taken with a running pick-up.

In an ideal world, of course, all passengers should be escorted by a Company representative to and from the aircraft.

When a passenger is occupying the co-pilot's seat and dual controls are fitted, they should be fully briefed as to the dangers of interfering with them — especially about using the pedals as a foot rest! If you can do so, remove the controls completely. When the co-pilot's seat is unoccupied, the seat harness should be secured away from the controls, preferably by being fully fastened.

In any aircraft, transistor radios, tape recorders and the like should not be operated in flight as they may emit radiations that could interfere with the navigation equipment (if you don't believe me, tune to Radio 4 on Long Wave and switch on a cheap calculator from the other side of the room — you will find the radio is completely blanked out by white noise).

All passengers should have their seat belts fastened at all times when seated, despite indications to the contrary (unless given permission otherwise by you), and before take-off should be fully briefed as to how to operate the release mechanism (some people may need some practice). Before take-off **and** landing (and whenever you deem it necessary, e.g. during turbulence), they also need to be **told** (it's no good just showing them the card) about the dangers involved in various aspects of aircraft operation, in particular the following:

a)   Your authority as aircraft Commander.
b)   Methods of approaching the aircraft, in particular the avoidance of propellers, exhausts and tail rotors. If other aircraft nearby have their engines running, it could mask the sound of a closer one. Propeller driven aeroplanes must always be approached from behind the wing, unless it's one with an unusual configuration, in which case the engine(s) should be shut down. There's always the danger that someone may bang their head on a wing strut or something. Pitot tubes are especially sensitive (and hot!).
     Children should be kept under strict control.
c)   Loading of baggage and hazardous items that must not be carried.
d)   Methods of opening and closing cabin doors (from inside and outside) and their use as emergency exits. Where **not** to step and what to hold on to.
e)   Hazards of rotor blade sailing and walking uphill inside the area of the rotor disc of a helicopter while rotors are running.
f)   When they can smoke (**not** when oxygen is in use!).
g)   The avoidance of flying when ill or drunk — not only is this dangerous to themselves, but if they are incapable

in the way of an emergency exit, other people could suffer as well (see **Fitness to Fly,** below).

h) How to use the seat belts and when they must be fastened.

i) What not to touch in flight.

j) Loose articles, their storage (tables, etc) and the dangers of throwing anything out of the windows (seat backs must be in the upright position).

k) The use and location of safety equipment, including a practical demonstration if required (if you intend to reach a point more than thirty minutes away from the nearest land at overwater speed, you need to do this with the lifejacket). When oxygen needs to be used in a hurry, adults should fit their masks before those of their children.

l) The reading of the passenger briefing card, which should be of at least A4 size, so it doesn't get lost in a pocket. It should also be as brightly coloured as possible, so that it catches the eye. Particular things to place on this card that always seem to be forgotten include instructions not to inflate lifejackets in the cabin and **full** door opening instructions (don't forget any little bolts that may be about).

m) How to get into the brace position (including that for rear-facing seats). If you ever have to give the order to adopt it, by the way, it is a good idea not to do it too early, otherwise the passengers will get fed up waiting for something to happen and sit up just at the point of impact.

You may (or may not) find the following sample brief useful:
'Welcome aboard this flight. I am the commander and I must ask you to take notice of any instructions you may be given by myself or my crew, and this includes any given by means of signs. Emergency exits include the window there and the door by which you came in. Full operating instructions for each are given on the passenger briefing card in the pocket of the seat in front of you which I would like you to read thoroughly, as it gives further instructions for the operation of the lifejacket, should it be required, which you will find under your seat. Other emergency equipment includes fire extinguishers which are there and there. For take-off and landing, pleasure ensure that seat backs are upright and all loose articles

are stowed away. You may not smoke during taxi, take-off and landing.'

Fitness to Fly

Although the symptoms of colds and sore throats, etc, are bad enough on the ground, they may actually become dangerous in flight by distracting you, or causing bodily harm by getting more serious with height (such as possibly bursting your eardrums, or worse). Neither should you ignore the side effects of medication bought over the counter, since they can affect the body's tolerance to Hypoxia (see also **Use of Oxygen**, below).

If you're under treatment for anything, not only should you not fly, but you should also check with the doctor that there will not be any adverse effects on your physical or mental ability, as many preparations combine chemicals, and the mixture could make quite a cocktail. Particular ones to avoid are antibiotics (penicillin, tetracyclines), tranquillizers, anti-depressants, sedatives, stimulants (caffeine, amphetamines), antihistamines and anything used for the relief of high blood pressure. No drugs or alcohol should be taken within a few hours of each other. In this case, even fairly widely accepted drugs such as aspirin can have unpredictable effects. It's as well to keep away from the office, too — nobody else will want what you've got!

Pilots generally are discouraged from giving blood when actively flying, and some dental anaesthetics can cause problems for up to twenty-four hours or more. Naturally, you've got to be certifiable if you intend to fly under the influence of things like marijuana (or worse).

Don't forget to inform the CAA (in writing) of any illness, personal injury or presumed pregnancy that incapacitates you for more than twenty days. There's also an upper age limit of sixty that affects Commanders on Public Transport flying.

Any pilot involved in an accident should be medically examined under the terms given in Accident Procedure (see earlier this chapter).

Whilst nobody should object to you taking a drink or two on an evening prior to a planned departure, you should remember that it can take as much as three days or more for **alcohol** to clear the body. Within twenty-four hours before a planned

departure most companies will expect you to exercise appropriate moderation, and possibly not drink alcohol at all within
twelve. This varies from company to company, the minimum
acceptable being eight, but twelve is quite common.

As far as passengers are concerned, all of the above applies
as well, though naturally they're allowed to drink. Despite this,
though, persons under the influence of alcohol or drugs, of
unsound mind or having the potential to cause trouble should
not be allowed on the aircraft. Certainly, no person should be
drunk on any aircraft. This is not being a spoilsport — drunks
don't react properly in emergencies and could actually be
dangerous to other people. Therefore, it is not only for their
own good, but for that of others as well. If you need to get rid
of obstreperous passengers, you can always quote Art 52 of
the ANO at them (or even use sarcasm), but don't forget you
will also need to fill in a Mandatory Occurrence Report.

See also **Incapacitation** (later this chapter) and **Casualty
Evacuation** in Chapter 7.

Use of Oxygen

Pure oxygen is a colourless, tasteless, odourless and non-
combustible gas that makes up approximately twenty-one per
cent of the air we breathe (although it doesn't burn of itself, it
does support combustion, which is why it's vital to our
survival, because the body turns whatever we eat into heat
energy. As we have no way to store oxygen, we survive from
breath to breath).

The amount of oxygen you use depends on your physical
activity and/or mental stress — for example, you need four
times as much when you're walking than sitting quietly. The
proportion of oxygen to air (twenty-one per cent) actually
remains constant to a considerable height, but as the air itself
gets less dense, so each lungful contains less oxygen in
proportion, which is why high altitude flight requires extra
supplies. Nothing extra is required below 5,000 feet, as ninety-
five per cent of what you would expect on the ground can be
expected. However, use of supplemental oxygen at or above
this height at night will be beneficial, particularly towards the
end of a flight.

Over prolonged flights at 8,000 feet, you may find measur-
able changes in blood pressure and respiration, although
normal healthy individuals should perform satisfactorily.

As you creep up to 10,000 feet, the symptoms of oxygen deficiency (otherwise known as Hypoxia), that is, impairment of vision (especially at night), lassitude, drowsiness, fatigue, sharp headaches and a false feeling of well-being, can catch you unawares. The intensity of them varies from person to person together with altitude, the duration of exposure and the amount of exercise being undergone (the more energy being expended, the more severe the symptoms).

If they occur at altitude (not necessarily as high as FL 100) without obvious cause, suspect Hypoxia (or hyperventilation, in which case don't use oxygen but breath slowly and deeply) and either descend or use supplemental oxygen (it's important to use oxygen before the onset of Hypoxia, because the condition itself tends to minimize the importance of its use).

Sometimes, however, unconsciousness may occur before the onset of recognizable symptoms, due to a high rate of ascent (or rapid decompression, which amounts to the same thing). You may get some symptoms as low as 8,000 feet amsl, but these are considered to be acceptable.

The amount of oxygen to be carried, and the proportions of persons on board to whom masks should be made available, varies with operating altitude, rate of descent and MSA. The rate of descent and the MSA are dependent on each other, in that it's no good having a good rate of descent if the MSA stops you. It may well be that, although you're flying at a level that requires fewer masks, the size of the MSA may demand that you equip everybody.

Anyhow, disregarding MSA, enough oxygen is required for continuous use by the crew and ten per cent of the number of passengers for any period that flight takes place above FL 100 (or when the cabin pressure altitude exceeds that height), and for all persons on board above FL 130 (Article 37 and Scales L1 and L2 of Schedule 4 of the ANO refer). Under these circumstances, not only must it be supplied for the crew, it must be used as well.

If you plan to use oxygen, it follows that enough should be carried for the flight and that masks are available for everybody. Adults should don their masks before their children do.

Preflight action includes ensuring that oxygen masks are accessible for the crew and that passengers are aware of their own masks' position. It is important to check the security of the circular dilation valve filter (a foam disc) on all masks, together with the pressure. Beards reduce the efficiency of masks.

Briefings should include the importance of not smoking and monitoring the flow indicator. All NO SMOKING signs should be on when oxygen is in use.

Further guidance will be found in AIC 102/88 (Pink 109) and the ANO.

Incapacitation

There is always a danger that whoever's in the other front seat may become incapacitated. In the obvious case, they collapse and fall across the controls. This problem is most acute if you have inertia reel harnesses that can't be locked.

Less noticeable is the sort of incapacitation that comes with boredom or lack of mental stimulation on longer trips, where you may physically be in the cockpit but mentally miles away. Even disorientation during instrument flight could be classed as incapacitation.

There's not much you can do against the first type aside from levelling the aircraft and commencing a gentle climb. Call for a passenger to help if need be, and tell ATC what's going on. Land as soon as you can under the circumstances.

The second type depends on the cause, most commonly (in the normal pilot's lifestyle) the low blood sugar caused by missed meals and the like. Although you may think it's better to have the wrong food than no food, be careful when it comes to eating choccy bars in lieu of lunch. These will cause your blood sugar levels to rise so rapidly that too much insulin is released to compensate, which drives your blood sugar levels to a lower state than they were before — known in the trade as 'rebound hypoglycaemia'. Apart from eating 'real food', you will minimize the risks of this if you eat small snacks frequently instead of heavy meals after long fasts.

There is a set procedure if a commander becomes incapacitated, and it's discussed in Chapter 1, regarding the First Officer's duties. However, do make full use of the autopilot and give yourself a chance by going to a more distant airfield if it has better facilities. Your first priority is to the passengers.

Meteorological Hazards

Hazardous weather conditions (as described below) should be reported to the appropriate authority on the frequency in use at the time.

Thunderstorms

The airflow is greatly disturbed anywhere near a **thunderstorm**, such disturbances usually being noticeable by the presence of strong up and down draughts accompanied by heavy rain and lightning.

Flight anywhere near them should therefore be avoided, but should this be impossible, it is best to maintain level flight and not attempt to change attitude or altitude as the speed of vertical air currents may well exceed the capabilities of the aircraft, thus causing it to end up in unusual attitudes. Fly by attitude at the recommended turbulence speed and maintain your original heading — do not correct for altitude gained or lost due to up and down draughts; allow the aircraft to 'wallow' through.

It's not a good idea to try and fly over the top of a thunderstorm, even baby ones near to larger storms. Similarly, try not to fly underneath, either, or make steep turns. Also, temporary blindness may be caused by lightning flashes, in which case it may (or may not) help to turn up the cabin lights.

All seat belts should be worn and tightened, and loose articles stowed. One pilot should control the aircraft and the other monitor the flight instruments — tough luck if you're by yourself!

You will probably need to operate all the de-icing equipment; check all electrical supplies and that pitot heating is on. Disregard any radio navigation indications that may be subject to interference. The use of **radar** will vary between types of equipment, but generally avoid all hooked echoes (like a figure 6), especially those that are rapidly changing. Either use iso-echo or a low gain setting (see also **Weather Radar** in Chapter 8).

In a thunderstorm, you can expect anything from lightning and turbulence through to hail, each with hazards of their own. Lightning, for instance, could explode a fuel tank, and then you are in trouble! A look at AIC 36/1987 (Pink 93) will give you other advice.

Wake vortices

These are sometimes referred to as wake turbulence, and are a by-product of lift present behind every aircraft (including helicopters) when in forward flight. They are particularly severe when generated by heavy aircraft such as wide-bodied jets. They take the form of horizontally concentrated whirlwinds streaming from the wing-tips, where the physical separation between the high pressure below and the low pressure above is removed.

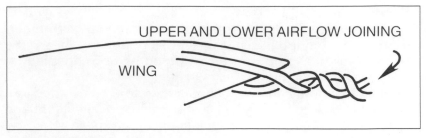

UPPER AND LOWER AIRFLOW JOINING

WING

The weight and speed of the causatory aircraft are the determining factors — the heavier and slower it is, the more severe the wake vortices will be. The presence of flaps, etc, will only have a small effect in breaking them up.

Wake vortices are most hazardous to other aircraft during take-off, initial climb, final approach and landing. Although there is a danger of shock-loading, the biggest problem is loss of control of your aircraft near the ground. However, not only can the effects be caught from other aircraft, but you can also get it from yourself, depending what strange antics you get up to.

The effects of wake turbulence become undetectable after a time, varying (according to circumstances) from a few seconds to a few minutes after the departure or arrival of an aircraft, particularly a heavy one.

Vortex wake generation begins when the nose-wheel lifts off the runway on take-off and continues until it touches down again after landing. Vortices will drift downwind, at about 400-500 fpm for larger aircraft, levelling out at about 900 feet below the altitude at which they were generated. Eventually they expand to occupy an oval area about one wingspan high and two wide.

Those laid down by large aircraft tend to move away from one another, therefore on a calm day, the runway itself will remain free of them, depending on how near the runway edge the offending wings were.

They will also drift with wind, so your landings and take-offs should occur upwind of any moving heavy aircraft, and before the point of its take-off and after the point of landing.

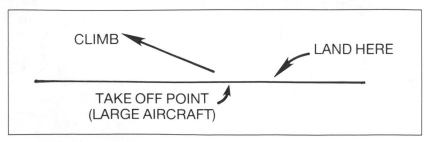

CLIMB   LAND HERE

TAKE OFF POINT
(LARGE AIRCRAFT)

You are safest if you keep above the approach and take-off path of the other aircraft, but for general purposes, allow at least three minutes behind aircraft greater than the light category for the effects to disappear, and further information together with techniques for avoidance will be found in AIC 90/1986 (Pink 89).

Standing waves

Where a high mountain range exists with an airflow of over twenty knots over it in stable conditions, then **standing waves** may exist downwind of the range, noticeable by the existence of turbulence and strong persistent up and down draughts. Fly parallel to the range in an updraught if possible, avoiding peaks.

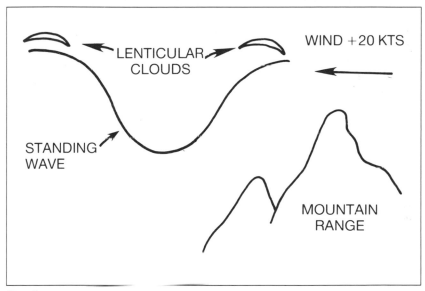

Standing waves.

Frost, ice or snow

These adversely affect performance, not only by adding weight, but also changing the shape of the lift-producing surfaces, thus affecting their stalling speed. In addition, there are the dangers of fuel freezing in the wing tanks, control surfaces freezing up, slush picked up on take-off freezing and stopping the landing gear from operating, to mention but a few possibilities.

It's a good idea to avoid flight in icing conditions whenever possible, but in any case, flight should not take place where icing conditions are expected in aircraft not equipped for the purpose — all such equipment should naturally be serviceable.

All ice should be removed before take-off, although hoar frost on the fuselage could possibly be left if the deposit is light and the hoar frost may be seen through. De-icing details should be entered in the relevant portion of the Technical Log.

The capability of an object to accumulate ice is known as its catch efficiency. A sharp-edged object has a greater catch efficiency than a blunt-edged one, due to the lesser deflection of air that it causes. Speed is also a factor. Due to the speed and geometry of the main rotor blades of a helicopter, their catch efficiency is greater than that of the fuselage. Therefore, ice accretion on the fuselage is not indicative of that on the blades.

Ice accretion can occur without causing noticeable vibration. On the ground this can be conducive to ground resonance, and bits of ice flying off rotor blades or propellers could be dangerous to persons on the ground. In flight, the extra weight and drag could cause descent and improper operation of flying controls.

Although all aircraft are different, expect icing to occur (in the engine intake area, anyway) wherever there is visible water vapour and the OAT is less than 10° C. Anti-icing should be switched on well in anticipation due to the presence of ice causing instruments to misread.

Try to restrict the use of de-icing boots until at least half an inch of solid (not slushy) ice has formed. Otherwise, the boots will merely stretch the ice covering and operate inside the resulting cocoon. Waiting a while at least gives you the ability to crack the ice off.

There are two main types of de-icing/anti-icing fluid, un-thickened (type I) and thickened (type II). One type tends to stick to the aircraft surface better and so remains effective against re-freezing for longer. Although most contain glycol, alcohol based liquids will have a detrimental effect on hinge lubricants and other greases. Although this is bad enough, the main problem will be water getting into where the grease was and freezing.

When de-icing with neat Kilfrost (TM) has been carried out on the ground, use the following table as a guide to its effetiveness. Regard the tailplane as equivalent to a wing, but only if it has been sprayed from above.

Amb temp degs C	Time in Hours				
	Snow	Frost	Fzg Fog	Fzg Rn	Rain
above +3	4				OK
+3 – 0	2	10		·75	1
0 – –5	1	8		·75	
–5 – –10	1	8		1·5	
below –10	1		1·5		

Reference should also be made to AIC 92/1987 (Pink 100), and **Winter Operations** in Chapter 7.

Windshear

This is the name given to sudden changes in wind velocity, whether horizontal or vertical. Officially, it becomes dangerous when the wind variations cause sufficient displacement of an aircraft from its flight path so as to require substantial control action to correct matters. Windshear exists when IAS changes by more than about ten knots purely due to changes in wind velocity — more severe examples will change not only airspeed, but vertical speed and aircraft attitude as well (severe windshear is considered to cause airspeed changes of greater than fifteen knots or vertical speed changes of more than 500 feet per minute).

Although mostly associated with thunderstorms (see previously), where you have the unpredictability of microbursts (as well as more constant downbursts) to contend with, it's also present with wake vortices, temperature inversions, mountain waves and the passage of fronts, and so can occur over any size of area. It's not restricted to fixed wing aircraft, either — helicopters can suffer from it as well. For instance, there will be a change in windspeed and direction above and below tree top level going in and out of a forest clearing.

All fronts are zones of windshear — the greater the temperature difference across the front, the greater the changes related to it will be (in general, the faster the front moves, the more vigorous the weather associated with it. The slower it moves, the worse will be the visibility, but you can still get windshear even then).

Warm fronts tend to have less windshear than cold ones, but as they're slower moving, you catch it for a longer time.

However, one of the most significant effects of windshear is, of course, loss of airspeed at a critical moment, similar to an effect known in mountain flying where a wind reversal could result in none at all!

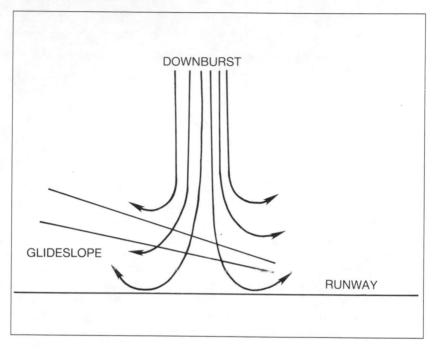

You could typically get this from a downburst coming from a convective type cloud, where initially you get an increase in airspeed due to the extra headwind. No problem so far, but if you do not expect the reverse to happen (as it will as you get to the other side of the downburst), you will not be in a position to cope with the resulting loss of headwind.

Windshear encountered near the ground (say below 1,000 feet) is the most critical, mainly because the lack of height prevents the acquisition of airspeed quickly — you know the old saying: altitude is money in the bank, but speed is money in the pocket.

The effects also depend on the type of aircraft and its situation, in that propeller driven types suffer less than do jets, and light aircraft tend to be less vulnerable than heavy ones — those with a good power to weight ratio will come off best. The take-off leaves you most vulnerable because of the little scope for energy conservation, less amounts of excess engine power and the amount of drag caused by the gear and any flap you may have, which is not to say that landing is that much safer, either.

Avoidance is the best cure, but anticipation is the most practical. This is done by alert observation of what's going on around you. In extremely simple terms, where windshear is expected, you should have a little extra airspeed in hand, and you can help yourself with the following:

a) On take-off, use the longest runway available.
b) Use more airspeed up to about 1,000 feet agl, but watch your climb gradient and don't use more than about ten knots.
c) Use less flap.
d) On landing, be more aware of missed approach procedures.
e) Set the prop RPM to maximum (for flat pitch).
f) Use full throttle if you have to — new engines are cheaper than a new aircraft. Don't allow the thrust to get too low, either.

In a jet, you are able to use higher angles of attack and still get a sizeable amount of lift for a moderate increase in drag, because the wings are designed that way. Various ways are used to inform you of the stall, and you want to keep the thing flying just above that point — something that may require some practice in a simulator.

Further details will be found in AIC 37/1987 (Pink 94), and your Company has to provide a formal windshear training programme relevant to type. There is an FAA video which is available from the CAA library to AOC holders only.

Shallow Fog

In **shallow fog**, you may be able to see the whole of the approach and/or runway lights from a considerable distance, even though reports from the aerodrome indicate fog. On descending into such a fog layer, your visual reference is likely to drop rapidly, in extreme cases reducing from the full length of the runway and approach lights to a very small segment of the approach lights.

This may give the impression that you are pitching nose up, making the chances of hitting the ground after corrective movements very probable. You should be prepared for a reduction in visual reference in the final stages of the approach and initiate a missed approach whenever you have the slightest doubt about the adequacy of forward visibility.

The minimum RVR for landing from a visual circuit is 800 m. If you can't get this, a missed approach should be undertaken.

Use and Location of Emergency Equipment

Every aircraft carries a First Aid kit that conforms to the standards laid down in the ANO (and is certified by an engineer). Life-jackets are commonly stored under the relevant seats when carried, and life-rafts should be securely stowed but easily accessible.

In addition to their uses for putting out fires, fire extinguishers have strange side-effects as well. For instance, the fumes given out by some are toxic, so you will need plenty of ventilation after their use. Also, be careful when using dry powder extinguishers on cabin fires — it ruins the avionics!

Two-Crew Operations

When you need to fly two-crew, there should be a clear division of responsibility between the handling and non-handling pilot. The Commander will nominate the handling pilot for each sector, who should always occupy the Captain's seat.

Standard take-off briefing — two-crew operations

Pilot handling	Pilot non-handling
Take-off brief (decision speeds, departure clearance)	Acknowledge
Initiates take-off	Monitors engine Calls airspeed
Calls after take-off check	Carries out same
Calls climb checks	Carries out same
Calls to set Navaids	Sets and identifies

Action in event of malfunction on take-off

Call any malfunction	Call any malfunction

(If P2 handling, then hand back to commander)

Decision — continue/abort	Standby and monitor
If abandon	Standby and monitor
If continue, take care of malfunctioning and instruct non-handling pilot	Checklist ready Carries out command

Both pilots should monitor any engine shutdown

Approach briefing — two-crew operations

Before commencing the approach, the commander should brief the co-pilot on:

1) Approach procedure
2) Tuning and identification of radio aids
3) Cross checking of altimeters
4) Height calls — 1,000 feet to cleared levels
5) Reference to DH — 500 feet above DH
           200 feet above DH
           100 feet above DH
           DH
6) Monitoring of approach
7) Specific warning if, on an instrument approach, the rate of descent exeeds 1,000 fpm or the ILS indicator exceeds half-scale deflection
8) Lookout for approach lighting
9) Action in the event of missed approach

In addition to the duties outlined above, the Commander should stress during his briefing the importance of the monitoring role of the other pilot. This is to include specific mention of the requirement to cross-check and warn the flying pilot of his approach to, and arrival at, cleared heights, altitudes and flight levels at all stages of flight.

Chapter 7
Special Aircraft Operations

General
External Slung Loads
Aerial Application
Fire Suppression
Aerial Filming and Photography
Casualty Evacuation/Air Ambulance
Pleasure Flying
Special Events
Line Patrol Flying
Police Operations
Parachute Dropping
Mountain Flying
Night Flying
Winter Operations
Aerial Survey
Air Testing
Mail Flights

General

Of necessity, most of this chapter will concern helicopters, because these are the machines which are used more than anything else for weird operations — you can't do much with aeroplanes except cart passengers and freight about, take photographs and spray crops. Where both types could be used, though, many techniques will have much in common.

Passenger handling itself is a specialized task. As I've said before, in General Aviation you are very much involved with your passengers, and as the flight is usually a special event for them they will naturally get quite excited and often engage you in conversation about all manner of things. Of course, a frequent business traveller may not get this familiar, but you will still be asked to join your passengers for lunch; not only out of courtesy, but as cheap entertainment as well — if you're not a good conversationalist when you start your career, you'll very soon learn! Other little things help customer relations as well, such as helping them with their seat belts, checking they're OK and settled down just before take-off and during the flight, and generally looking after their well-being.

All of this is to do with pure salesmanship. A lot of repeat business for any company will revolve on whether their pilots get on well with the passengers, and if you're not naturally gregarious, think twice about charter work as a long-term way of earning a living.

Otherwise, some of the more exotic things you can do with helicopters include water sampling (where you hover very low over a body of water and a scientist dips the equivalent of a jam jar into it), or frost control (where a large barrel of oil is lit to provide smoke that will indicate the level of an inversion. You then fly with your rotors just above the smoke to bring the warm air down and thus prevent frost on crops. Very interesting at night at 100 feet!).

Everything else in this chapter is otherwise fairly standard, though not boring, I hope!

External Slung Loads

A helicopter will be used to lift specialized items in areas where a crane is impractical or more expensive. In theory, you can lift anything, provided the capacity for the payload is available; I have even been asked to quote for the lowering of 800 feet of telephone cable down a mine shaft — unrolled! However, more common tasks are logging and the placing of air conditioning or ventilation equipment on the roofs of tall buildings.

You will find it useful to check out the following:

CAP 426   — Helicopter External Load Operations
ANO Art 29   — Suspended loads

Rule 47	— Marshalling Signals
ANO Art 42	— Picking up and raising of articles
ANO Art 43	— Dropping of articles

You should only get involved in load-slinging if you have the proper experience, and you get that by being trained properly and supervised. In some companies, 'training' is once around the circuit!

If you're experienced and have done some slinging in the past year you can probably get by with a full briefing from the Chief Pilot. If you're not current then expect no less than two observed sectors if loading permits, otherwise you will require some training circuits.

When engaged on external slung load work, the Certificate of Airworthiness of the aircraft changes from Public Transport to Aerial Work, therefore no passengers should be carried (you would be forgiven for thinking that you would also get away with Duty Hours, but you're still regarded as being on Public Transport, even though the helicopter isn't — in fact, you may even need an official exemption from the full equipment scales required for Public Transport).

The ideal complete team on the ground consists of at least three handlers at every point of pickup or deposit, so in a simple lift from A to B, six would be needed, although this could be reduced if adequate air to ground communications are available (all procedures given here are based on the assumption that they are not). One person would be for marshalling and the remainder for hooking up, etc. Marshalling signals are given in Rule 47.

There should be as many ropes, strops, nets, hooks, etc that can be made available, as more will always be required than you think. Woven polyester rope is suggested for slings, although ordinary rope will do, provided it doesn't have a tendency to bounce up if it breaks.

At the very least, you need one set of slings at each drop-off point, so that while the first load is being undone you can be on your way back with a sling and not waste flying time. All slinging equipment should be able to withstand four times the anticipated load because flight conditions may increase the load's weight artificially.

All ground crew should be provided with hard hats (with chin straps), goggles or eye-shields, protective gloves and a metal probe for discharging **static electricity**, which comes from a number of sources, the main ones being engine and precipitation charging (the last is due to friction between the aircraft's surfaces and airborne particles). There is also a risk of static from the presence of thunderstorms.

Although the capacitance associated with this phenomenon is small, voltages as high as tens of kilovolts can exist which are capable of throwing people to the ground. In addition, static electricity near to a potentially explosive cargo or fuel tank is obviously dangerous. It's for this reason that a **static discharge probe**, which is earthed to the ground, is applied to the hook before any other contact takes place and the procedure kept up as much as possible.

Before doing anything else, you should check the following carefully:

a) **Helicopter Condition**. The rear doors need to be removed so that used harnesses may be placed inside quickly from either side — very often drop-off points are in places where you can't land but only come to a very low hover. Also, there is a little less weight for the machine to carry.

You shouldn't need to fly the helicopter from the other seat, but if it is required, then consider carrying a suitably qualified co-pilot if payload permits.

A mirror should be set up at the front so you can see the operation of the hook and the behaviour of the load. The hook mechanism itself must be checked for consistent electrical and mechanical operation, as must all standby release methods. All hooks must be enclosed ones.

b) **Condition of sling equipment**. Any worn or frayed items should be discarded.

c) **Preparation of loading and unloading areas**.
Non-involved personnel should be absent, and there should be no loose articles lying around that could be blown around by the downwash and cause damage. Approach and departure lanes should be into wind.

d) **Performance planning**. Calculation of the payload available and fuel requirements must be done using the performance graphs given in the Flight Manual, bearing in mind you will need power in hand to hover Out of Ground Effect (OGE). Lateral C of G limits must also be kept in bounds — be especially careful of the effects of load swinging (see later).

e) **Preparation of loads**. The weight of each load should

be known and clearly displayed. The methods of suspension must be understood and some are explained shortly.

Sand and aggregate should be kept dry and, if possible, weighed immediately before loading; a good soaking will increase the weight dramatically, and you may therefore get a surprise when you come to lift it. Small pieces of steel or timber should be bundled and nets used when the load consists of a number of small articles.

f) **Personnel briefing**. All concerned should be aware of the following:
The hook-up operation
The setdown operation
Hand signals to be used
Direction to move in case of engine failure
Number of trips between refuelling stops
Manner of retrieving slings and nets
Use of protective equipment
Accident procedure

Hooking up

For the **hook-up operation**, the marshaller should be positioned at least 25 m from the load with his back to the wind so you can see him from your high position.

If the marshaller needs to reposition, he should cease marshalling first — accidents have been caused by marshallers moving backwards into unseen obstructions.

Using standard marshalling signals, he will position you over the load where the loaders apply the static discharge probe to the hook and place the eye of the net or sling inside it.

The loaders then give an affirmative signal to the marshaller who subsequently gives the 'move upwards' signal until all the slack has been taken up, at all times keeping the helicopter over the load. As the strain is taken, the loaders guide the strops as necessary, taking care to be free to move away quickly should the need arise. At all times in the event of engine failure, the ground staff must move in the opposite direction that the helicopter would go, e.g. JetRanger to the right, staff to the left. They should not turn their back on the load, nor get directly underneath it. Neither should they wrap lines directly around their wrists or bodies. After they have finished, they should clear the area as soon as possible.

As the weight is taken up by the aircraft and the rope stretches, the difference in weight and performance will immediately become obvious — it will feel as if you're attached to a large rubber band!

Once you're hovering and the marshaller is sure that the load is properly suspended (and you are sure you can lift safely, flashing the landing lamp once to indicate this), the marshaller will check the area behind you for other aircraft and give the affirmative signal (you will find it difficult to do a half-turn to check for yourself!).

The machine will feel quite sluggish, as if it's tied to the ground. Move forward slowly, giving due regard to the load's inertia.

Once in flight, you should take great care to cause no risk to third parties by keeping away from almost anything underneath that could be damaged. Only in the case of imminent danger to the aircraft should a load be jettisoned, usually as a result of excessive swinging, where the load is in danger of hitting the aircraft (commercially, dropping loads is definitely regarded as a non-macho thing to do, but it is you that's doing the flying!).

External loads increase the frontal area of the whole aircraft, which naturally increases the drag. Thus, you will require more power to maintain a given hover height, climb rate, airspeed or altitude. A load may be easy to lift, but may present so much drag in flight that it causes severe difficulties, particularly where you may reach power limits too quickly to maintain forward flight.

If you're flying with a long line, you will have more need to anticipate the movement of the load and develop a high degree of co-ordination and patience. It's not the sort of thing that can be learnt in any way other than by having lots of practice.

Setting Down
Approach into wind as much as possible, coming into the hover high enough not to drag the load.

Because of inertia, all manoeuvres should be anticipated well in advance and made smoothly (not suddenly) with reference to the speed of the load over the ground. If operating into a confined area, the load will tend to pull you down as the wind effect is lost, so a little speed in hand under these circumstances is desirable, even if it's not what you would normally expect to do.

Once in the hover, you again come under the guidance of the Marshaller, who signals descent until the load touches the ground and the cables become slack. The cables are released after the helicopter has moved to one side so that they do not foul the load.

A manual release is provided if the electrical one doesn't operate, and once it has done so, you should see a 'load released' signal from the marshaller, whereupon you hover by the side of the load while the replacement sling is placed inside the cabin.

You should behave at all times as if the load has not been released.

Load Behaviour

When using a single point sling (usually used for logs), the rope should be doubled or a swivel used as the rope could unravel if the load starts spinning, causing the eye to loosen and come apart (Fig 1). A two point sling with less than a forty-five degree angle to the hook or tag line is usually the common method for most loads, with a four point sling being used for box-like ones (Fig 2).

Where the sling may catch or damage the load, use spreader bars for stability (Fig 3). When carrying a single pole or log, wrap the rope or chain twice around the end of the pole (Fig 4).

Tag lines (short lines attached to the underside of a load) are useful for loaders to grasp on the setdown. They should have a safety latch and weigh at least 5 kg (Fig 2).

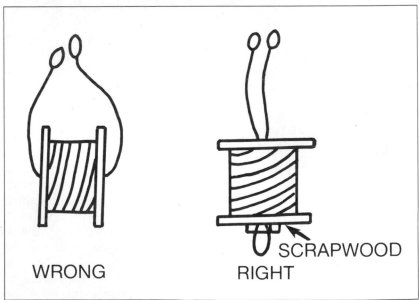

WRONG   RIGHT   SCRAPWOOD

Chains work well and store in a smaller area than cables, but with heavy loads they can bind and not tighten up where they cross over a load, allowing slippage.

Most things can be carried in a net. When using nets, loads should be carefully and evenly stacked in the centre in order to stop anything spilling. The net should be stretched around the load on the ground before pick-up. Individual light loads, such as jerrycans or containers, should be lashed together, since the net may not completely enclose the load at the top. If there are many small items, consider a tarpaulin as a liner, or use a top cover.

There is no sure way to predict how each load will fly, but loads with an uneven shape will tend to spin and, if they are slung without reference to their centre of gravity, could affect the flying characteristics of the helicopter. A drogue chute can be used to stabilize the load, but a windsock type will fly better than a pure parachute, which will oscillate to spill the air being forced into it. Naturally, these must be kept well away from the tail rotor (Fig 3).

Logs or cut timber usually fly poorly unless a tail is installed. This can easily be made out of a tree bough or a piece of plywood (Fig 5).

Oscillation or excessive vibration of a load can commence due to a number of factors, usually from a combination of the stability characteristics of the load and the forward speed of the helicopter. Heavy or dense loads, such as bags of cement or drums of kerosene, will not usually present problems due to their mass, but large volume loads of low density are liable to commence oscillating at a certain critical speed, found by experimentation. You can dampen oscillation by reducing your airspeed to at least ten per cent below the critical one, going slower if necessary in combination with increasing power.

Placing the aircraft in a turn could provide centrifugal force sufficient to stop any oscillation. Turning is also the usual remedy when the load starts to swing, but this will also increase the effective weight of the load, possibly placing it outside the lifting capabilities of the aircraft (a good reason for not being too tight on payload). Thus, application of centrifugal force in these cases could make things worse.

Special precautions must be taken in the case of bulky loads which have a tendency to float, such as empty containers. In these cases, permeability to air can have a stabilizing effect — leaving doors open on containers reduces drag considerably and can help keep the load facing in one direction.

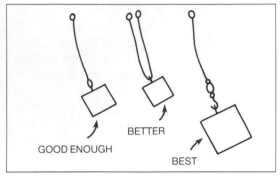

FIGURE 1

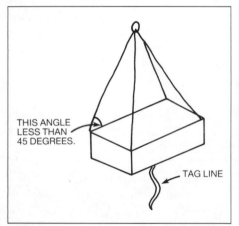

FIGURE 2

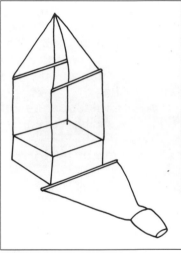

FIGURE 3

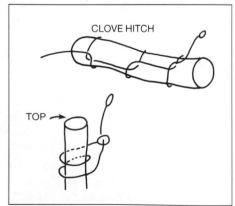

FIGURE 4

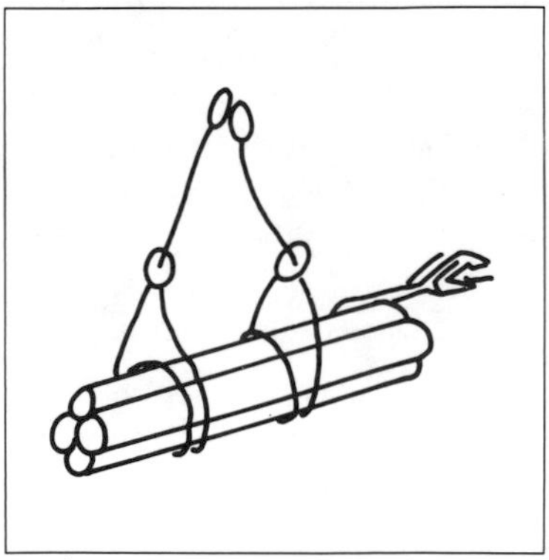

FIGURE 5

Scaffolding and planking are prone to swinging violently with only a few knots change in airspeed. Items with an aerofoil shape could even have a tendency to generate their own flying characteristics.

Aerial Application

Aerial application (of insecticides or fertilizers) consists of either crop-spraying or top dressing, the latter being used in forestry.

Top Dressing is more akin to load slinging, except that you use engine driven devices in the form of buckets to spread solutions over forests. The techniques are similar to crop spraying, with the difference that it can generally be done in stronger wind conditions. Like crop spraying, it is characterized by always being in, or very near, the avoid curve and many other situations that you are taught to avoid normally. You can tell by looking at forests that have been sprayed in the early stages of their growth as to whether the spray pilots were successful or not — you very often see some trees shorter than others. That's where they missed!

Crop-spraying, like slinging, is very satisfying when a good rhythm is obtained by using an efficient team that keeps the aircraft in the air as much as possible. Unlike slinging, however, you will be operating a heavy machine with unwieldy spray booms attached to it at some speed in fairly confined areas, and the low level manoeuvres will require a high degree of co-ordination. There is usually very little wind to help you, either, because of the legal restrictions on wind speeds and the possibilities of **Spray Drift** (see later). It therefore becomes very demanding halfway up a mountain at 3000 feet with high temperatures and an airspeed of about five knots!

When using a helicopter, the idea is to fly at between 35-45 knots at a height of about ten feet along the 'grain' of the crop, at the end of the run pulling up and pivoting around to face the other direction on the end of the boom that is pointing into wind so that you start where you left off. Thus, you turn into wind at the end of each run, all the while progressing along the crop towards the wind direction.

To make money out of it, there must be the likelihood of 10,000 acres of application within an area of about fifty miles diameter over a season (about four months). Set prices are usually charged for an area, which means that the quicker the

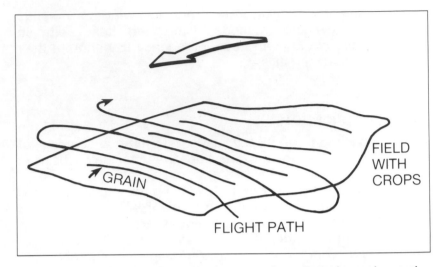

FIELD
WITH
CROPS

GRAIN

FLIGHT PATH

job is done, the quicker another can be started — about the only way to maximize income in this sort of work. As a general rule, expect to spray between 300-600 acres per working day. The aircraft should be placed in a central part of the area, and its production (normally measured in acres per hour) will depend on payload available, endurance, dead time between sites, volume of work at each site, terrain, pilot's experience, time spent on the ground reloading, rate of application and weather (I think that's all).

Organization, however, is most important. Some crops may require different chemicals, and if you keep changing the load the whole pattern of work will be disrupted. Thus, grouping together crops that require the same spraying on a regular basis can get rid of not only dead ferrying time, but also unnecessary cleaning of tanks.

Aerial Application takes place under a 'Certificate' granted by the CAA, which is broadly comparable to an Air Operator's Certificate (see Chapter 10). Under the terms of this, a Ground Operations Manager must be present at all times and he must have certain minimum qualifications.

In addition, the ground team will also contain a field support engineer, who monitors aircraft performance and attends to routine servicing. The same person could combine both jobs.

There may also be a flagman, who marks out the areas to be sprayed and the routes to be followed. Although an experienced pilot should be able to produce reasonable results in an emergency without markers to guide him, it isn't recommended for prolonged operations.

Other ground staff include loaders, who mix and load the solution. The loader's job usually requires fast action in order to keep things going as much as possible, but when things are happening quickly, there is more danger of spillage and subsequent contamination.

To minimize weight, whatever solution you use will be much more concentrated than normally used in agriculture, except that solids would be about the same. During aerial applications, exposing yourself and the ground staff to the spray must be regarded as a possibility.

Direct contact between the skin and concentrate should be avoided, the most common exposure point being around the wrist. Skin contamination can be minimized by the use of rubber gloves and boots, and by wearing clean clothing which includes long trousers and sleeves (which is just what you need on a hot day).

It's not essential to use anything waterproof unless you actually expect to get drenched. Flaggers can avoid exposure to whatever is being sprayed by simply keeping out of the way of each pass.

Hoppers and tanks should not leak in flight, not only for your protection, but also to help prevent affecting non-target areas.

Spray Drift is the movement of whatever you are spraying to where it was not intended to be. It's undesirable not only because it reduces the amount of chemical available to do the job, but it will cause actual damage in non-target areas due to concentrated amounts accumulating downwind, sometimes exceeding the rate actually applied to the target. Spray drift is affected by greater wind velocity at height, volatility of the solution, inversion conditions combined with spray pressure, nozzle spray angle and air movement around the aircraft.

You can reduce the chances of it by producing large droplets that are released close to the target. This can be done by:

a) Flying as low as possible
b) Locating nozzles away from wing or rotor tips
c) Placing the spray boom well below the wing of aeroplanes or as far forward as possible on helicopters
d) Orienting nozzles backward and spacing them to produce a uniform pattern
e) Using low nozzle pressures
f) Using larger orifices in the nozzles
g) Spraying when winds are light and the air is cool. Unfortunately, in the UK, this generally means about

0400-1000; these must be the most unsociable hours in aviation!

h) Using herbicides that do not produce damaging vapours

Spray drift can also be reduced by modifying the solution. This can be done by using additives which produce more viscosity, or with an invert emulsion system, which will apply a mayonnaise-like material. These both have disadvantages, in either needing specialized equipment or mixing techniques.

If you are trying to increase the volume of solution over a particular area, you are better off tinkering with the nozzles than reducing speed or raising spray pressure. This will help to avoid the production of small droplets, or 'fines', that are more likely to drift.

There are some crops, however, that require good coverage and small droplets, the opposite of what is needed above. This is where you need to be a bit of a chemist as well as a pilot in order to satisfy the customer.

Accurate records are also essential, not only as aids to the business but also in case of later complaints of drifting (which is possibly Trespass, by the way). When keeping records, it is helpful to note such items as nozzle size and spacing, wind velocity and weather conditions, rate of application and time on task, together with a diagram (which you should have made anyway, for planning purposes).

Fire Suppression

Involvement with fire suppression is subject to the normal restrictions, such as weather or night, although fixed wing fire bombing operations do take place in darkness. You may be asked either to help fight the fire itself, contain it or simply channel it in a specified direction, perhaps towards a natural barrier such as a cliff top.

The most obvious use of an aircraft is as a water bomber, but this will tend to be restricted to large aeroplanes, although some ways of using helicopters (in similar fashion to top dressing or by using an internal tank in a Chinook) are gaining in popularity — helicopters are at least able to make use of handier sources of water, like swimming pools or small rivers. However, forest and moorland fires also require vast amounts of manpower, who are usually tired by the time they get to the fire from the long walk to get there! Thus, the helicopter will also be used as transport for fire-fighters and their equipment, as well as for observation (if you are used on observation, your passengers will have some rank and experience, since they will be directing ground forces from the air).

Thus, the transportation of men and materials is just as useful here as any other time. Expertise in external slung load work on your behalf is essential as portable equipment will also need to be moved. Experiments have been made using the helicopter with hoselaying, acting as water towers, using a fire bucket to turn the helicopter into a water bomber, etc, but these activities are really combinations of load-slinging and top dressing, discussed elsewhere.

There are some differences, though. Your accuracy will need to be considerably sharper than usual for several reasons; one is that there will be no marshallers to guide you in the target areas (a bit hot, there), and another is that chemical fire retardant (highly concentrated foam detergent) is often used and not welcome when sprayed over already tired firemen by mistake! A third is that evaporation will take its toll on whatever is dropped, ensuring that so much less of what you carry is actually effective.

Also, you will very likely not be the only aircraft about. The combination of lots of smoke (hence poor visibility) coupled with heat turbulence and the presence of many other aircraft buzzing about could prove to be extremely dangerous.

For ground support, in addition to load-slinging gear, you will also need mobile fuel and provision for Fire Brigade radio equipment, not to mention a few aircraft spares. It is possible that the Fire Service will have their own trained ground staff, but take along your own just in case.

After the fire, if wind conditions permit, you may be asked to lift an unrolled hose to drain it. This saves exhausted firemen from having to under-run miles of hose before they roll it for stowage on their appliances. That alone should be good for a few beers.

Aerial Filming and Photography

Aerial filming and photography flights should be planned so that emergency situations would put structures or persons in the vicinity at **no** risk. No flight should take place outside the provisions of Rule 5 unless an exemption has been granted (in practice, when using a helicopter, you can get an exemption to operate down to 200 feet for photography, but you will need to keep a record of when it was taken advantage of, as you would with any other).

If a door needs to be removed for any reason, loose articles and surplus seat belts should naturally be secured and manoeuvres carried out where possible so that the side of the aircraft without the door is uppermost. Occupants in the vicinity of the open door should wear a bit more than the seat belt supplied. This point is controversial — very often a photographer will expect the door to be off, not have a mount and just use a normal seat belt. In this case, I also like at least a rope around their middle loosely attached to an anchor point as well, but a professional outfit — which includes your company — will have its own despatcher's harness.

If used, a camera mount will normally be fitted by the company supplying it, but you should oversee the work and annotate the loadsheet accordingly.

When the mount is in place, the C of A changes to Aerial Work, therefore no passengers should be carried without an exemption, so you will need one to carry the photographer. The mount should not be fitted unless there is a Supplement to the Flight Manual covering its installation.

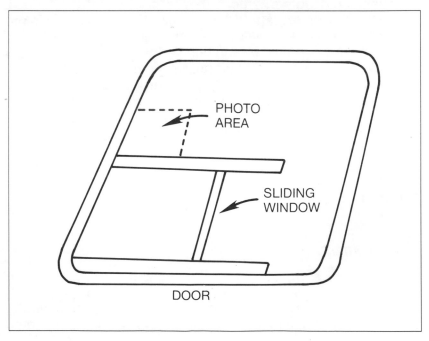

If given a choice, the photographer should sit on the pilot's side — on the top part of most pilot's windows is an area which, if the target is kept inside it, will give him the field of view required.

It's important to try and get what's wanted first time, not only for economy, but also because of noise nuisance. Camera crews are famous for wanting 'just one more shot' and 'a little lower', but you shouldn't push yourself or the machine. At times considerable cross-controlling will be needed for certain panning shots, but it's impossible to give complete guidance here and you will have to exercise your discretion as to the flying required. Film crews are also notorious for wanting to do silly things — the less they know about aviation, the sillier they will be!

Bear in mind the height/velocity curve when using a helicopter — the JetRanger requires at least 450 feet to regain the 60 knots needed for a good engine-off landing from a high hover.

Operations should inform the local emergency services of your activities.

Casualty Evacuation/Air Ambulance

Patients just being moved from one hospital to another do not qualify for exemptions from any regulations that may be allowed for saving life, although special provisions may apply for duty hours (see Chapter 3) — the emergencies referred to in the exemptions apply to the aircraft and not the patient.

There are two types of ambulance flight, Intensive Care Transport (ICT) and Ambulance Taxi Transport (ATT).

Some are a mixture of the two, such as standby ambulance helicopter facilities at races such as the Isle of Man TT, or the British Grand Prix at Silverstone or Brands Hatch.

Trained crews exist for these occasions with established procedures, so basically all you will be called upon to do is fly and ensure that the medical crews do not forget anything like crash helmets — this is most important for the diagnosis of head injuries, as blood will no doubt cover everything else.

Whatever you get involved in, the following should generally be avoided:

a) Anyone with previous or present signs or symptoms suggesting epilepsy or any other form of fit.

b) The unconscious patient, unless in-flight attention is available.
c) Patients with any severe haemorrhagic type of injury, unless in-flight attention is available.
d) Abdominal or chest injuries if altitude changes of up to 1500 feet are likely to be involved.
e) Those under the influence of alcohol or drugs, unless prescribed by a qualified doctor.
f) Persons of unsound mind or anyone who may be a potential danger to the aircraft or persons therein.

'Walking Wounded' passengers, that is, those who are infirm due to age, ill health or otherwise, may be carried subject to the approval of the qualified medical personnel who should accompany them and be responsible for them.

Patients of whatever condition should not be placed anywhere near emergency exits and their locomotive devices (wheelchairs, etc) should not impede escape paths.

If your Company does a lot of Casevac work, it may be worth while retaining a doctor to advise on certain cases, especially where infectious diseases are concerned.

Routes should be planned to take into account changes of altitude and rates of descent. You will need to accelerate or decelerate with care.

Aside from the patient's condition, the consent of both referring and receiving hospitals is required, together with confirmed arrangements for road transport at the departure and destination airports. You also need to make sure that the type of aircraft is what is wanted, together with the details of staff and equipment that may be carried.

Specialized equipment, if carried, should be properly installed, and instructions on its use must be available to all attendants. Some of it could actually be classed as Dangerous Goods (such as Aeromedical Oxygen), so you may need an exemption to carry it. Anything that needs to be fixed to the aircraft (e.g. stretchers), or connected to its systems, must be through an airworthiness/manufacturers' approved system. All equipment must be compatible with the aircraft environment (for instance, equipment used in road ambulances may be unsuitable for flight).

Oxygen (if used) must be sufficient to cover the duration of loading, flight, technical stops and unloading, plus about one and a half hours of reserve for eventualities.

Other passengers must be limited to the number of seats available after stretcher equipment has been fitted. Patients should be carefully strapped in for take-off and landing, and attendants must be briefed on how to do it. They must also be briefed on crash and ditching procedures, the position and method of use of emergency exits and equipment.

Flight Attendants accompanying the patient must have the medical experience necessary to deal with the case, and knowledge of aviation medicine sufficient to predict and treat symptoms arising from flight.

Doctors must be qualified and registered in the states concerned with the skills necessary to look after the patient. A doctor is always required on ICT flights and on ATT flights which are other than simple escort cases; in these instances, written confirmation should be obtained from the customer, nurse or agent. If in doubt insist upon the inclusion of a doctor.

Nurses must also be registered in the states concerned and work under direct instructions of an accompanying doctor (or apply those given before flight by one). Nurses must not be used on their own on ICT flights or when there is any possibility of the patient's condition changing.

Paramedics may be employed with the agreement of the patient's doctor. Their training may not be valid in some states.

Pleasure Flying

The aim of pleasure flying is to carry a group of people, generally members of the public who have never flown before, for a short period in a Company aircraft for a fee.

It can be very lucrative, provided that the operation is slick and smoothly controlled. It's also an ideal opportunity to promote aviation in general, so everybody involved should take care to ensure that the customer's association with aircraft (and the Company) is a happy one. It's for this reason that the machine must be handled smoothly with no sharp manoeuvres, unless they're specifically asked for with all passengers being in agreement. The only types of flying generally recommended are spot turns and sideways movement in the hover (for helicopters) and normal climb, descent and cruise. Oddly enough, hovering manoeuvres are quite popular.

In addition to the public actually flying, there will also be those attending the associated event. Any site chosen must be organized and staffed in such a way as to afford the maximum safety for all concerned.

Don't forget the exemption to enable you to fly nearer than 3000 feet to assemblies of over 1000 people.

When the Company receives a request for pleasure flying, the size and location of the site, the type of event and the anticipated numbers need to be noted. A site inspection then needs to be arranged. This must be done by somebody who knows what the requirements are, i.e. a qualified pilot if possible (when you do pleasure flying, the positioning of the aircraft must be paid for as well, so if the site turns out to be unsuitable and is rejected on the day, you've all wasted your time). In assessing the suitability of a site, its physical characteristics and position relative to areas available for emergency access must be taken into account, together with areas for emergency use by aircraft.

For instance, it may be acceptable for downwind take-offs to occur (provided performance is OK) if emergency vehicle access is better in that direction.

The site must conform to standard requirements (for which see the **Technical Bits**, later). You are allowed some discretion if, when assessing a site, an otherwise perfect location is spoiled by one or two major obstacles which, while encroaching on the Company minima, nevertheless may be avoided by curving the flight path. If operating at an airfield, though, you should be alright on this point.

Even where exemptions are not required (such as from Rule 5 (1) (d) (i) — closer than 3000 feet to 1000 persons in attendance at an event), the CAA Flight Operations department must still be notified at least seven days prior to the event on a special form that they provide. It may or may not be included in the Ops Manual. Local emergency services must also be notified.

All the following notes are geared to helicopters in particular, but may be adapted for aeroplanes.

On arrival at the site on the day you should check that the area is roped off properly and is the same area as was agreed originally — beware of tents and marquees, etc, creeping up on you. If you don't use the agreed area, then (by arrangement with your FOI) you will have to inform the CAA within seven days as they will have been informed of the original proposals.

Next, report to the event organiser and check the times of any other activities that may affect you, e.g. aerobatics, balloons, parachuting or whatever. Give him a written brief on what you want his tannoy announcements to say (preferably every half hour) about your activities, for instance:

'Helicopter pleasure flights from the . . . (give the position). See the show and your town from the air. Take your cameras and enjoy yourselves from the ultimate view-point. We take credit cards as well as cheques.'

He may have been given some free seats and run a competition to get rid of them, or possibly have just given them to his friends. Therefore you will need a positive means of identifying the freebies, say by headed notepaper or something. You may be plagued by people claiming they are from the organizers or the local papers asking for free flights, but unless you can identify them, politely refer them back to the organizer. He will also need to know your start time.

On rearrival at the Operational Area set out the fire extinguishers and safety equipment just inside the roped area and carry out whatever checks you need on the fuelling equipment. This will save time later when the pressure is on. Show the marshallers around all the equipment.

It's a good idea to keep the emergency equipment accessible, but out of sight as the general public are often put off by the sight of anything designed to help in an emergency (like check-lists). Where local authority emergency services are available on site, the rescue equipment is not necessary but take it anyway, because they may be called away and you will have to stop flying until they come back.

Standard rescue equipment consists of the following:

a) a vehicle capable of carrying everything — not a wheeled trolley, but something self-propelled. A car or van will do.

b) 22 kg Dry Chemical fire extinguishing agent, 1 x 7.5 kg CO_2 or 1 x 3.5 kg BCF extinguisher and 1 x 20 gal premixed AFFF foam unit with a minimum discharge rate of 16 gallons per minute.

c) 2 helmets with visors
2 pairs flame resistant gloves
2 fire tunics or donkey-type jackets
Stout boots

d) Release tools as follows:
1 axe (rescue, small, non-wedging or aircraft)

1 x 24 inch bolt cropper
1 x 40 inch crowbar
1 harness knife
1 flame resistant blanket

e) Medical equipment as follows:
6 BPC9 dressings or equivalent
6 BPC12 dressings or equivalent
6 triangular bandages
6 foil blankets
1 pair scissors
1 basic First Aid kit
2 stretchers

(BPC9 and 12 are now out of date, but there will be an EEC equivalent, no doubt. Scissors will be found in the average First Aid kit, anyway).

There should be only one entry and exit to the operational area, usually under the control of the cashier.

The **minimum** personnel required to run the site effectively will be three, one to collect money and brief passengers (the cashier) and the remaining two to marshal passengers in and out of the area and to operate seat belts, etc.

If for any reason, such as last minute sickness, you cannot get enough people, then you can get away with one marshaller on passenger movement provided that all embarkation and disembarkation is done from one side of the aircraft, one door at a time. It is not recommended, however, as passengers *en masse* must be regarded as thick as two planks — they will take every opportunity to walk into a tail rotor or a propeller, regardless of how many warnings you give them. A large version of the briefing card is recommended as a sort of briefing board that they can read in the queue.

While Marshallers are also allowed to be the rescue crew, they're not expected to wear their firemen's uniforms all the time. They should nevertheless be dressed in such a manner that instant reaction to an incident is not hampered by only having shorts and T-shirts on.

When putting up the sign with the Company identification (and the price) on, set it up about ten yards or so from the cashier's desk. That way, if people are put off by the charge, you don't give the wrong impression by having lots of people turning away at the last minute. Also, it saves the cashier answering the same questions all day.

You will need plenty of other signs for distribution around the event as, unless you're careful, regulations will ensure that you're far enough away for people to think you're nothing to do with it (this doesn't apply to air shows, of course).

Next you should brief the loaders, ensuring that they know that people should always approach and leave the helicopter from the front and that nobody should be allowed further aft than the rear skid support (or forward of a similar point on an aeroplane).

They also need to know about the opening and closing of doors and the operation of seat belts (all of this should be covered anyway in the standard passenger brief).

The most dangerous time is when the passengers get out, so that's when marshallers must be most wary. When the aircraft lands, outgoing passengers should be out of the area before the others are ushered in. Never close the throttle to ground idle while passengers are embarking or disembarking, as you are then able to lift into the air and get out of the way of anyone you see about to run round the back end — believe me, they will! The tail rotor is still dangerous at whatever speed it's going.

With reference to refuelling, it's very tempting to just carry on until the last moment when you've got a long queue, but be careful about your fuel reserves. Not only is it good airmanship to land with a reasonable amount on board, but you must have a thirty minute break every three hours anyway. Passengers (and employers) understand a helicopter stopping for fuel, but not for you swanning off for a hamburger somewhere.

There is another safety point as well. In a way, helicopters are regarded in the same sense as a fire engine — for instance, the public make no distinction between an old fire engine on show or a new one actually on duty. If there's a fire, they will turn to anything for help. The same goes for a helicopter. If there's a severe accident somewhere, it's possible that you could be asked to ferry someone to hospital. Do you know where the nearest one with a helipad is, and will you have enough fuel to get there should something happen?

When dealing with the customers, fill the machine up on every lift. Children less than two years old and carried on an adult's knee should have an approved seat belt extender provided for them — don't expect to carry more than one. If your machine takes four passengers, don't fly with less than three on board. If only two turn up, then they should wait or come back later when others have arrived.

Don't take money from one passenger and seat him in whilst waiting for more custom. This is for two reasons; firstly if nobody else comes along you're obliged to go up with just one person (highly uneconomical), and secondly you will have to make inane conversation by shouting whilst the customer is waiting, because usually you're the only one with a headset.

If business is really bad, then sell the remaining seats (quietly!) at half rate.

Talking of economical flying, and bringing up the subject of freebies again, if the show organizers send along more than one, then split them up and send them up one at a time.

That way, at least the costs are covered by the other revenue-paying passengers on each trip, whereas if you take all of the freebies up at once, you lose money on the whole lift.

You will need to identify those who have paid as well. This is usually done by sticking labels on them, date-stamping their hands, or whatever. Don't sell more than two loads in advance in case something happens and you have to return all the money.

If asked how long the flight is, say six miles or so — it sounds better than three minutes!

While the aircraft is flying, brief the next load something like this:

'When the helicopter lands, please stay here until you are called forward as we have to unload the other passengers first. You and you go to the right hand side as you look at it, you to the front and you to the rear. The other two please go to the left hand side, you to the front and you to the rear.

When you get in, please do not step on the floats (if fitted) but use the foot rests which will be pointed out to you. Once you are in, we will do up the seat belts and close the doors. After you land, we'll get you out, so just sit tight and wait for us.

Just two very important safety points — please don't touch the door handles in flight and keep away from the tail rotor — always move towards the front. Any questions?'

Again, this sort of stuff should be on the standard Passenger Briefing Leaflet anyway — you could hand out a few to keep people in the queue occupied, as it is a fair bet they will not listen to you properly, anyway. It may be a good idea to have one enlarged and pinned to a large board so that it can be read from a distance.

The cashier will need a small float of change. If in doubt as to what constitutes an infant — charge.

Be polite, the passengers are paying your salary, after all. Keep calm with difficult ones, they will go away in the end.

Keep in mind the possibility of a CAA representative hovering around, so act accordingly.

When it approaches closing time and it's obvious that not all people will get a trip, cease selling in good time. Announce it over the tannoy if necessary.

The Technical Bits

The Operational Area, which is under the positive control of the Company, encompasses the Helicopter Landing Site, the taxiways, HAAs and IAAs (see below for definitions) and take-off, climb and approach slopes.

It has side surfaces rising upwards and outwards to 100 feet at a gradient of 1:1 from its edges unpenetrated by obstacles and will be fenced, roped off or otherwise protected from intrusion by unauthorized persons.— therefore it should not include a public right-of-way (rope and stakes used for demarcation and public control are not considered obstacles for this purpose, although they may be for Performance planning).

Figures given below are derived from performance figures for the Bell 206B for +20°C and 1000 feet PA at maximum AUW — you will need equivalent figures for your machine.

The Take-off Distance Available (TODA) for each take-off direction consists of:

> The **Horizontal Acceleration Area** (HAA), which has a minimum width of 30 m or twice the rotor diameter, whichever is greater. The length must accommodate the Take-off Acceleration Distance required, which in turn is one third of the Take-off Distance to 100 feet given in the Flight Manual. Thus, the HAA is approx 300 feet or 92 m in worst case conditions, but may vary.
>
> The **Take-off Area**, which has the same width as the HAA and twice the length, making it 184 m.

The total length of the TODA is therefore 282 m.

The Inner Approach Area (IAA) for each landing direction has the same width as the HAA and must be long enough to accommodate the 'Emergency Distance from 100 feet' as detailed in the Flight Manual — 770 feet or 234 m.

The TODA and the IAA are essentially the same patch of ground, except that the TODA is slightly longer. As both the HAA and the upwind third of the IAA must be obstacle-free and are at opposite ends of this area, the whole TODA should therefore be selected as obstacle-free in the first place.

The Liftoff and Touchdown Area should be the same as any other landing site, that is having a diameter of at least twice the length of the helicopter, including rotors.

Taxiways (used if Liftoff and Touchdown areas are remote from everything else) should have a minimum clearance of 7 m from obstructions either side of the main rotors giving a width of 25 m.

Take-off, climb and approach slopes (which may be curved) should not be established over large areas of water unless you have flotation gear. They should be obstruction-free with a gradient of not less than 1:8 and 1000 m long with areas suitable for emergency landings.

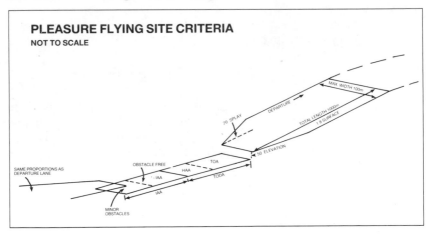

PLEASURE FLYING SITE CRITERIA
NOT TO SCALE

Special Events

Vast amounts of people being moved into a major sporting event (such as The British Grand Prix at Silverstone) render the **feeder sites** used for their lifting and dropping off liable for special treatment. These events are good for business — one day at Silverstone keeps some companies in profit for the year!

Like Pleasure Flying sites, Flight Operations need to be notified (at least twenty-eight days prior to the event in this case), but there are other considerations as well.

First of all, if you sell single seats to the public, rather than selling the whole capacity of the aircraft on a 'sole use' charter basis, then you will either need a full Air Transport Licence or an exemption. It also needs to be done in your own right; you can't do it on the back of someone else. Whoever holds the AOC must apply for these exemptions from Branch 2 (ATL) of the CAA, nominating the positions of the intended aerodromes. They will consult Flight Ops as to the suitability of said aerodromes who will apply Pleasure Flying site criteria (as found in the Ops Manual) to support their judgments. Again, there is a special form to fill in which will cut out most of the lack of communication over this subject, and you should find a copy in the Ops Manual.

Secondly, you will need to arrange with the destination for arrival and departure slots, which are usually at a premium. Because of the numbers of aircraft involved (approx 126 H1 types alone at Silverstone in 1988), there will be a briefing for all concerned well before the event, at which all companies are expected to send a representative. At the very least a Notam should be issued.

H1 helicopters are less than 15 m in length, and **H2**s are between 15 m and 24 m; they therefore require different treatment at their feeder sites.

A feeder site is one where more than five movements take place in any one day in connection with an event, as a result of which they require special facilities (a movement is a take-off **or** a landing). If using H1s you can get away with normal equipment as used for pleasure flying, but H2s need something a bit more macho.

Actually, it's basically the same, but the vehicle must have four-wheel drive and there must be a minimum of 60 gallons of water and 5 gallons of foam concentrate, with equipment able to deliver it at a rate of 40 gallons per minute. A minimum of 100 lb of CO_2 or 50 lb of dry powder or BCF is also required.

The rescue and medical equipment requirements are also more comprehensive, needing transfusion and resuscitator gear to be readily available in addition to:

1 large non-wedging axe
1 small non-wedging axe
1 grab or salving hook
1 1" cold chisel
1 4 lb hammer
1 fire resistant blanket

1 heavy duty hacksaw with six spare blades
1 suitably large ladder
50 feet of 2" line
1 pr 7" side cutting pliers
1 24" saw
1 large slotted screwdriver
1 large Philips screwdriver
1 pr tin snippers
1 pneumatic rescue chisel with spare cylinder
1 chisel and retaining spring
1 quick release knife with a sheath
3 prs flame resistant gloves
1 24" bolt cropper
1 3'6" crowbar

Line Patrol Flying

Electricity Boards carry out their line inspections generally with a helicopter, but it's possible that something like an Optica could be used if no hovering is required. However, anything fixed wing will largely be useless, so here I will mainly refer to helicopters.

On these occasions, observers from the Boards will be carried and the sorties will be flown in accordance with their normal procedures, which are pretty exhaustive. All of their staff will have been fully and professionally trained to exacting standards.

They need to be, as following of power lines calls for a high degree of proficiency and concentration on the part of all concerned. The very nature of the exercise (flying as close as fifty feet to the lines inspected) means that for most of the time you will be flying very near the avoid area of the Height/ Velocity envelope. This needs to be studied and will be found in the Flight Manual. Select a minimum speed for yourself (say twenty knots) so as to place the aircraft as close to the envelope edge as possible.

The CAA assumes that the flight will not take place in the avoid area, and so exemptions from Rule 5, etc, have tended to be geared towards looking after third parties on the ground not directly connected with your activities. However, the flights are still Public Transport and entering the avoid curve (see *Glossary*) is therefore prohibited. If prolonged incursions are likely, then consider using a twin.

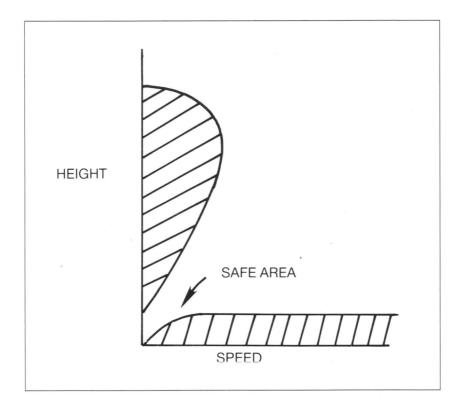

Even where a single-engined machine could be used, it's usually over areas that are not suitable for forced landings or are unable to afford safety for the passengers. While it's expected that you shouldn't fly unless you can alight without danger to persons or property on the surface if you have an engine failure, each aircraft should still have a full restraint harness for each occupant, together with a protective helmet and flame-proof overalls, or clothing with suitable shoes.

Any exemptions granted for line patrol operations will be subject to certain conditions, notably no flying at night or over congested areas, and all flights to be confined to within 300 feet of the lines concerned (but no closer than one and a half rotor diameters to the lines when level, or one diameter plus thirty feet when above their level). Also, the lines should be crossed vertically at least 100 feet above them (common sense dictates that you should do this over a pylon rather than the lines themselves). You will not be allowed closer than 100 feet to any people or vehicles directly concerned with line oper-ations and 200 feet to any structures other than those connected with the lines themselves. You shouldn't, but if you do have to go under a wire for any reason, get your skids on the ground as near to a pylon as possible.

Don't plan on doing more than two to three hours per day due to the high workload.

As well as getting the proper permissions, other problems involved in flying so low include insurance. Ensure that whatever you get also covers you for frightened animals bolting and causing havoc — this usually happens because of sharply changing noise levels caused by rapid manoeuvres. If you can't help flying over animals, at least try not to chase them through the fence!

Line patrol should not normally happen if the visibility is less than about two miles, and one mile if raining. These limits are higher than basic because moisture will stick to the windscreen at slower speeds. Things are further complicated if you have no windscreen wipers, as precipitation will not blow away either. Under those weather conditions, speeding up to get rid of water is not what you want to be doing! Give serious consideration to aborting if rain is anything near heavy. Also line patrol should not normally be attempted if the wind strength is above twenty-five knots.

Lines are patrolled at twenty or so knots, a little above pole height and to one side. Observers will normally be on the opposite side to you so the lines will be closest to them. They make commentaries on tape which are later transcribed into useful information.

Always try to follow the line as near into wind as possible. If downwind operations are inevitable, consider reducing all-up weight as appropriate (a lightly loaded aircraft is desirable in any case). If the wind is in the order of ten knots or so, being downwind generally will only ensure that the transit time along the wire is too fast — if any more it is likely to be rough as well, especially in the mountains.

Monitor vital instruments and be particularly aware of the danger of an overtorque or overtemp situation. Don't forget the possibilities of tail rotor and wire strikes, and other lines (especially tower lines) crossing — the observers will be too busy to assist your lookout.

If a closer examination of the line is called for, DO NOT try to come to the hover and backtrack, but gain height and speed, positively identify the area and make a conventional circuit and approach to come to the hover alongside the line into wind.

Police Operations

The only exceptions granted by the ANO are for flying in close proximity to crowds and the requirement to fly sufficiently high over a built-up area to enable a safe landing to be made in the event of engine failure.

Presently, either a police force will own its own aircraft or charter from operators as and when required. As they may need to charge another force for the use of their aircraft from time to time, it may be thought that reward is given for the use of an aircraft, thus there is some discussion as to whether the force concerned needs an AOC. As a result of all this, the CAA exemptions department has been working overtime, not only from the requirements to hold an AOC, but from those of the ANO as well. I suppose they could always use the same argument that the Gas and Electricity Boards use to escape liability for anything, i.e. they're not selling anything, but merely providing a service for which a charge is recovered (that's why you can't sue the Gas Board).

Parachute Dropping

No parachute dropping should be undertaken unless (as a pilot) you have been approved by the British Parachute Association and the parachutists themselves are in possession of an Operations Manual authorized by them. You get your certificate by passing a check ride with a TRE who in turn has been approved by the BPA. The normal regulations for the dropping of articles from aircraft also apply.

In addition, the aircraft flight manual should include a Supplement issued by the CAA to cover parachute dropping. For some strange reason, parachutists do not seem to be classed as passengers or freight, so it's a good question as to whether a parachute trip is actually Public Transport or not.

Parachutists should be strapped in at all times except immediately prior to dropping, and before take-off they should be instructed in the proper manner of securing seatbelts so that they don't flap around whilst in flight.

There should be no loose articles in the cabin, and seats must be removed, as must dual controls if a parachutist intends to drop from the front seat (of a helicopter). There should be no other passengers.

If dropping from a helicopter, static lines should not be used and doors must also be removed (see also Flight Manual limitations on flight without doors).

A typical freefall drop will require one pass over the drop site into wind at approximately 2,000 feet, where the jumpmaster will drop weighted paper markers. You then commence climbing to the drop height, turning downwind and keeping the markers in view all the time. When at drop height, come over the site again at about sixty knots into wind, and the jumpmaster will guide you to where he wants to be.

When dropping, both sides of the aircraft should be used if possible so as to preclude the possibilities of lateral centre of gravity limits being exceeded.

Mountain Flying

Mountainous areas are strange — general principles common to other areas will be vastly different in them. You must be prepared to adapt your flying techniques as the need arises to suit both the peculiarities of various regions and the type of aircraft.

With reference to **performance**, the maximum weight for a given altitude (and vice versa), as well as the cruising speed in relation to altitude and All-Up Weight, need to be known in advance. It's also useful, in a helicopter, to know the hover ceiling In and Out of Ground Effect for any weight.

Aircraft performance changes drastically when both temperature and height increase — just the opposite to flying in cold weather, in fact. As far as altitude is concerned, low-level operations (below about 5,000 feet) probably will not need you to get concerned about taking notice of airspeed placards and power limitations. You will find that at least seventy-five per cent power is available to a fair height, but don't tread the line too carefully between what's available and what's required!

Power available is reduced with height, and propellers and rotors turn at the same TAS, so as you increase altitude, higher pitch and power settings will be required. Larger control movements will also be needed, due to the increased rarity of the air, and there is more lag as a result. Higher temperatures will have a similar effect.

As altitude or temperature is gained, the dynamic pressure applied to the ASI is reduced for any TAS, therefore the IAS will begin to read less in relation to TAS. Thus, if you maintain a particular IAS, your groundspeed will increase relative to it and you could be going faster than you think. Landing and take-off distances will therefore increase in sympathy with altitude and temperature.

If you allow for all these effects as part of your flight planning, then fine, but if you get used to operating from a particular place with a particular air density and hence a corresponding take-off run, you may get caught out one day when things change. That's what graphs are for!

The psychological effects of mountain flying, such as disorientation, vertigo and apprehension, will reduce as your confidence increases, and this will be assisted by a knowledge of what to expect, some of which follows.

There will often be a temptation to fly below the level of the surrounding ridges, thus depriving you of your normal horizon. In this case, frequent cross-references to instruments are essential to prevent the exaggerated aircraft attitudes caused by flying with reference to ridge lines.

When passing close to the ground, you will get an impression of increased speed. The nearer you fly to a ridge, the more this will be so.

Climbing along a long shallow slope is often coupled with an unconscious attempt to maintain height without increasing power. Unless you keep a constant eye on the ASI, you're in danger of gradually losing speed — if your airspeed is reducing, then either the nose has been lifted or you are in a downdraught.

The strength of up- or downdraughts can frequently exceed your climbing capabilities. Downdraughts will be associated with a loss of height or airspeed for the same power (the loss of airspeed is due to inertia at the point of entry). A lack of cloud above (descending air) is a possible indication of a downdraught.

If you get into a downdraught, do not fight it, but guide the aircraft towards the lifting slope. If in a helicopter, it is possible to get help from the ground cushion, but the effect will be less on a slope or grass.

When valley flying, make use of upslopes or slopes exposed to the sun to take advantage of any updraughts that may be around. The aircraft should be placed on a converging course to the line of the ridge and positioned to obtain a straight flight path approximately one-third up the slope and two across or two up and one across, which are generally the area of smoothest flight (Fig 1A). However, local conditions could vary this.

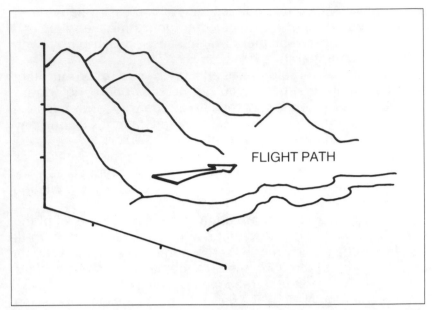

Figure 1A.

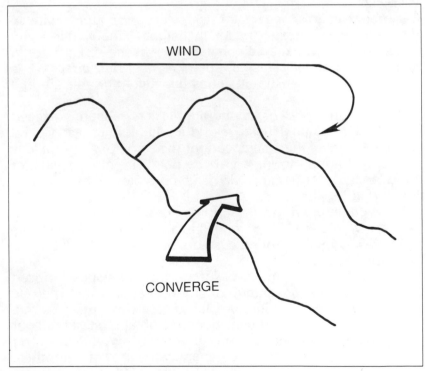

Figure 1B.

It's quite possible to climb on a lee slope taking advantage of the updraught formed by stronger wind returning on itself (Fig 1B), but beware of exceeding power limitations as speed is reduced. Also, there is so little room to manoeuvre if something goes wrong. If you find you have to do this, converging on the ridge line at forty-five degrees gives you the best chance of an escape route.

Similarly, try and avoid flight along lee slopes, but if you need to (because life is sometimes like that), smoothest flight will be obtained by flying as close as possible to the ground (say at about six inches or so!). It helps if you are close to trees, as friction effects will slow the wind down a bit, though naturally giving you a bumpy ride which can sometimes get quite irritating. This gives even less room for error, though. If the relative humidity is high, you could watch for the presence of rotor clouds, which will indicate the presence of wind currents and turbulence.

When cruising downwind, along a lee slope or not, sudden wind reversals could make the aircraft exceed VNE or even take away your airspeed completely.

If bad visibility and rain are likely to be a problem, choose a more mountainous route, even if the winds are a little stronger — Fohn effect will often provide a clear passage.

Winds can be very difficult to predict and their associated up and downdraughts can be formidable. Smoke may be used to detect wind direction, as can water, but this may only give half the story. For instance, it is not uncommon for the windsocks at each end of Banff airstrip in the Rockies to be 180 degrees at variance with each other!

The most important thing to watch after is the funnelling of wind as it progresses down a valley, so although the mean windspeed may be reported as five knots or so, you may find it as high as thirty knots in some places, and not necessarily coming from the expected direction, either! (This may be due to other effects, such as anabatic or katabatic winds, but they will all be subject to Bernoulli effects as well, although these are minimal compared to those of the wind itself).

Close to the ground the air moves in laminar fashion, but the depth of the laminar section and the gust spread will vary considerably, depending on the nature of the surface and its heating. The movement of air over a crest line has a venturi effect, giving an increased windspeed over the summit and a corresponding reduction of pressure, which could cause the altimeter to over-read slightly. On passing over or round an obstacle, the air may become turbulent or have formed into rolls which have a vertical or horizontal axis. Updraughts would be on the windward side and downdraughts on the leeward side.

The laminar flow will become broken if the ground becomes abrupt, or there are trees, and the wind is strong. Turbulence

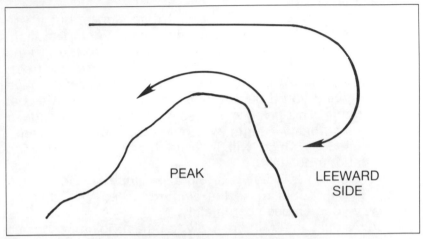

Figure 2.

will occur on both sides, resulting in an updraught close to the leeward side and a downdraught close to the windward side as the air is made to curl (Fig 2).

The general effect of a series of ridges is to form rolls between the crest lines (Fig 3). This may cause a dangerous

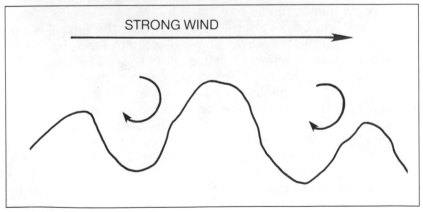

Figure 3.

situation to arise where a downdraught can exist on an upslope where normally an updraught would be expected, as in Fig 1 A. As a result, on top of steep ridges there may be an area of nil or reverse winds which is difficult to locate on the first recce.

The vertical distance to which a mountain chain will influence the movement of air is about three to five times its height, variable with windspeed. Horizontally, the effect is variable and most noticeable in stable conditions with a windspeed of more than twenty knots, when standing waves will form, mentioned previously at the end of Chapter 6.

As you know, you can recognize the existence of these by the presence of lenticular clouds, but you will also see ragged

Figure 4.

cloud around the peak (Fig 4). These should be avoided at all costs due to the turbulence associated with them, especially at the winds speeds that lead to their creation. In addition to the dangers of airframe fatigue by shockloading, momentary loss of control may occur, not to mention discomfort to your passengers.

Landing Sites on peaks or crests (for helicopters) usually present you with more possibility of an escape than do sites on flanks or valley bottoms. Wherever possible, landings should be made on ground higher than the immediate surroundings, enabling the approach direction to be varied according to the wind and giving a clear overshoot path.

Where conditions allow, always select a landing site as far forward to the windward edge as possible. This avoids the danger of suddenly finding yourself in dead or reversed airflow (as if on a lee slope) and makes overshooting easier.

If landing on the sides of a slope, use the windward sides.

Leeward sides should only be used in cases of operational necessity. Consider using smoke grenades to find out the wind direction. Don't forget you will not have the full effects of a ground cushion, if at all.

The reconnaissance should be carried out in many phases, each one being closer than the last until you are able to feel your way onto the landing site. Constant reference should be made to the altimeter to prevent descending below the level of the landing point due to the loss of natural horizon.

In checking out the landing site, approach at a converging angle into wind (thirty degrees or so). Particular note should be taken of escape routes, up- and downdraughts and turbulent areas. As you carry on, continuously confirm the suitability of the landing site and maintain a constant angle of approach.

A fairly flat approach should be used, so as to minimize the use of collective pitch to establish the hover. The angle of approach is best increased as the wind strength increases up to an almost vertical approach in a windstorm, although you would be mad to go mountain flying in any mean wind speed above fifteen knots (funnelling may increase this somewhat). Steep approaches should be avoided anyway, due to the aforementioned large handfuls of power and attitude changes that may be required in the final stages. The engine may be able to cope with it, but can your tail rotor?

Always be prepared to break off an approach at any time even if only seconds from success. Never commit yourself till the very last moment. Short cuts do not exist with mountains — they have been around a lot longer than you have!

Landing sites on the bottom of valleys often have difficult access, and frequently leave no escape route once an approach has started. It's important to ensure a safe reserve of power is available before being committed. In any case, placing the aircraft downwind near to ground should be avoided. Always go low and slow when approaching downwind with a last minute turn into wind (Fig. 5).

If landing in snow conditions, try to land with the sun behind you, as the aircraft shadow will give a useful guide to the ground slope and surface and provide a useful focus for a sight picture approach.

For **take-off**, beware of the effects of altitude on performance — extensive hovering should be avoided. Consider a jump take-off if little power is available (proceed to the edge with full RPM and tip yourself over the edge — very exhilarating for passengers!).

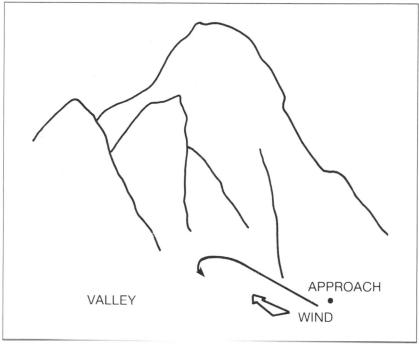

Figure 5.

Night Flying

Current regulations don't allow single-engined night flying on Public Transport, but occasionally positioning may take place with the pilot only on board.

Searching for an overdue aircraft in low light conditions causes lots of problems, and route planning should take account of this. Particular care must be taken to maintain radio contact. It remains your responsibility as to whether night flying shall be undertaken, bearing in mind there is no VFR at night.

For twenty minutes before going, it's a good idea to prepare your eyes by either dimming the lights or wearing dark glasses.

Generally, planning for night flying is much the same as for day, although there are some aspects that demand some thought. The route should be plotted on the chart in the normal way, but navigation in practice will be carried out using electronic aids or features that are prominent at night such as town lighting, lighted masts or chimneys, large stretches of water (big black holes), aerodromes, motorways, and the like.

Navigation is easier the higher you are, and it's a good idea to mark the MSA on each portion of the map where it changes.

Night flying can be pleasant — there's less traffic, you tend not to go in bad weather and the air is denser, so the engine and flying controls are more responsive. However, the change in working patterns can cause reductions in personal performance which should be monitored closely.

One of the optical illusions you might come across is the apparent motion of a stationary object, which isn't helped by rain on the windscreen. Apart from reducing visibility, it's a particular threat when attempting to fix your position by reference to a single light source.

When little or no light is on the surface and a prominent one comes into view, it may give you an overwhelming sensation that the light is above the horizon, which could lead you to pitch into a steep attitude in keeping with the resulting false horizon.

Sometimes the effect is little more than an uncomfortable climbing sensation even when you're straight and level, but an unobscured windscreen could make objects appear lower than they really are in relation to you.

This will be more apparent with high intensity runway lighting, which may also give you the same effect that actors have on stage, where they can't see the audience due to bright lighting.

Changes in colour and contrast at night may also cause confusion. The lack of normal contrast will upset your altitude perception, making you feel further away and higher than you are. As a result, on a final approach you may be too low and fast.

The solution to these sort of illusions is to use every piece of sensory information you can, including landing lights and instruments. Problems will arise if several of the above factors affect you at once, especially if the landing point is sloped — this is where more frequent cross-referencing of altimeters is important.

If used, landing sites for helicopters must be checked out in daylight on the same day as they are to be used at night. Pre-flight checks allow for night flying — a torch must be carried and two landing lights are preferred by the Powers That Be.

Permission to enter the rotor disc area by outside persons on the ground is given by flashing landing lights.

In a helicopter, hovertaxi higher and slower than by day making no sideways or backwards movements. Great care should be exercised to point the **Schermuly flares** to a safe place at all times (that's a bit difficult when they're fitted and the fuelling truck pulls up right alongside them). The flares should not be armed at this stage, but at the holding point immediately before take-off and disarmed at the same place after final approach. They should be disarmed after reaching cruising altitude, if this is high enough.

The maximum useful height for discharging a flare is approximately 1,800 feet. Its burn time is eighty seconds, during which time it will fall approximately 1,500 feet.

Therefore, having established autorotation after an engine failure at night, the first flare should be discharged immediately or on passing through 1,800 feet, whichever is later. Don't bother doing it before this, as they will be useless.

Due to switching arrangements, and depending on the height at which your engine stops, it may not be possible to set off more than one flare before landing, but if possible, the second should be discharged between 800-1,000 feet agl.

In all autorotations at night, a constant attitude approach should be maintained at all times, which will keep the beam from the landing light in the same position on the ground (if you flare, it will shine up into the air, from which position it's no good to you at all!).

Winter Operations

See also **Meteorological Hazards**, in Chapter 6.

There are some benefits to flying in cold weather. The denser air means that the engine works better at least. Thus, there's correspondingly less danger of exceeding temperature limits.

However, winter operations are associated with many hazards, too, including freezing precipitation, low ceilings and cold temperatures. Rapid changes in these are typical.

The chill factor caused by the resulting airflow from revolving propellers or rotors can reduce the ambient temperature by several degrees. When it gets to below −20°C or so, contact gloves need to be worn to prevent local freezing when your skin comes into contact with cold metal. You may also need to wear tinted goggles or sunglasses.

Always dress accordingly — in the case of a forced landing it could be that the clothes you wear will be the only protection that you have. Extra time for pre-flight planning should always be allowed.

The **pre-flight** inspection should include you — a person improperly dressed and making a series of short exposures will get fatigued more quickly. It's important to maintain blood sugar levels as more calories are consumed in the cold.

Special attention should also be paid to the following:

a) That the correct oil and grease grades are used and that any special equipment (such as winter cooling restrictors) are fitted to assist the engine to maintain correct operating temperatures.

Note that de-icing fluids are pretty efficient de-greasers as well, particularly alcohol based ones.

b) You have proper tie-downs and pitot/engine covers, together with static vent plugs, etc.

c) That the heating systems are working properly and don't allow exhaust gases into the cabin (if you're getting a regular headache, check for carbon monoxide poisoning).

d) That de-icing and anti-icing equipment is working properly and that all breather pipes, etc, are clear of anything that could freeze. Just because an aircraft has de-icing, it doesn't mean that it's cleared for flight into icing conditions (light icing is half-an-inch in forty miles).

e) That the aircraft has not been cold soaked below the minimum operating temperature allowed in the Flight Manual.

f) That all frost, ice and snow has been removed, particularly on lift-producing surfaces. Hoar frost may possibly be left on the fuselage if it can be seen through, but beware of flying into cloud where more will stick. It must be removed from places where its dislodgement could cause ingestion, e.g. engine cowlings.

Use de-icing fluid if possible — scrapers do not leave pretty results. Also, fluid, if it's thick enough, helps prevent further ice forming (see Kilfrost table in Chapter 6).

Don't forget to fit engine blanks, etc, before using fluids.

g) That you check any particle separators fitted as water seepage may have frozen inside the engine, resulting in abnormally high N1 and JPT readings (in a turbine).

h) That the skids of a helicopter are not frozen to the ground.
i) That you unstick windscreen wipers and moving parts (including rotors and propellers) by hand.
j) That windscreens are defrosted. Don't forget to have a cloth handy for demisting the windscreen from the inside when it mists up.
k) Check control linkages and flying control movement.
l) Pitot heat operation — don't just accept a flicker on the ammeter.
m) That water drains are not frozen.
n) Carb heat operation.

Wherever possible, the first start of the day should be an external one. With a turbine in cold weather you can expect a lower achieved N1 before light up with abnormally high JPT peaks, eventually settling down lower than normal (air intake icing in turbine engines can be detected by a rise in JPT and N1 for the same torque setting, but remember that use of de-icing may affect performance).

Oil pressure will be slow to rise, but will be high after starting. Temperature, on the other hand, will be very slow to rise at all. Allow the electrics to warm up before use.

In a helicopter, don't wind up to flight idle too quickly due to the risk of spinning or yawing on the pad. The cyclic should be central so as not to move the aircraft in any direction.

If the helicopter has been frozen to the ground, one skid may come free first on take-off which may cause dynamic rollover. If the aircraft has not already been freed, pull collective until ready to lift and crack it free with a little controlled pedal movement. You could also try gently circulating the cyclic.

Taxi slowly and with caution if the taxiways are clear of snow. If not, in a helicopter, taxi higher and slightly faster then normal to keep out of the resulting snow cloud. In an aeroplane, act as if you have no brakes. Ramp markings may be covered in ice — be aware of other people's problems.

Marshallers should be well clear and move slowly themselves. If the heater is required to be off in the hover, ensure the blower is on, to help clear the windscreen.

Taking Off

In snow conditions, the accepted take-off method in a helicopter is the towering type, because a normal one may result in a large snow cloud with a possible loss of visual reference to air and ground crews alike (you may be able to blow a lot of loose snow away with a little application of collective before the take-off proper).

If a white-out does happen, apply maximum available power for an immediate climb and apply forward cyclic, keeping the ball centred and using the A/H if necessary.

After getting airborne in an aeroplane, exercise the gear once or twice to dislodge any slush, etc, that may have stuck to the legs. With any piston engine, use carb heat **regularly** and check the instrument readings frequently for indications of carb icing. When using carb heat, have it full on or off, but not on for prolonged periods — it increases fuel consumption markedly (see also **Engine Handling**, Chapter 8).

The Cruise

Icing can be experienced from sea level up to 44,000 feet, but mainly it can be expected between 3,000-24,000. There are two types of icing cloud, stratus and cumulus, the most likely altitude for which will be 10,000 and 5,000 feet respectively. The most probable icing temperatures in relation to altitude will be − 3°C at sea level decreasing to −24°C at 20,000 feet, but mountain wave clouds can be loaded with heavy ice at remarkably low temperatures (remember that low pressures coupled with low temperatures will cause your altimeter to read high).

The instant answer with icing encountered *en route* is to change altitude. If you are in freezing rain, the warm air will be above you. If you are in sleet, stay where you are, as you may get freezing rain above and below you. Going higher may also take you out of the cloud tops, but more ice may accumulate *en route* underneath the wing as more of the lower side is exposed to the airflow.

Landing

Helicopter Landing Sites should be selected with a view to being able to pull out of a resulting snow cloud if necessary (refer to **Operations from Contaminated Runways** in Chapter 6 for a discussion on landing with fixed wing aircraft).

Carry out a normal approach, using a constant attitude with minimum changes. Aim to keep the helicopter forward and downward until a few inches above the snow. Use the aircraft shadow, a smoke grenade or the landing light to provide texture to the surface. Try hovering higher than usual before actually committing yourself to try and blow the looser stuff away first.

When you do commit yourself, you will need to confirm the firmness of the surface, not usually a problem if landing at a camp or something, as the ground crew will have done this for you. The danger lies when you're going to an unchecked landing site for the first time. Touch down without delay, as far as possible treating it as a sloping ground landing.

Bounce the skids a little to see if there's a crust, but don't forget to keep your RPM to flying levels until you're sure you're on firm ground.

If shutting down on an icy surface, shut down carefully anticipating ground spin. Handle all controls gently.

After final shutdown, fill any fuel tanks to prevent inner tank condensation. Remove batteries if the temperatures are forecast to be below −10°C. Ensure that aeroplane propellers are aligned so that water can drain out of the spinners — then you won't get a nasty surprise caused by lumps of ice inside causing imbalance and vibration.

If operating away from base, ensure that the battery is fully charged before departure, and consider taking a spare, together with an external start cable. Check that heaters, blowers, etc, work and that snow deflectors are fitted. Also, note whether tie downs and covers are serviceable. De-icing fluids should always be carried, as should a small amount of food. Consider the use of a support vehicle if the extra equipment required for winter operations becomes excessive.

Aerial Survey

Aerial survey is the process of photographing areas of land from varying heights, the results generally being used for map-making. As a result, this activity takes place at great heights, but it may get exciting and bring you down to 300 feet depending on the results required.

Aerial survey can give good job satisfaction, especially if you can see the results and the target appears in every frame as requested by the surveyor!

When doing low-level work, you will be given a large-scale map with flight patterns marked on it, and you do everything by pure map reading. The pattern can be star-shaped, consisting of sets of two or three parallel runs at angles to each other over the target. The equipment used is something like the Zeiss trilens, which will take one flat and two oblique photographs at the same time.

Close map-reading is not so easy at higher levels, however, although flying from town to town will generally be accurate enough. At really high levels, like Flight Level 10 or so, you will need a navigation aid, something like Decca Navigator.

Air Testing

If you're a junior pilot, you may well find yourself doing quite a bit of this, anything from just engine running to full C of A air tests, although many engineers these days are cleared for engine runs.

The reason why junior pilots tend do them is because they are pretty boring and are regarded as a waste of time to anyone except engineers.

Nevertheless, Air Testing demands your full concentration and everyone due to fly in the aircraft later deserves it also.

One point to bear in mind is that the aircraft is only technically serviceable for the air test — to all other intents and purposes it is unserviceable. If in doubt, insist that an engineer goes with you — if he won't fly in it, then don't you bother either.

The least taxing are straight engine runs. When a sliver of metal is detected in oil, there usually follows an engine run for anything up to two hours or so (I have known one run for five) to see if it happens again.

Then there are compass swings where you place the aircraft on a series of headings on an isolated spot well away from large hangars and other aircraft, while a chap with a landing compass stands outside in the cold and rain taking readings. Comparison of aircraft readings with his, adjusted with certain formulae, give the corrections.

The shorter air tests tend to concern themselves with the proper rigging of flying controls. The longer ones creep into the full-blown C of A air tests which are Extremely Official and done in accordance with strict procedures.

In order to do one of these, you must be on the Maintenance Contractor's approved list of test pilots (approved by the CAA, that is), which means having some experience on type and being able to fly accurately.

The basic idea is to perform a series of prescribed manoeuvres (timed climbs, for instance) while an engineer takes notes of temperatures and pressures, etc. The results are plotted on performance graphs (by you) so they can be compared against the standard figures in the Flight Manual (this is where you see how accurate your flying really is, when the plotted points end up all over the place instead of being in a straight line).

Before you start, though, you need to be sure that the props or rotors are as clean as you can get them, because their state will make a surprising difference on the climb figures.

Mail Flights

These involve much night flying in 'orrible weather, and newspaper flights come under this heading as well. The main thing to watch is that the cargo is loaded properly, as it is a great temptation just to pack the thing to the gunwales and go, because everything is done in a hurry. Because there is such a rush on, there will often be a penalty clause imposed on the Company if things are delayed, so you may well find commercial pressure to depart on time, even if the payload calculations aren't done and the load isn't secured properly.

With reference to the load, if your aircraft weighs less than 5,700 kg, actual weights must be used, and regarding security, bags must be lashed down **leaving you an emergency exit after the load has shifted!**

One last thing — you don't know what is in mailbags, so consider lining the aircraft floor with plastic, just in case something nasty leaks out.

Chapter 8
Technical Matters

General

Every Ops Manual, despite the adoption of the aircraft Flight Manual as part of its structure, will still need a Technical Section dealing with aspects peculiar to the Company's type of aircraft. You may feel you've been taught enough of it already, but things like oil and fuel requirements and specimen performance data will still need to be emphasized. Also, the check lists in the usual standard of Owner's Manual are nowhere near good enough for UK Public Transport operations, so these will need to be expanded, too.

Whilst too much information should not be duplicated between the Flight and Operations Manuals, enough technical details ought to be included to provide a ready reference guide. The basic idea of a Technical Section is to include information that may be relevant to a pilot in flight with anything of a detailed descriptive nature being left in the Flight Manual. This is more important in smaller aircraft with no room for a complete library up front.

Information will need to be provided on such topics as crosswind take-offs on ice covered runways, action not included in checklists or drills, special handling techniques and many others. Emergency drills may need to be placed on different coloured pages.

Thus, if you operate several types of aircraft, you will have some duplication of the same paragraphs in every Section but with different information in them. You may feel there are some paragraphs missing here — I'm just covering the more unusual aspects not commonly found or expanded on and usually forgotten in Ops Manuals. The advantage of doing things this way is that the Manual can be changed easily when the Company's aircraft change.

If you haven't thought of it already (because most pilots tend to be mechanically-minded), it will be well worth your while digging a little deeper into engineering principles and practice in general. Not only will it help you stay alive, but you get more out of engineers when you speak their language.

Crew Complement

Most General Aviation aircraft are normally operated with a single pilot unless circumstances dictate otherwise. The 1st pilot (who is normally the Commander) sits in whatever seat is detailed in the Flight Manual, the only exception to this being an instructor or TRE qualified on type who may, for training purposes, occupy the other seat and yet be in command of the aircraft.

Responsibility as Commander is only taken by the co-pilot should the Commander become unfit to fulfil his duties (see also **Incapacitation** in Chapter 6).

Leading Edge Protective Tape

Protective tape is used on leading edges of helicopter rotor blades (and some aeroplane propellers) to protect against wear and tear from impact by dust or precipitation. A partial loss of it can dramatically affect aerodynamic efficiency, resulting in the need to apply a substantial increase in power during hovering manoeuvres. It will also cause a loss in RPM during autorotation.

The most likely time for the tape to come off is during or after flight through precipitation (typical — just when it's wanted!), so you need to check it out before take-off. If it looks like wearing out, then remove or repair it before the next flight, removing an equivalent amount from each blade, as it may have also been used for balancing purposes. It will be put on in short strips of anything between six to eighteen inches (so you are not flying with a great length of it hanging off) which should be removed as a whole — don't just cut bits away.

If tape comes off in flight (noticeable by a distinctive 'chuffing' sound, sometimes accompanied by vertical bounce), reduce power and speed and make gentle manoeuvres while landing. If it comes off before landing, just carry on.

Propeller Overspeed

If engine control is lost and RPM rises above the maximum, reduce airspeed and feather immediately.

If you're not quick enough, damage could be caused due to over-revving and the feathering system may not be able to cope with the extreme RPM. DO NOT attempt to unfeather the engine but land as soon as possible.

Failure of Feathering System

Most feathering systems don't function below a certain low RPM (typically 700-1,000). This is so you don't start with the blades feathered.

However, there are further implications — if your engine fails due to a major mechanical fault, you may not be able to catch the propeller quickly enough for feathering. The usual reaction is to close the throttle of the dead engine first; opening it a little may increase the RPM so that feathering can take place properly. Keeping your speed up may help as well.

If the propeller fails to feather, reduce your airspeed to a minimum (but not below scheduled engine-out climb speed) and allow the RPM to stabilize as low as possible.

Try again. If the propeller still fails to feather, try to reduce speed sufficiently for its rotation to cease, which will cause less of a drag penalty than a windmilling prop, even if it has stopped in fine pitch.

Not only will your single-engined climbout performance be affected, directional controllability will be, too, although you should be OK down to Vmca.

Engine Failure/Autorotations in Helicopters

Engine failure in a helicopter is detected by a noticeable decrease in engine noise, yaw in the same direction as blade rotation, loss in height/speed and ENGINE OUT audio/visual warnings (if fitted). Sometimes these extra warnings are needed because there's so much noise you can't tell whether the engine has failed or not anyway. While speed is of the essence, there is usually time enough to verify actual engine failure with instruments.

Success at engine-off landings largely depends on pilot skill, so full use should be made of every opportunity to practice under varying conditions. For all practical purposes, however, your gliding distance is about equal to your height, or, put simply, what you can see between your feet.

Blade inertia means that loss of RPM at the entry into autorotation is most critical — high angles of attack from high collective pitch settings may cause enough drag to slow the rotors drastically. Pitch MUST be reduced as soon as possible without regard to passenger comfort, but calmly all the same.

Try to establish the cause of engine failure — if it's fire, close the throttle immediately, but if not, consider initially closing it only to idle speed (or not closing it at all) as the engine may be able to provide enough power to enable you to downgrade the incident from catastrophe to mere disaster (make sure a sudden burst of power doesn't give you a nasty surprise if the engine comes alive again). The discussion that follows will consider the throttle as being fully closed.

Several factors may affect the rate of descent, such as gross weight, air density, airspeed and rotor RPM. Changing airspeed, though, is about the only one you have direct control over that allows you some flexibility (you can alter the RPM, but they must still remain in a small speed band to be effective). Changes in airspeed can have dramatic effects on the rate of descent. If the recommended IAS is sixty knots (fairly common), for instance, speeds of either thirty or 100 knots could increase RoD to as much as 3,000 fpm. Turns will have a similar effect, but the results will be worse if pedals are used, so try and use the cyclic only for these.

Each helicopter will have an optimum rate of descent that will give the longest range consistent with it. Where winds or density altitudes are high, expect to increase speed a little. Decrease it when winds are calm or density altitudes are low.

If you deliberately decrease the RPM in order to increase range (and possibly lessen the rate of descent), don't forget you will have to build up your RPM again before landing.

Don't worry about the avoid curve in autorotation, either — this is only a function of the pitch angle of the blades, so if you're in flat pitch it does not exist.

Having entered autorotation:

a) Select landing spot
b) Transmit MAYDAY
c) Warn passengers
d) Turn off electrics, but NOT battery (you need the intercom)
e) Close throttle if required

Plan to slightly overshoot your desired landing spot, and when about seventy feet from the ground, use rearward cyclic to slow the aircraft vertically and horizontally. Continue the flare progressively in order to be at the correct speed for landing at ten feet, applying collective pitch as flare effect decreases to check the descent more positively.

As the flare ends and the kinetic energy of the rotors is used when the collective is raised, the airflow through the rotors is reversed, assisting you to level the aircraft ready to cushion the landing as you apply the required collective pitch. Try and stop any drift or yaw until the aircraft has stopped.

This is where correct use of airspeed during the descent will have had the most beneficial effects. As the kinetic energy stored in the blades is what slows you down, it follows that any you have to use to slow an unnecessarily fast rate of descent is not available for the final stages of touching down.

Try not to let the rotor RPM drop below about seventy per cent, as head resonance in some helicopters may cause ripples in the tail boom — but protect yourself before the aircraft.

With high skids fitted, as near a zero speed landing as possible should be achieved due to the couple caused between the body and the skids when they contact the ground — but again, you are more important than the machinery!

After landing:

f) Close throttle
g) Close fuel valve
h) Turn off Battery
i) Evacuate aircraft
j) Follow the Accident Procedure in Chapter 6.

Ground Resonance

Peculiar to some helicopters, this is indicated by an uncontrollable lateral oscillation increasing rapidly in sympathy with rotor RPM. If corrective action isn't taken, the aircraft will break up. This condition will only occur if the undercarriage is in contact with the ground.

It's best avoided by landing or taking off as cleanly as possible, but if it does occur, the helicopter must either be lifted off the ground or the collective lowered fully with throttle closed.

Tail Rotor Failure

This may be detectable in the early stages by vibrations, buzzing, stiff pedal movement or unusual pedal positions for given altitudes. If not, sudden failure will ensure that thrust from the tail rotor becomes fixed at anywhere between zero and maximum.

Structural failure is apparent from noise, sudden yaw and severe vibration, possibly coupled with a sharp nose-down trim change. **Drive** failure will cause an uncontrollable yaw. In this case, there may also be an engine overspeed.

The immediate reaction should be to enter autorotation, keeping up a little forward speed on touchdown in order to maintain some directional control. As speed is reduced towards touchdown, the aircraft will yaw progressively with less control available in proportion. It may be worth trying to strike the ground with the tailskid first, which will help you to keep straight.

If **Control** failure occurs, it may be possible to find a power and speed combination that will enable you to maintain height until you can find a suitable landing area.

If you want to try and use a run-on technique, get the wind off to port (if the blades rotate anti-clockwise), so that the fuselage is crabbing left, and control descent with a combination of throttle and collective pitch, applying more power from either source just before touchdown so that the aircraft runs on straight. This is not always the best solution, as applying power to an already overstressed tail rotor may make things worse.

Landing with a power pedal jammed near full should be easier to control, since the rotors are fixed in a position appropriate to the high power settings required for a normal landing. If the pedals jam the other way, you will probably need more speed because there will not be enough anti-torque thrust available.

Sometimes, failure can be due to **tail rotor breakaway**, which is effectively a stalling of the tail rotor. It has amongst its causes high density altitudes, high power settings, low airspeeds and altitudes and vortex ring.

Your helicopter will be more susceptible to it if the tail rotor is masked by a tail surface, and it can be especially triggered by tail and side winds.

Recovery is due to a combination of full power pedal, forward cyclic, reduction in collective or autorotation.

Hydraulic Boost Failure

Indicated by feedback forces felt in the controls when making manoeuvres. They will be negligible when the controls are held in a fixed position. The usual system is to check that the Hydraulic Cb is in and that the HYD switch is on. Select switch off if power is not restored.

Reduce forward speed and control inputs to a minimum, making necessary movements at a rate of travel not faster than one full displacement, stop to stop, per second.

Overpitching

In a helicopter, overpitching is a condition where the rotor RPM are too low to maintain flight, giving the impression of 'labouring'. It is the nearest equivalent to stalling and is commonly caused by being overweight for the particular conditions. Reduce power to maintain RPM.

Mast Bumping

This is a symptom of helicopters with teetering rotor heads where cyclic input occurs with a low G-loading on the head, causing the head to exceed flapping limits and strike the mast with disastrous consequences (like the head falling off). Reduced or zero-G conditions should therefore be avoided.

Loading

Loading presents similar problems for any aircraft throughout the spectrum, but heavier types will have things like Maximum Zero Fuel Weight to contend with, in addition to having larger areas in which to place loads and therefore presenting more chances for mistakes to happen (this is a good time to mention that there will be local weight restrictions for particular areas, such as not more than 150 lb per square foot, or not more than 250 lb in the baggage compartment).

The loading section of the Ops Manual will contain details of where and how to load freight, baggage, passengers, etc with worked examples of the associated paperwork. In an Ops Manual dealing with large aircraft, it will occupy a section by itself, but for smaller types it's convenient to include it under Technical.

Some aircraft have a proper cargo fit, but problems may be caused where one that normally carries passengers is used without modification, with the subsequent improper use. Naturally, in small aircraft where the emergency exits are obvious, this really only involves the removal of seats, because the aim is just to substitute loads while using the same fixtures and locations. However, where you get involved in removing galleys and otherwise converting the cabin in larger aircraft, the exercise becomes a little more difficult (just because a Flight Manual contains details of freight loading limitations, it doesn't necessarily mean that any modifications you make by reconfiguration of the cabin are specifically permitted. Those figures may only have been used for basic certification procedures). These potential problems are the reason why you may need to be certificated on your training forms as being cleared to change aircraft configurations.

There are two aspects to Loading, the weights concerned and their distribution. Every aircraft has certain weight restrictions which must not be exceeded laid down in the Flight Manual and, as a Commander, you are legally bound by them. Most of them are commonly found with fixed-wing aircraft, and you get some nasty surprises sometimes. For instance, the tendency to put fuel in wings means that you have unusually shaped fuel tanks to contend with, so when you place fuel amounts against moment arms you won't get a straight line variation. Some aircraft therefore use fuel/ moment arm tables where every fuel load has a different moment figure.

If you're faced with one of these, it's not sufficient just to subtract the closing fuel moment from the start one, otherwise you could end up with something strange. For example, 1,000 lb has a moment of 1843 and 300 lb a moment of 558. The result for 700 lb is not 1843−558 (1285), but the actual figure of 1274. Not much difference, but sufficient to cause an insurance company to have qualms about paying up if you have an accident.

The **Maximum Taxi (Ramp) Weight** is the maximum permitted weight at which the aircraft may be moved, either under its own power or otherwise. The **Maximum Take-off Weight** is that laid down in the Flight Manual as such. This is **not** necessarily the **Maximum Permitted Take-off Weight**, which is the maximum weight at the commencement of the take-off run that varies due to performance factors such as length and slope of runway, temperature, humidity, obstacles and altitude (see Chapter 6). Any maximum take-off weight less than the full maximum due to performance factors is known as the **Restricted** (or Regulated) **Take-off Weight** (RTOW) and is the starting point for calculating maximum payload available.

Sometimes, of course, RTOW is the same as MTOW, but this will only tend to happen at larger airfields or landing sites which give plenty of room for manoeuvre (Maximum Taxi weight, if you haven't already guessed, can be higher than Maximum Take-off Weight, and you should be able to burn off the difference before getting airborne!).

Confused? You soon will be!

Maximum Landing Weight speaks for itself, and is established to help prevent the forces of impact with the runway being transmitted through the undercarriage to the rest of the aircraft, which can only happen if the weight is kept within certain limits (thereby also assisting you to reduce the downward velocity better at the point of landing). This weight may very well be restricted by performance considerations in similar fashion to Take-off Weight, and could well be a factor in further reducing your payload at the start of a flight.

As fuel is carried in the wings of most aeroplanes, excessive payload weight (in the cabin) relative to fuel weight will increase the design bending moment of the wing, being most critical with a full load and zero fuel. A **Maximum Zero Fuel Weight** is therefore established to limit the weight in the cabin, being a weight beyond which any increase in load must consist entirely of fuel.

In addition to the above Technical weights, there are Operational Weights, the most important being the **Aircraft Prepared for Service Weight** (APS), consisting of the basic weight plus or minus changes to seat layouts, fixed equipment, unuseable fuel and crew equipment, such as flight guides. It is the basis of the loadsheet, and is sometimes the same as the **Dry Operating Weight** which is an APS weight that also includes supernumary crew, baggage etc.

Wet Operating Weight, on the other hand, will include the weight of useable take-off fuel plus engine additives.

The **Traffic Load** is the weight of cargo, passengers, baggage and mail and will include the weight of loading equipment (pallets, nets, etc).

The **Allowed Traffic Load** (not necessarily the same thing) is just the **payload**, which is calculated by subtracting the Operating Weight from the Regulated Take-off Weight.

In an aircraft with under twelve seats, unless you have dispensation, you must use actual weights for passengers, whereas otherwise a statistically derived standard weight (which will include baggage) may be used.

The **Maximum Compartment Weight** is the maximum that may be loaded in any specific compartment, subject to restrictions on floor loadings, and loose equipment weight is additional equipment which may or may not be included in the APS weight.

Now we come to weight distribution. Incorrect loading naturally affects aircraft performance, and will possibly prevent the thing from even getting airborne. A Centre of Gravity too far forward will make it more difficult to raise the nose on take-off, possibly overstressing the nosewheel as a result, and make the flight less economical by excessive use of trim tabs, which causes more drag. There are certain advantages to having the C of G towards the rear (by making the tailplane contribute to total lift, which also reduces the power required), but excessive aft C of G will make the aircraft less stable, more fatiguing to fly and will cause similar drag and nosewheel problems (but in reverse) as excessive forward C of G. Don't forget also that there will be local weight restrictions that are concerned with the actual strength of the fuselage at that point, so an ideal C of G may have to be adjusted for this.

Passenger seats occupy the whole floor space evenly, so this load-spreading principle needs to be borne in mind when loading freight, such as dividing bulk loads into smaller packs (cargo should ideally be distributed so as to represent the presence of passengers). This makes it easier to provide decent restraint on each pack, because access areas to exits above and around the cargo need to be established for use **after** the load has moved after an emergency stop.

You may find it helpful to line the floor with something waterproof if you're not sure what you're carrying — people who use the Royal Mail don't know about Dangerous Goods regulations and may send something flimsy that leaks something horrible all over the place.

Loads must be restrained by means of nets or straps (or a combination of both) and must be distributed over available fixtures, e.g. seat attachments.

There are many ways of expressing C of G position, ranging from a simple statement of fact (such as seventy-five inches from a specified point), through using a graph in the Flight Manual (which will give an envelope in which it may be plotted), to using index numbers on larger aircraft which are more manageable than the telephone numbers you would have to use if the calculations were done conventionally.

However, fine detail is outside the scope of this book, and we are dealing with smaller aircraft and their operation anyway. There are ways of making life easier with regard to loading on these, the most common of which is a **Load Plan**.

The idea of this is to save the constant working out of C of G on loads that are fairly standard. Weight ranges need to be worked out, especially for helicopters, as frequently the aircraft will be loaded by non-technical staff (such as oil rig workers), who will want as little detail and as much flexibility as possible. These weight ranges should not be confused with the standard weights used for convenience on larger aircraft. C of G limits used in Load Plans will have to be more stringent.

Units used and weight conversions should be known by everyone, and the same principles will apply to all aircraft. When going for an AOC, the Flight Ops Inspector will want to see pre-worked examples for worst case situations (this will include full and empty tank positions). Any flights outside the conditions of a Load Plan will need the C of G and a Loadsheet to be worked out in full.

The following example Load Plans may be used for the Bell 206 helicopter with the fuel and payloads as shown (just adapt the method to suit other aircraft). The Load Plan number should be included in the Tech Log before flight. The figures assume an APS weight of **up to** 2,100 lb and a maximum weight of 3,200 lb. Pilot and passenger weights may be **up to** 200 lb including baggage. When there are less than four passengers, baggage may be loaded on the rear seats or in the baggage hold to suit passenger convenience, but maximum weight in the baggage hold is 250 lb. Fuel loads above 75 gallons assume a range extender is fitted.

Notice the specific instructions as to what to do with baggage.

Load Plan	Pax	Fuel
B3	3	50 gallons
B2	2	83 gallons
B1	1	93 gallons

Passengers will be loaded front to rear with the passengers occupying seats thus:

First	Forward passenger seat
Second	Starboard rear passenger seat
Third	Port rear passenger seat
Fourth	Centre rear passenger seat

As you can see, everything needs to be spelt out so that anybody in the Company can refer to the details and get everything correct with all possibilities catered for.

Generally, if you need to reduce weight, then that is done by manipulating the payload, not the sector fuel.

Loadsheets

Loadsheets are not required for aircraft below 2,730 kg, or for training, positioning or private flights, but you will still need to know your C of G as a matter of airmanship. Loadsheets should be drawn up outside the conditions imposed by a Load Plan and should account for all items of the laden weight. Generally it could be used in the circumstances below, although you could probably think of more. The position of the laden C of G must be specified, together with the load distribution, but it will be sufficient to note its position within a range unless it's required for other purposes, such as airworthiness or performance.

Wherever practicable a copy must be left behind with a responsible person or organization. If this can't be done, then the completed loadsheet must be placed in a fireproof container together with the Tech Log.

Occasions when you need a loadsheet include:

a) When loads outside load plan provisions are carried, such as for passengers with more than the anticipated baggage allowance, or extra fuel to cater for a longer trip.
c) With any combination of doors removed
d) With camera mount and cameraman on board
e) With an underslung load
f) With freight only
g) When parachute dropping

Engine Handling

Pulling full power just because it's there is not always a good idea. The limits laid down in the Flight Manual may be there for other reasons; for instance, the engines could actually have been de-rated because the transmission was not designed to take that much. Excessive use of power will therefore ruin your gearbox well before the engine (and this will show up as metal particles in the oil).

Maximum Continuous Power is the setting that may be used indefinitely, but any between that and maximum power (usually shown as a yellow arc on the instrument) will only be available for a set time limit.

While I'm not suggesting for a moment that you should, piston engines will accept their limits being slightly exceeded from time to time with no great harm being done. Having said that, the speed at which the average Lycoming engine disintegrates is approximately 3,450 rpm, which doesn't leave you an awful lot of room when it runs normally at 3,300. Turbines are less forgiving than pistons and give fewer warnings of trouble. The closer tolerances to which they are made means that the limits set for these engines are much more critical than they would be in a piston engine. It's for this reason that regular power checks (once a week) are carried out on them to keep an eye on their health.

In a turbine engine, power used is indicated by the torque-meter (you will also have mast torque to contend with in a twin-engined helicopter). In a piston, you get this with Manifold Pressure combined with RPM.

Too much Manifold Pressure relative to RPM will cause over-boosting (the same as labouring a car engine by being in too high a gear), which will cause detonation, or pre-ignition. This in turn will unnecessarily increase the operating tempera-ture, but the real harm to the engine is caused by the shock waves that result from the piston getting the effects of the power stroke when it doesn't expect it. Prevention of pre-ignition (or 'pinking' in a car, which is the same thing) is done by adding substances to the fuel.

The 'LL' in 100LL stands for low lead, but there is still about four times as much as is required to do the job it's intended for, namely to prevent pre-ignition.

In addition to the lead (in the form of TEL — tetra-ethyl lead), a scavenging agent (ethylene dibromide or EDB) is also added to ensure that the lead is as far as possible in a vapourized form, ready to be expelled from the cylinder with the other exhaust gases. Unfortunately, this is not 100% successful, but the results are best at high temperatures and worst at low ones.

These unwanted extras result in fouling of spark plugs, heavy deposits in the combustion chamber, erosion of valve seats and stems, sticking of valves and piston rings and general accumulation of sludge and restriction of flow through fine oil passages (come to think of it, using expensive fuel in your car may well be just as bad in other ways as using the cheap stuff!).

You obviously need less priming to start a warm piston engine than a cold one, but you may still need a little even where you would not expect to. This is especially true with fuel injected types, where the feed pipes lie across the top of the engine and consequently get warm, with the resulting vaporiz-ation of the fuel inside them. You then need a short burst of pressure to ensure the presence of fuel in the first place.

Leaning makes the engine run hotter and give more power for less fuel; it also improves scavenging and hence wears the engine less. A 112 hp aircraft cruising at 4,000 feet and eighty-five knots will burn five gallons per hour when rich but only 4.5 when leaned, giving a range of 116 miles as opposed to 100 — a saving of sixteen per cent. Not only that, at height, the engine will not work at all if the ratio of fuel to air is not correct.

For better **economy**, lean off slightly in the climb, but never take off with reduced power or too lean a mixture. It may save fuel, but the extra is needed to cool the engine at low speed settings. When levelling at cruising altitude, the combination of increased IAS and throttling back cools the engine rapidly. Don't be in such a hurry, and do your serious leaning five to ten minutes after establishing the cruise. Close the cowl flaps before levelling off. In the cruise, better fuel consumption may be obtained at slower speeds and lower power settings, but consider the cost of extended running time.

Leaning also increases exhaust temperatures. Try leaning to ten degrees lean of peak EGT (without exceeding the maximum) — this does, however, lose about five knots. Don't forget to enrich the mixture before increasing power when cruising at peak EGT or when increasing to more than seventy-five per cent power. Move the engine controls slowly and smoothly, particularly with a turbocharged engine. The absence of power caused by harsh movements, which on older engine designs will result in a cough and splutter, can be very embarrassing.

Apart from sympathetic handling, the greatest factor in preserving engine life is temperature and its rate of change. Over and under leaning are detrimental to engine life, and sudden cooling is as bad as overheating.

If you close the throttles at height and dive down to a landing, the thermal shock is worth about £100 in terms of lost engine life. Don't use the cowl flaps as airbrakes! Use them to warm the engine after starting and to cool it after landing (allow the temperatures to stabilize before shutting down, especially on turbocharged aircraft).

Although many flight manuals state that as soon as an engine is running without stuttering it's safe to use it to its fullest extent, it's always a good idea to warm up for a few minutes before applying any load, at least until you get a positive indication on the oil temperature (and pressure) gauges.

Similarly, many engines have a **rundown period** which must be strictly observed if you want to keep it for any length of time. As engines get smaller relative to power output, they have to work harder. Also, in turbines, there are no heavy areas that will act as heat sinks (such as the fins on a motorcycle). This results in localized hot spots which are safe if cooled properly, done with the assistance of circulating oil inside the engine (seventy-five per cent of the air taken into a turbine is for cooling purposes).

If you shut down too quickly, the oil no longer circulates, which means that oil may carbonize on to the still hot surfaces. The real danger here is with the build up of carbon if this is done too frequently, which may get big enough to prevent the relevant engine parts from turning, often just at the wrong moment! This coking up could seize the engine within fifty hours or less. Another point to note with turbines is the possible heat deformation of the metal, because it will be of a thinner gauge than that used in the average piston engine.

Even on a warm day, if it's humid, **carburettor icing** is always a danger, especially at small throttle openings where there's less area for the ice to block off in the first place.

The difference between the OAT and the temperature in the venturi can be anywhere between 20-30°C, so icing can be expected even when the OAT is as high as 10°C. There could be icing caused from water in the fuel precipitating out under certain conditions, and impact icing.

With smaller engines, use full settings whenever you apply carb heat — e.g. the system should either be on or off. However, continuous use of hot air should be avoided, if only to keep the fuel consumption down. If you have a temperature gauge in the intake, then by all means use partial heat, but even this should be used sparingly as it could raise the temperature to a more critical icing range (see below).

If ice is present, rough running may increase as the melted ice goes through the engine. Be careful that you don't get an overboost or an excessive increase in RPM when you reselect cold.

Of course, fixed wing aircraft have some advantage if the engine stops due to carb icing, in that the propeller acts as a flywheel which keeps the engine turning, thus giving you half a chance to do something about it. In a helicopter, where you don't have this effect because of the freewheel drive which allows the machine to autorotate, the practice of only selecting hot air when you actually get carb ice is not such a good idea.

In this case, you will have to learn to take more notice of your instrument indications in order to detect any problems early, particularly noting Manifold Pressure and RPM readings, comparing them before and after heat is applied. If they return to the same positions, then no ice was forming.

There is a critical range for ice formation, and this will be indicated by an arc on the temperature gauge, typically −2-32°C (gauges are supplied on helicopters because of these problems).

If you keep the temperature above the top range, then there is no problem (there is an added bonus in that full heat will help stop overboosting, but some machines will require full cold to be applied for take-off and landing). Conversely, where temperatures are low, keep the carb air below the band.

Most of these problems are avoided with fuel injection, where the fuel is metered to the engine according to its power requirements, automatically taking air density into account. Ice is not formed because there is no venturi to cause temperature drops. The only control you have (apart from the throttle) is ICO. The biggest operational problem with fuel injected engines is blocked jets.

Further thoughts on carb icing can be found in AIC 1/85 (Pink 68).

Aircraft Husbandry

A company can tell how well its pilots look after their aeroplanes by the amount it spends on servicing — the lower the costs, the better they are.

Aircraft should not be parked on soft or sloping ground, and suitable chocks should be placed under the main gear wheels of aeroplanes. Aircraft should be parked into wind whenever possible, with the nosewheel in line with the fore and aft axis. Control locks and covers should be used whenever convenient (especially when wind speeds are expected to be high, in which case consider picketing as well), and all doors, hatches and windows should be closed when the aircraft is left unattended.

Anti-collision lights should be switched on immediately prior to starting engines, but it is suggested (in accordance with military practice) that this be done immediately the aircraft is occupied, always having due regard for the capabilities of your battery, that is. Speaking of which, always leave the light switches on when leaving the aircraft, because that provides a good indication that you've left the Battery Master Switch on.

Engine ground runs and taxying should only be carried out by duly authorized pilots or engineers who are responsible for ensuring that there is adequate clearance when taxying in the vicinity of obstructions. Where space is limited, a marshaller should be used, but remember you are still responsible if you hit anything.

Maintenance

There are two types of maintenance, Scheduled and Unscheduled, which basically speak for themselves.

The purpose of controlled maintenance is to ensure that the aircraft concerned is kept to an acceptable standard of airworthiness throughout its operational life. Depending on the performance category in which the aircraft is placed and its maximum authorized weight, there will be different types of maintenance schemes intended to carry this out, but the main problem is that the nature of General Aviation means that very often aircraft are not seen by an engineer from one scheduled check to the next.

Aircraft whose weights do not exceed 2,730 kg come under the general umbrella of the Light Aircraft Maintenance Schedule (LAMS). Those exceeding this weight must be maintained according to a maintenance schedule approved for each one by the CAA.

The Maintenance Schedule (which is only valid for a given period) contains the name and address of the owner or operator and notes the type of aircraft and equipment fitted. It lays down the periods when every part of the machine will be inspected (including the Check A) together with the type and degree of the inspection, including the periods of cleaning, lubricating and adjustment.

Maintenance Schedules are written specially for each aircraft (although they can share the same one) so it can be awkward to change Maintenance Contractors as the equivalent of an Annual Check may have to be carried out before an aircraft is accepted by the new one.

Types of check include fifty-hour, 100-hour and Annual, the last being where the C of A is renewed as well (unless the MAUW is less than 2,730 kg). There are variations on this, but regular checks (such as fifty- and 100-hour checks) can be extended by five or ten per cent respectively to take account of scheduling requirements, but this facility should not be used as part of normal operations (lack of planning on your part doesn't justify an emergency on an engineer's part). These checks are also valid for a period of time — sixty-two days — so the servicing will still have to be carried out, even if no flying has taken place. This can also be extended for a short time at the engineers' discretion. Some maintenance companies submit schedules for checks to be taken at seventy-five or 150 hours, and vary other aspects of their operation.

In between these checks there will also be times where particular components will need to be changed, either on a planned or emergency basis.

A Certificate of Maintenance Review is issued after every Annual Check and a Certificate of Release to Service after a regular service (or sixty-two-day inspection). Both documents should be current at all times. A Certificate of Release to Service is not valid by itself — it must be backed up by a Certificate of Maintenance Review.

When a company applies for an Air Operator's Certificate (see Chapter 10), Flight Operations 7 of the CAA will want to ensure that this aspect of your operations is satisfactory. It's not so much a problem if the maintenance is done in-house, but if your Company has sub-contracted this out, a written agreement needs to be in force between the two parties detailing exactly who does what and the general divisions of responsibility.

You would be forgiven for thinking that there are certain things that an engineering outfit gets up to that can be taken for granted, but such is not the case. For example, you would expect them to supply tools, spares and suitably trained personnel as a matter of course, but your contract needs to spell this out in detail (it could be placed in the Operations Manual and cross-referenced, though).

Engineering companies have Engineering Manuals and expositions, which are equivalent to Ops Manuals, and their standard procedures will also be laid out in these, so between the two of you, you should be able to cross-reference everything quite satisfactorily.

Just in case this is difficult, here's a small sample of what you may need to include:
   a) Operator's name and AOC number, and equivalent details of the engineering support organization.

b) Title and reference number of the Exposition or Engineering Manual concerned.
c) Any sub-contracts arranged for either party for anything specialized, such as Avionics.
d) Specific responsibilities for compliance with statutory requirements, Service Bulletins, mandatory modifications, provision of spares, tools, personnel and the compilation of and amendment to any technical publications that may be about, including the completion of log books.
e) The control of deferred and repetitive defects; somebody needs to keep an eye on the Tech Logs as they are returned from each flight to make sure that the same faults don't keep recurring.

The agreement should also include any termination or expiry arrangements (not financial) and any action that may be taken without the Company's approval, or which need agreement.

While on the subject of maintenance, let me mention oil cans, which come sealed so that you need a special implement to open them. Actually, you can use a screwdriver, but whatever you use, don't bang it down on the lid to get into it, but gently prise it open. This stops you getting slivers of metal in the oil which may disagree with your engine.

Weather Radar

The point of this item is to detect rainfall with the intention of avoiding any associated severe weather. As a result, it's possible to deduce areas of turbulence from the shapes of concentrated precipitation and how they move. If you're flying where there is no weather to detect, it's therefore difficult to guesstimate where the turbulence is. The wavelength used by the equipment (typically 10 cm) is too small to detect anything other than water droplets, but this can be optimized for the type of rainfall you wish to detect (down to 3 cm).

Operation is quite simple, but full use on the ground should be avoided (not below 500 feet, in fact). Naturally, you've got to check the operation of the equipment before departure, but most sets have an internal procedure for this. When you do switch it on, it should be set to Standby for at least three minutes first, to allow things to warm up.

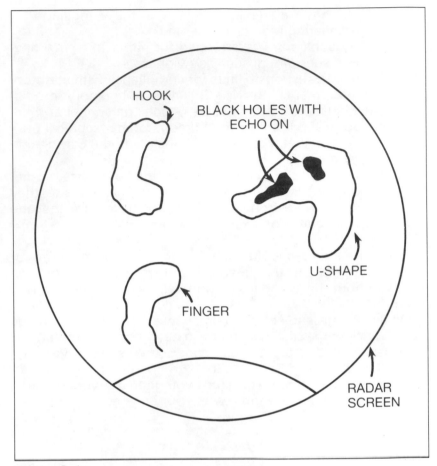

Weather Radar.

You will have several scan ranges to choose from, possibly from 250 miles down to five. Once airborne, there will also be a tilt capability which will point the antenna upwards and downwards, useful for estimating the height of clouds. In the same way, you will also get some ground echoes (good for detecting coastlines).

If you haven't got the luxury of colour and computer controlled echo highlighting (and have to rely on steam radar), there are certain distinctive storm patterns to look out for, such as the hook, finger and U-shape (they all look similar to the figure 6, in fact). The heaviest precipitation, and the heaviest turbulence, will show up as black holes. These will be best detected in Contour mode.

Busbars

Most multi-engined aircraft have left and right main busbars and a battery master busbar (bus for short), but there the similarity ends. There are so many variations on the theme that it's quite difficult to keep track of them all, and getting acquainted with a new type of aeroplane can be rather complicated, especially when the Flight Manual is less than perfect. It helps in these cases to understand the philosophy behind buses (which are notoriously complicated).

The lighter an aircraft is, the better, so it would clearly be impractical (if only in terms of weight saving) to run a wire from the battery to every component used on an aircraft. A better solution would be to run a single wire to a collection of electrical appliances and serve all of them from the end of that line, which is what a busbar is all about.

Physically, an electrical busbar is a metal bar with provisions to make electrical contact with a number of devices that use electricity. There's nothing to stop you having main buses supplying secondary ones. Essential things to know about buses are: what they power, how to re-route power to them and how to isolate them, a bit similar to fuel tank arrangements.

All aircraft must have standby electrical power systems, just in case the normal one goes down. For small aircraft, this is usually the main battery, which is oversized for this reason. The problem with it is, it's time-limited and although there is a theoretical minimum, it's not always safe to rely on more than about ten minutes or so.

It's helpful to know which equipment (on which buses) uses the least power, and these will actually be listed in the Flight Manual. It's perfectly possible to navigate successfully by only turning the VOR (or whatever) on every 10 minutes and off one minute after having fixed your position. The same principles apply to everything else, and will go a long way towards conserving battery life.

Fire

Fire has three elements — fuel, air and heat. Take one away and it stops.

On the ground, engine fire drills may vary considerably between different types, and these will have to be memorized, but there are some general points that can be made. Firstly, prior to evacuating the aircraft, make sure the parking brake is off, so that it can be moved somewhere safer if things get out of hand.

If the fire has been caused by spilt fuel, has spread to the ground under the wing, and the other engine has been started, taxi clear of the area (more specifically, the fuel on the ground) before evacuating the aircraft. If the other engine has not been started, evacuate first, carrying out what drills you can.

If you're able, use the radio to summon help, and don't forget to go with the fire extinguisher. Remember that human beings *en masse* need very different handling than when encountered singly.

In the air, initial shut down actions are similar everywhere — after performing vital actions from memory, e.g. identifying the source and so forth, refer to the checklist to see if you haven't forgotten anything.

If the engine has been secured promptly, the fire should go out quickly after the fuel supply has been cut off. You will find, however, that structural failure of the wing will be imminent after about two minutes if the fire is uncontrolled, which is a sobering enough thought to make you commence emergency descent **immediately**, no matter how good it looks.

If you've got fire extinguishers in the engine bays, delay actuating them until the engine has been secured and you've no reason to suspect a false alarm. That is, unless you can actually see signs of a fire.

In the cabin, whether in the air or on the ground, the priority is to get out, and as soon as possible, because if the flames don't get you, the fumes will. The only difference between the two situations is how quickly this can be done, and what you can do about it.

To help you identify the source, smoke associated with electrical fires is usually grey or tan and very irritating to the nose or eyes (it doesn't smell too good, either). Anything else (say, from the heater) tends to be white, but you may get some black from upholstery.

If you think you have an electrical fire, it's no good just using the extinguisher, because you may just be treating the symptom and not the cause. Switch off the Battery Master as soon as you can after calling for help, then do something about the fire.

However, whatever you do, transmit a Mayday — you can always downgrade it later.

Chapter 9
Legal Matters

A Point to Bear in Mind
Law in General
UK Air Transport Law
  Authorized Persons
  Statements
  Interviews
  Production of licences
  Log books
  Prohibited Airspace
  Public Transport or not?
International Air Law
Employment
Health and Safety at Work

A Point to Bear in Mind

It's quite simple — I am not a lawyer. I have had some training in it as part of wider Transport examinations, but I cannot lay claim to any great theoretical knowledge. However, in just the same way that you don't have to be a doctor to diagnose a headache, a layman in some circumstances is allowed to have views on what is usually regarded as the province of experts. And that is what this chapter contains; my views, which may very well have suffered from the attempt to translate laws into plain English. Therefore, if you need it, get proper legal advice. In other words, sticking to the medical theme, a headache may be a symptom of something worse . . . .

Law in General

You have probably had enough law by now to last you a lifetime! The trouble is that there's a lot more relating to normal commercial life which affects you as well.

The background to some of these laws is international, but most come about in the normal way that UK law is made, the most distinguishing feature of which is that not all of it is written down (don't worry — most of what concerns you is, and there's reams of it, too!).

Very briefly, but accurately enough for our purposes, UK law commences with the Common Law, which derives its power from having been around from 'time immemorial', a phrase which technically means from before 1189. What is most important to you here is the Common Law Right of Silence, which means that you're not obliged to say anything to **anyone** on the very reasonable premise of not being expected to incriminate yourself (new legal developments do not propose to take this right away, but merely allow juries to take your silence into account).

Common Law may be specifically altered in plain words by Acts of Parliament, which are another main source of law. 'Specifically' is the operative word, as all laws need to be very carefully drafted. If you think about it, the essence of any prosecution and subsequent judgement is down to the respective parties' interpretation of them (especially the judge's!).

Actually, law arises from these judicial interpretations as well, because notice is taken of them in later proceedings, depending on the status of the court in which they were made. Interpretations made in the House of Lords (which is the highest court in the land) are binding on any lower courts, but not the other way round — what a Crown Court may think has no bearing on the House, although it does in Magistrate's Courts, which are of course lower in status. This rule is known as **judicial precedent**, and should not be regarded as making laws as such.

In addition to passing specific laws, Parliament may pass an Act which grants a suitably qualified person (or body) authority to make laws, especially where things get a little technical or are strictly for a local area (such as bye-laws). This is because the average MP can't always be expected to understand everything, and there's naturally not enough time for Parliament to get involved with every little thing. This is known as **delegated (or subordinate) legislation**, which at least has the benefits of being flexible and time-saving.

Delegated legislation is brought to the notice of the public mostly by way of **statutory instruments** (an 'instrument' is merely another name for a document), which is where we come in, because that is how the Air Navigation Order (and most other laws that affect your professional life) have been made. It's also how various Authorized Persons and examiners have come into being. For instance, Section 60 of the 1982 Civil Aviation Act grants the power to regulate Air Navigation by Order in Council (the ANO is both **Statutory Instrument** No 1985/1643 and an **Order in Council**. To make it valid as an Order, the words 'certified to be true' — that is, by one of the Lords or others of Her Majesty's Privy Council — must appear beside the authenticating signature at the end of it. The Documentary Evidence Act 1986 requires this in order for it to be **admissible evidence**, for which see later).

The major point concerning this type of law is that it can be invalid under certain circumstances, whereas an Act of Parliament cannot (Parliament is supreme, of course). When this happens, such law is known as being **ultra vires** when it purports to deal with subjects outwith its terms of reference (**ultra vires** is Latin for 'outside the powers').

This could be where some of the conditions concerning its existence are not fulfilled, such as the print size in the SI document not being the same as specified. You may think this is a bit of a technicality, but this method of law-making is regarded as needing strict controls, for obvious reasons, and every effort is therefore made to give the citizen the benefit of the doubt, as it's not on to deprive anyone of their rights because somebody got the procedures wrong. There was a gentleman who escaped a parking ticket by virtue of the fact that the yellow lines he was parked on were two inches thinner than the regulation size.

In this way Parliament keeps a tight control on any authority that may be created by Act of Parliament, because the end result could be that Civil Servants end up making unauthorized laws, and they aren't elected.

In order to be properly enforceable, subordinate legislation must also be given **judicial notice**, so that it can be admissible evidence in a Court of Law. It is worth noting that the Civil Aviation Act 1982 does not appear to grant this to its subordinate legislation, which has the effect of shifting the burden of proof of being **intra vires** (or within its terms of reference) to the maker of the law, rather than to you to prove the opposite, that is, that it may be **ultra vires**. In the absence of provisions requiring judicial notice to be taken of it, subordinate legislation must be pleaded (and proved) by the party seeking to rely on it, but this virtually never happens.

Although delegated legislation need not necessarily be brought to the notice of Parliament (because there's so much of it), the Act behind it usually requires it to be done by Statutory Instrument submitted to **Affirmative** or **Negative Resolution** procedure.

The difference is quite simple; where the affirmative resolution procedure is used, SIs do not become law unless actually approved by Parliament — in other words, a vote of approval is specifically given. Negative procedure means the opposite; they are law unless rejected by parliament within forty days.

In the case of the Civil Aviation Act 1982, as to whether a particular procedure is used or not depends on Schedule 13 to it, and this expressly provides that negative resolution procedure is to be used, except in the case of noise certification, which uses the affirmative. There is no general rule of law as to when an Instrument may be unenforceable due to failure to comply with the correct procedures, because each case turns on its own circumstances.

A **penal** statute (that is, one which involves penalties for its contravention), however, must be strictly observed, a classic case being that of Ronald Biggs, who could not be extradited from Brazil because the extradition treaty in question had not been laid before Parliament as required. Since Civil Aviation subordinate legislation purports to be enforceable by criminal proceedings (i.e. you get punished if you break it), it occupies the same position.

In a **remedial** case, however, some latitude would be allowed, such as where a person was being refused the grant of a licence which would enable him to make a living because the law had not gone through the proper procedure.

Interpretation

Words used in delegated legislation mean the same things as those used in the Act behind it, unless there is a clear statement otherwise. Interpretation of all laws must be done in terms of:

a) a combination of the common law rules for interpretation of statute
b) the particular enabling Acts
c) the context of the regulation concerned

using the **Interpretation Act 1978** as a guide; **not** the circumstances of the case.

This is precisely because such legislation cannot necessarily be taken to mean what it says, as a result of the possibility of bad drafting, which may leave the law open to interpretations the enabling Acts do not permit, from which injustice could result (Commissioners' Decision 1/74).

As far as we are concerned, the first interpretation is made in the cockpit. You (as Commander) have the final authority as to the disposition of your aircraft (Chicago Convention, as embodied in the Civil Aviation Act, 1982), therefore your word is law until overturned by judicial review on an application made within three months by a person with a lawful interest.

In the case of any dispute, the question of interpretation is always primarily a matter for the courts, with the above methods of guidance being used as support in case of ambiguity. Any judgements resolving this would probably take place in accordance with the **spirit** of the law, e.g. what, in the judge's opinion, was the presumed intention of those who made it. Provided a literal interpretation isn't absurd, then it applies regardless of any inconvenience it may cause (subject to the doctrine of precedent).

In short, regulations made under Civil Aviation subordinate legislation are subject to the same Parliamentary control as the enabling powers and must be interpreted and applied in accordance with them.

So to summarize, whether a law affects you or not depends on:

a) The validity of the law itself
b) If it's valid, whether it's enforceable
c) Whether it's been interpreted correctly in the particular circumstances,
d) Whether the court actually has jurisdiction.

With reference to jurisdiction, Section 99 (3) of the 1982 Act says that, for the purposes of conferring jurisdiction, any alleged offences under the ANO or Section 81 do not take place in an actual place, but only in a deemed place.

This means that cases can be heard at selected places, thus there is some flexibility where a British registered aircraft acts dangerously towards a Dutch ship in international waters, where the jurisdiction can be given to the place where the offender is caught, for example. This point is also useful to you, in that it means you may not have to go to the court nearest to the place you're supposed to have committed the offence, but could choose by manoeuvre something more convenient, like where your solicitor lives.

UK Air Transport Law

Although you are usually concerned with law that directly affects you as a pilot, Air Transport Law in the UK is made in the same way as any other, i.e. by a mixture of Common Law, Acts of Parliament and delegated legislation which sometimes implements international agreements (see later).

Where the question of interpretation arises, reference is sometimes also made to Road Transport Law in comparison.

The Civil Aviation Authority was created as a **statutory body corporate** by section 1 (1) of the Civil Aviation Act 1971.

Under this Act, which received Royal Assent on 5 August 1971, the Aerospace Minister for the time being in office was made responsible for the organization and development of Civil Aviation in its many and varied aspects. Thus the CAA actually came into being in early 1972, combining under one Authority functions previously carried out by various organizations such as The Board of Trade, the Air Registration Board and the Air Transport Licensing Board.

As a corporate body (which as an entity only consists of its Board Members, or the equivalent of shareholders in a Limited Company, acting collectively), the functions of the CAA are specified in the statute creating it. The 1971 Act was repealed and replaced by The Civil Aviation Act 1982, which was a **Consolidation Act**, not debated in Parliament (actual changes to the 1971 Act would have been done by a Civil Aviation (Amendment) Act 1982, a subtle difference). The manner in which the CAA is to perform its functions is given in Section 4. The regulation of the carriage of passengers for reward takes place under Section 64. Section 60 authorizes things to be done by Air Navigation Order, which may pass functions on to the CAA, but this is not mandatory. Section 2 (4) points out that the CAA is not to be regarded as a servant or agent of the Crown, but Section 20 (2) allows it to act on behalf of the Crown in clearly specified cases.

There was an oversight in establishing the CAA, in that the ARB (a company limited by guarantee, which carried out many of its functions previously) was subject to the jurisdiction of the Parliamentary Commissioner, whereas the CAA is not. This increases the difficulties of getting redress for wrongs committed.

Just for reference, here is the full list of functions that may be conferred on the CAA by (or under) an Air Navigation Order, from Section 3 (c):

a) Registration of aircraft
b) Safety of air navigation and aircraft (including air-worthiness)
c) Control of Air Traffic
d) Certification of operators of aircraft
e) Licensing of aircrews and aerodromes

There seems to be nothing in the above that permits an ANO to specify who enforces it (the ANO could authorize any government department to do flight crew licensing, for instance, but not a non-government one, other than the CAA).

As the above functions are specified by delegated legislation, it has no power to concern itself with anything not mentioned. There are two reasons for this.

The first is that those activities would be **ultra vires** anyway, and the second concerns the fact that the CAA is funded by charges schemes, i.e. other people's money. Funds utilized for anything not authorized are improperly used, the technical term being 'misappropriation of funds'. If the bringing of a prosecution, for instance, facilitated the performance of a **primary** CAA function, then at first sight it might seem that it could use its funds to do so. The problem is that prosecutions (criminal ones, anyway) are brought by the Crown (R v Fred Bloggs, for instance) so these activities would have to be specifically allowed under the terms of Section 20 (2) of the Civil Aviation Act 1982.

Close inspection of Section 2 also discloses that the CAA is a **juristic person** (e.g. artificially created, as opposed to a 'natural' one), meaning that it is very definitely subject to the **ultra vires** doctrine. This means that the burden of proof falls upon that person to prove its right to do anything, which is the reverse position to the case of a natural person, who is innocent until proven guilty — the end result of this is that an offence must be proved beyond reasonable doubt in every respect before a prosecution brought by a juristic person can be upheld against a natural person.

Any natural person (say an investigator) laying information before a court on behalf of a juristic one (say, the CAA) must be duly authorized. This is Rule 4 (1) of the Magistrates Courts Rules 1981, which is in fact an instruction to officers of those courts to ensure that such is the case. If he's found out then (or later) not to be authorized for any reason, then the person who laid the information (him) could actually be considered to be the prosecutor, which means the wrong person is described on the charge sheet, and possibly lacks the proper authority to bring charges in the first place.

Authorized Persons

An Authorized Person is one who has been given authority by the CAA to perform certain functions on its behalf. Paragraph 15 of Schedule 1 to the Civil Aviation Act 1982 permits the CAA to authorize any member or employee of it to do so. Because of the constraints of delegated legislation, the activities of Authorized Persons must necessarily be restricted to those permitted to fall within the CAA's responsibility, that is, those in Section 3 of the enabling Act.

CAA Resolution 21, dated 5 June 1975, notes that a quorum for the purposes of authorizing anyone to perform functions on its behalf shall be one member (a quorum is a minimum number of people). Therefore, a minimum of one member of the Board of the CAA must form a Board Meeting to do this.

Thus, the appointment of an Authorized Person must be made by at least one person authorized to authorize, so to speak, be it a Board Member or somebody duly delegated (I can't imagine a Board Member doing it all himself). If the card carried by the AP does not carry any proper indication that the authorizer was in fact so authorized then it may not be valid (this may sound a bit of a cheap point, but as the CAA is not a natural person in its own right, its range of action is limited without proper procedures).

To enable it to be produced in Court as part of a case, that is, to be **admissible evidence**, a document must be properly authenticated, otherwise it serves no useful purpose. Paragraphs 16 and 17 of Schedule 1 (of the 1982 Act) also provide that a document received in evidence should have the seal of the CAA on it, and that the seal itself is not valid unless authenticated by the signature of the Secretary of the CAA (or somebody duly authorized by the Board).

In the light of this, unless a document carried by an alleged AP has such a seal and signature on it, then there may be no proof (acceptable to a court, anyway) that he is in fact an AP, and therefore probably should not have wasted your time asking all those questions in the beginning.

A constable is an Authorized Person, but do not forget to ask for his warrant card or note his collar number. A policeman in **full** uniform is deemed to be properly appointed (if he's not wearing his hat, or his buttons are undone, then he's not properly dressed in uniform. He may be from the plain clothes division, of course, but a 'constable' in the normal sense of the word doesn't usually mean 'detective').

Statements
Statements (made by you) can cause a problem, especially with reference to your Common Law Right of Silence. If given, a statement should give **all relevant points**, not just answers to the investigator's questions (they may be based on a wrong interpretation of the law). What is actually relevant is naturally open to argument, which is why you should either have expert assistance or stay silent. Where a jury is allowed to take notice of your exercise of your Right of Silence, you could explain that you were not convinced that such points were being covered.

As nothing generally happens except by agreement (which means a contract is formed), there is an implication of confidentiality between you and the interviewer, essentially meaning that all that is discussed by yourselves should not be relayed to third parties — this includes within the CAA.

Interviews
Interviews are statutory inquiries to which certain rules of procedure will apply, on top of those of natural justice. 'Statutory Inquiry' is actually defined (in the Tribunals and Inquiries Act, 1971) as 'an inquiry or hearing held or to be held in pursuance of a duty imposed by a provision contained in, or having any effect under, any enactment'.

According to Sections 7 (2) and 7 (3)(c) of the 1982 Act, the CAA is in all civil proceedings a Tribunal supervised by the Council on Tribunals. Where the CAA requests an interview, which is a civil proceeding, Regulation 25 (2) of the CAA regulations imposes upon them a duty to disclose certain information relevant to those proceedings prior to it, which could include copies of the evidence to which the inquiry relates. Pursuant to Section 12 (1)(a) of the Tribunals and Inquiries Act, it is the CAA's duty to furnish a written statement of its reasons for the establishment of an inquiry if so requested at the time when notice of the inquiry is given.

Production of Licences
The ANO says that (unless engaged on Public Transport, Aerial Work or International Navigation) you must produce your licence to an Authorized Person within a reasonable time after such a request from them (this request must obviously be made personally; firstly because you will need to check their credentials, and secondly because a request to send your licence somewhere is actually one to 'surrender', which is not the same thing according to the 1982 Act. The Act itself specifically mentions 'custody', 'production' and 'surrender' as three separate things, so the intention clearly is to regard them as such).

A 'reasonable time' is as long as it takes to reach inside your navbag in an immediate post or pre-flight situation. If you can't do this (maybe because you fall outside the conditions that require you to carry your licence), you are allowed to nominate a police station at which your licence will be produced within five days of the original request. Actually, the relevant Article, 63 (3) (a), is not at all clear as to whether your part in the matter is producing the licence or specifying the police station, so it is possible you may not have to go yourself.

As the Civil Aviation Act only allows provision by the ANO for access to aerodromes and places where aircraft have landed for the purpose of requesting to see your licence (not your home, for example), and as (according to Section 3) the CAA has functions concerning the licensing of aerodromes, it could be argued that such access is only permissible to licensed aerodromes. A constable, of course, can go anywhere within the limits settled by the Act and the ANO.

In practice, anyone wanting to see your licences will actually come and visit you if you are willing to permit this to happen, but you may be entitled to be paid for your time, like any consultant, provided you give advance notice that there will be a charge.

Log Books

The five days option for production at a police station doesn't apply to log books, though, so it's not known what would happen if you did not have it with you, since it's not the sort of thing you carry around in your briefcase.

There are couple of points to note about your log book. First of all, it's your personal and private property, not having been issued to you under the ANO.

Secondly, according to Article 23, only two classes of people are required to keep a personal flying log book:

    a) Flight Crew members of UK registered aircraft
    b) Regardless of aircraft registration, those who are flying in order to qualify for licence purposes

The Civil Aviation Act itself does not mention Log Books, except to mention fleetingly that an Air Navigation Order is allowed to make provision for things to be done to 'documents' other than licences, which presumably includes them. However, since the word 'issue' is mentioned in the same breath, and log books aren't issued to you, then maybe it doesn't. In any case, filling in log books is not within the ordinary meaning of the expression 'air navigation'.

Actually, the question of log books can also provide another useful illustration of how people's idea of what the law says can vary. Article 63 (4) of the ANO says that everyone required by Article 23 to keep a log book needs to produce a personal flying log book if requested to do so within two years of the last entry. Simple enough, at first sight. But . . .

One of the defined classes of person in Article 23 is 'every member of the flight crew of **an** (not **any**) aircraft registered in the UK'. If you refer to Article 106 (1), you will find that the definition of 'Flight Crew' includes anyone who undertakes to act as a pilot of **the** aircraft. It could follow, therefore, that to be flight crew (and subject to the requirement to produce a log book, or anything else for that matter) there must be an undertaking, at the moment of the request for production, to act as such on a particular aircraft.

Therefore, even leaving aside the point about particular aircraft (and this applies to licences as well), once you've finished flying and are off duty there is no longer an undertaking to act as flight crew, therefore you're not subject to the requirement to produce a log book when requested. In other words, as you're only Flight Crew between chocks away to chocks on (or rotor start to rotor rundown) that's when the requirement exists — the request to produce should be made between those times.

Looked at this way, the log book referred to in Article 63 (4) could be construed as merely a record of undertakings to act as flight crew of a particular aircraft which is closed after each one and must be produceable for two years. If this is the case, then a copy of the Tech Log for each flight will do, provided it has your name and address on it, as required by the ANO.

It is possible that the traditional log book we all know is not the same thing as the statutory personal flying log book referred to in the ANO!

It just goes to show how much care must be taken both in setting up laws and reading them — that's why it's a specialized job to draft Acts of Parliament.

Prohibited Airspace

This may only be created by the ANO itself (the 1982 Act permits aircraft to be stopped from flying over such areas as may be specified in the Order. It also allows the ANO to provide for exemptions). Therefore, unless specified in the ANO, or exempt under the terms given in it, prohibited airspace does not exist. Mere 'notification' of its existence may not be enough.

This produces another way of looking at Rule 5. If you think about it, areas which you must keep away from (i.e. not closer than 500 feet, etc) are really miniature areas of prohibited airspace, most of which keep moving around!

Public Transport or Not?

WARNING! This subject is extremely complicated and liable to cause acute brainfade!

Public Transport is defined in the ANO, specifically Article 107, as being where **valuable consideration** is given (or promised) for the carriage of passengers or cargo on a flight (it actually says in the aircraft, but I suppose you can take that for granted).

In addition, it covers anyone or anything that may be carried free on that flight, not being employees of any **air transport undertaking** that may be operating it (although it looks as if it's worded otherwise, company directors and anyone working on behalf of the CAA, such as Authorized Persons and TREs, are employees for this purpose). Thus, if you carry a passenger (say, a friend) on a Base Check who is not an employee or a director of your Company, it will be considered to be Public Transport, even though valuable consideration is not promised or given.

If the valuable consideration allows a particular person to fly an aircraft, then that is also Public Transport (unless it's being bought on HP or a conditional sale agreement). Presumably, this is meant to cover self-fly hire, or maybe trial lessons, since the phrase used is 'fly the aircraft' rather than 'fly in the aircraft'. Although that person may not be an employee of the operating organization, crews are not passengers (although they may be for insurance purposes, but see Article 106 (1)), so I don't quite see where this one fits in, as PT only exists when **passengers or cargo** are carried for valuable consideration.

However, these clauses are the only ones to affect the average professional. Otherwise, in broad terms, you are allowed to win prizes in air races (up to certain limits) and recover direct costs and a pro rata contribution to the amount of hours flown every year if you go to air shows and the like.

If a payment is made to a (registered) charity (with CAA permission) that allows someone (maybe a prize-winner) to fly **in** an aircraft, then that is a private flight.

Equal contributions to the direct costs of a flight borne by the pilot if up to four persons (including the pilot) fly in an aircraft are exempt, but direct costs do not mean HP payments, insurance, hangarage . . . . There must also have been no advertising for that flight, except within the confines of a flying club, in which case all passengers (over eighteen) must be members of that club. It also helps if the pilot is seen not to be employed as such (this situation is what anyone else would call 'cost-sharing').

A similar situation exists where a pilot reclaims direct expenses paid out on behalf of his employer.

There are sundry other exemptions, such as joint or company owned aircraft. Remunerated parachute dropping (and positioning for it) is regarded as aerial work (107 (9)).

Let's have a closer look at the words 'valuable consideration' as an example of not-so-good drafting.

The word 'consideration' means money or something of money's worth that is more than merely nominal. It is a legal expression referring to something that is used to bind a contract. For example, the chocolate wrappers sent in to a manufacturer to obtain a free gift have been held to be 'consideration'.

The word 'consideration' by itself would have been enough to do the job, but somebody saw fit to add 'valuable' in front of it, which changes the position somewhat, because now everybody has to rush around trying to decide what that particular word means, and subsequently how valuable should consideration be to qualify for inclusion in the ANO? The real problem with all the above conditions, though, lies in the field of insurance. You may (or may not) know that there is no such thing as a 'contract' of insurance.

This is because you are betting; in this case, that you crash your aircraft before a certain date. The insurance people, of course, are betting that you don't (or is it the other way round?).

The trouble is that insurance companies are well known not to pay if they can get away with it, so if it can be proved that you were doing illegal Public Transport flying, you may well find that your insurance is invalid as well, not to mention being caught for third-party liability in some cases.

Anyway, enough of digression. Back to the subject. Article 6 says that an Air Operator's Certificate is needed for all flights that may come under the definition of Public Transport — 'an aircraft cannot fly for Public Transport otherwise than under and in accordance with the terms of an Air Operator's Certificate which may be granted to the operator'. It could be argued, therefore, that the offence is actually against the aircraft.

Article 6 was originally Article 3A of the ANO 1960, and was inserted as an afterthought to it to cover AOCs that would be unenforceable during the time gap until section 1 (2) (a) of the coming Civil Aviation (Licensing) Act 1960 came into force on 30 March 1961. This section was later repealed by the 1972 Act, so from that time the ANO could no longer legally make provisions for an AOC with enforceable terms (the 1982 Act says that only statutory instruments are allowed to establish enforceable terms; in other words, no enforceable law — that is, by criminal proceedings — can be made below the level of a statutory instrument, which of course an AOC is not. AOC terms are laid down by the CAA, which cannot issue SIs).

By the way, the term 'operator' above has been held by leading counsel to include the pilot (any person with the management for the time being of an aircraft is regarded as being the operator). Reference to Road Transport Acts shows that if it had been intended that a 'driver' was not to be an 'operator', then the proper wording was available to do the same in Aviation. Article 99 provides that if the ANO is contravened in relation to an aircraft, then both the Operator and the Commander are liable.

Actually, the imposition of Public Transport conditions is only permitted by the enabling Act (of the ANO) where the aircraft is used for a **commercial, industrial or gainful purpose** (specifically Section 60 (3) (f)). What it says is that 'An Air Navigation Order may contain provision as to the conditions under which passengers and goods may be carried by air and under which aircraft may be used for other commercial, industrial or gainful purposes.'

Quite a mouthful, but the use of the word 'other' in conjunction with the Rules of Interpretation of Statute infers that 'conditions' may only be imposed when aircraft are being used for gainful, etc, purposes (notice the absence of the words 'valuable consideration'). As these rules are meant to be enforceable by criminal proceedings, they become penal situations, and as such must be strictly construed in accordance with the enabling statute.

So what may be relevant as to what is or is not Public Transport is not the presence of any consideration, but if there is, whether the aircraft is being used for a commercial, industrial or gainful purpose. Therefore, all you really have to do is pin down who the user is and see what his use of the aircraft is to see whether Public Transport or Aerial Work conditions apply.

Since, in most circumstances, light aircraft are chartered to a sole user, most 'charter' flights could in fact be called private flights (if it were not for the ANO) unless the aircraft is actually being used **during flight** for commercial, industrial or gainful purposes by its user.

The user (that is, the hirer) is using the aircraft for his own purposes (unless buying and selling is actually going on in the back) and the 'operator' is the pilot in command. Whoever hires out the aircraft to the user could be held to be their agent in respect of maintenance and all the other things that are needed to keep the aircraft flying.

If passengers are being carried for separate fares, on the other hand, then the aircraft is being used in that way by the person with the right to the money collected.

But beware! The terms of an AOC could be enforceable if made as the terms of an **Air Transport Licence**. If an aircraft is being used for the carriage for reward of passengers or cargo, then the CAA may apply air transport licensing even if the aircraft is not being used for anything resembling Public Transport or commercial or other gainful purposes.

All that being said, what about the situation where you're asked to do a job and you're not sure what's going on? Do you feel up to actually asking for a certificate to say a flight is not Public Transport?

This is plainly impractical, so you need to know a few ins and outs to protect yourself (please note that the intention in writing all this down is **not** to enable you to do illegal Public Transport flying!).

A workable PT flight (ANO definition) must have the following:

a) An Air Operator's Certificate issued to 'the operator'
b) The crew must have current licences (e.g. CPL/ATPL) and be type rated, base/line checked, etc., in accordance with the operator's Operations Manual (indeed, the whole flight must be conducted in accordance with it).
c) The aircraft must have a (current) Transport Category C of A, Certificates of Maintenance Review and Release to Service, Technical Log (with Deferred Defect Sheet), Passenger Briefing Leaflets and all legally required equipment (fire extinguishers, placards, etc).

You may be able to get around these requirements by ensuring that the person hiring the aircraft does so with a separate contract than the one he hires you with, and you will be better off if you can also prove that you were not paid, or at least you were an employee of the hirer's organization (if you do this, you may have to show that the enabling Act only permits an Air Navigation Order to make different pilot licensing provisions according to whether the person concerned is actually **employed** or merely **engaged** in a flight crew capacity).

You could also get base and line checked by a proper company and put it through their books, but do not forget you must use their Ops Manual and other documentation.

Finally, you could resort to drastic measures and form a company for a short time that doesn't have in its memorandum and articles of association any references to gainful use of aircraft or hiring them out by the hour.

There is a Common Law rule that you cannot buy or hire from yourself — this is the basis upon which co-ownership groups and non-profit members clubs are run in every walk of life. However, Article 107 (3) says that any agreement between any such organizations **or members of them** (this also means within the same group) in respect of a situation where valuable consideration would normally be expected would be considered as if it had been given anyway. This is **notwithstanding any rule of law as to such transactions**; in other words, the Common Law purports to be specifically overridden, yet it is not clear from the enabling Act that the ANO is permitted to do this.

An **unincorporated non-profit members' club** can be created for a specific purpose or occasion and could exist for one flight or a day only, being dissolved once it has served its purpose. Such clubs should pay for their own operating costs to avoid the inference of valuable consideration. For instance, it should not be too difficult for a group of parachutists to form a club for the day for the purposes of hiring an aircraft.

However, the paperwork must be sound and, as I said, these are drastic measures, so try and get legal advice here.

Legally, there is nothing to stop you (as a pilot) obtaining your own Air Transport Licence or AOC, should you feel the need.

International Air Law

The idea of International Law is to reduce the possibility of a phenomenon known as **conflict of laws**, and the resulting confusion that could arise where, say, a claim for damages is brought in a French court in respect of injury to a Dane whilst travelling on a ticket bought in Holland for a journey from Germany to England on an Italian plane.

International Law (Public or Private) consists of internationally agreed rules that courts of participating states apply to cases which have a foreign connection, the private side of things affecting individuals and the public side affecting states. Public International Law takes precedence over Private, which in turn is superior to State law, although ultimately (short of war) International Law is unenforceable where the original consent establishing it disappears.

Air Law has mainly evolved through agreements between 'high contracting parties', taking the form of various International Conventions or Treaties, too numerous to mention here. These form the basis of Public International Law which in turn can be incorporated into the law of individual states, an example in the UK being the UK Carriage by Air Act 1961 in relation to the Chicago Convention of 1944 (in fact, the Chicago Convention and its annexes are also embodied into Section 60 (2)(a) of the Civil Aviation Act, 1982).

A **Convention** is an agreement that many nations are at liberty to enter into and the word **Treaty** is used to indicate agreements between two (or more) States that bind only themselves. The **Tokyo Convention 1963**, for instance, relates to offences committed on board aircraft (but not to offences committed by aircraft, as such).

Thus, Conventions can cover many subjects, including the agreement of standards for navigational equipment and documentation, but they can also establish governing bodies, such as the International Civil Aviation Organisation (ICAO).

ICAO is a worldwide body convened by governments while the International Air Transport Association (IATA) is an equivalent body established by the airlines. Although IATA is a private organization comprising virtually all the scheduled airlines of the world, it nevertheless has strong links with ICAO and governments, and is often used by many airlines as an agent for securing inter-airline co-operation.

IATA consists of many committees, but the most significant is Traffic, which negotiates many detailed arrangements between states and airlines. Other airline organizations exist, particularly within Europe, which operate on a similar basis.

In addition to certain freedoms granted by Conventions over the years (such as flying over certain territories, taking tech stops and collecting or discharging passengers), other rights of commercial entry are established by **bilateral agreements**.

These agreements provide for route(s) to be flown, estimate traffic capacity, frequencies of service and establish other precise rules under which operator and crew licensing are accepted by the respective parties to the agreement.

Employment

As soon as you start working for somebody a contract of employment is deemed to have started. There are reams of papers written on the ins and outs of contracts, but basically once a contract is formed there are rights and duties on either side, made the more binding if something called **consideration** (remember that?) is given by anyone to seal the bargain. This consideration need not be money, nor need it be adequate.

Unless you're a freelance, you will normally be deemed to have entered a contract of service where you have a **master/servant** relationship with your employer.

If you are self-employed, you will be regarded as an **independent contractor**, and subject to a different legal position if a passenger decides to sue for any reason (your employer may be able to drop you right in it).

If a passenger does want to sue, you have greater protection if you are actually an employee, because the come-back is then on your employer, as you're a part of his business (he does have a let-out if he can prove that you were acting **outwith the terms of your employment**, but as long as you haven't done anything stupid, you should be OK).

Aside from whether you're paid by PAYE, you can identify the essential difference between the two in the way that you're treated. An independent contractor is outside the employer's business and is told merely what has to be done, and not how.

Most contracts are fairly free and easy, it being up to both parties to state what they want out of any given situation. However, contracts of employment (and sales of goods, incidentally) are regulated by law and thus there is less freedom of movement, although the bias is on your side, helping to protect you and allow more collective bargaining (this last only applies if you're in a union, of course, but there are none for General Aviation).

Although any contract may be made verbally (which will override any written contract, by the way, subject to provability), the law lays a duty on the employer to give you a written statement within thirteen weeks of starting work detailing conditions about such things as pay, hours, holidays, pensions, sick pay, notice, disciplinary rules and any other procedures which may affect you.

In case you do not get a written statement, you may be able to use what actually goes on between you as evidence of the presence of a contract.

Employer's Duties

    a) To pay wages as agreed. You are entitled to receive a written itemized pay statement, regardless of the method of payment. It must contain certain minimum items.

     b) To indemnify against liability and loss (if you lose as a result of doing his work).

     c) To provide a safe system of work (this includes premises and appliances — and aeroplanes).

     d) If an employer does issue a reference, it is subject to the law of defamation. Be careful, though, to distinguish between a false statement and an expression of opinion made without malice.

Your duties

     a) Obedience. It's your duty to obey a lawful order, but there are proper processes for your dismissal if you don't.

     b) To show good faith, that is, you are obliged to work in your employer's best interests.

Like any contract, one for employment will take place according to the agreed terms and conditions, but if there is any dispute, it will be judged according to what is **reasonable**.

In the case of termination, there may be claims for damages on either side, provided it could be proven that damages were suffered as a result of the action.

The usual problem is unfair dismissal on the employer's part, though, and there are strict procedures that enable you to go to an Industrial Tribunal should such an event happen. I suggest you check out your local Citizen's Advice Bureau for the latest information.

There is an Equal Pay Act which allows women to receive the same pay as men for performance of equivalent work. It also makes it illegal (with certain exceptions) for discrimination on grounds of sex, and it applies both ways.

Neither is an employer allowed to discriminate on race grounds.

Health and Safety at Work

This applies to Aviation as well, and there is actually a Common Law duty of care for whoever employs you to ensure that the aircraft flown are airworthy and fit for Public Transport in every respect. You are required to do a pre-flight check, to be sure, but not being a qualified engineer, there are some things about an aircraft's condition for flight that you just have to take on trust, which become the Operator's responsibility. If something turns out to be wrong, then despite the adherence to authorized maintenance schedules, there could be negligence involved.

The recent amendments to the ANO (see Article 106 (1)) mean that there are cases in which crews cease to be passengers carried under the terms of Public Transport. Under these circumstances, there is a lowering of safety standards applicable to working conditions, as they are obviously no longer protected by those conditions.

Reference

As you will recall from your licence studies, law can be quite a turgid subject at the best of times. If you haven't fallen asleep already, here is a useful selection of reference books:

Shawcross and Beaumont: *Air Law* (Butterworths)

Archbold: *Criminal Pleading, Evidence and Practice,* 39th ed., (Sweet and Maxwell), 1976

Brian Harris: *Criminal Jurisdiction of Magistrates,* 9th ed., (Barry Rose), 1984

Wade: *Administrative Law,* 5th ed., (Oxford University Press), 1982

The preliminary notes on Statutes contained in Halsbury's Statutes (Butterworths)

Wade and Philips: *Constitutional Law,* 7th ed., (Longmans), 1965

Josling and Alexander: *Law of Clubs,* 5th ed., (Oyez-Longman), 1984

The Concise Dictionary of Law (Oxford University Press), 1986

Kiralfy: *The English Legal System, 3rd ed.,* (Sweet and Maxwell), 1960

Francis Bennion: *Statute Law, 2nd ed.,* (Oyez-Longman), 1983

A C D Mitchell: *Guide to Operational Aviation Law* (The Avrisk Group), 1986

Chapter 10
Setting Up a Company

General

Financial Matters

Obtaining an AOC

The Operations Manual (Again)

Back to the AOC

Running Things

General

Most pilots are quite happy working their way up the career ladder, graduating on to larger and larger types as their experience grows, and don't concern themselves with the possibilities of operating their own aircraft.

One day, though, there will come an opportunity to set up your own Company and obtain your own Air Operator's Certificate, a typical scenario being where you come across somebody with his own aircraft who would like to offset the costs of operating it against some income. Or it may be that you come into some money yourself and feel able to go it alone. More common is the situation where you fly somebody on a charter who is new to flying, they become impressed and decide to buy their own aircraft, and because you were their first pilot you very often get made an offer you can't understand.

There is nothing wrong with this, but think seriously before leaving employment with relative security for something that may only last a few months. One rule of thumb (which works very well) is that the more attractive the package offered, the less stable the job. Another is to subtract twenty-five from the physical age of anyone who is keen on Aviation for its own sake, and wants to make a business out of it to get their mental age. If you can, find out something about the company your prospective employer runs. Have they got credibility? Are they well established, or is the man you are talking to just a waffler with access to a lot of other people's money rather than his own? (See how many of his cheques bounce, and how much of what he says will happen actually comes true).

Signs that a company won't last long include excessive flamboyance on the part of the Boss, who naturally pays for everything, treating all and sundry to lunches, drinks, etc (if it was really his money, he wouldn't be doing that). Statements to the Press that are less than complimentary to other companies around should also be noted, as should excessive hype and illogical spending on non-essentials, where the basics aren't being looked after — e.g. spending money on smart new offices rather than servicing the aircraft.

I don't mean to put you off unnecessarily from anything that could lead to greater things, but a little scepticism in the early stages of such situations could save you and a lot of other people plenty of aggravation later on. There are several ways to protect yourself. One is, do not move at all — bide your time and see what actually materializes out of your prospective employer's promises. A lot of people say a lot, but not much actually happens — they give the illusion of movement without actually progressing anywhere (like 'reorganization' in a large company). The more urgency projected, the more sceptical you should be.

Another way of protecting yourself is to have somewhere else to go to if things fail to materialize; an even better way is to estimate the amount of work you can expect to do for a year and insist on payment of the whole lot in advance. If they want you enough, they will produce the goods. In fact, to work in aviation at any level (as opposed to playing in it) needs a more businesslike approach than most people think, at least as far as mental attitude is concerned. The whole idea of doing the job is to earn money; if you happen to enjoy it, you're lucky, but you're doing yourself and other pilots a disservice by underselling yourself just because you're keen to fly.

You suffer the same fate as companies who undercut — in the end, the waters just get stirred up, nobody makes any money at all and very few survive.

Financial Matters

If despite all that gloom, you still want to carry on, then please let me add one more word of warning — you will need much, much more money than you anticipate. Not for nothing is it said that to get a small fortune in Aviation, you need to start with a large one! But it need not be that bad provided that things are done properly from the start.

First of all, if you need to borrow money, you'll find it easier to borrow a lot, and don't just cover the cost of the equipment. You'll need as much slack as you can get to cover cash flow while you're waiting for customers to pay, and emergencies, so don't stint — ask for a million or so. I'm not kidding! Aviation is the sort of game where things work out cheaper only if you can afford to fork out the money from the start. If you buy your own bowser, for instance, instead of positioning your helicopter to the local airfield for fuel, you will probably cover all that empty flying and unnecessary landing fees inside three months, but you have to have the money in the first place — paying as you go along should be avoided as much as possible, as it will usually kill any project stone dead.

On that basis, don't depend purely on loans. In fact, you probably won't get a loan until the lender sees some input from another source (preferably yours), so you may need to find a Venture Capitalist who would be willing to invest in your project. These sort of people supply money in return for stock (shares in the Company), typically expecting to be free of their obligation in about four years or so with a handsome profit (although they could make a loss). The major benefit to you is that they provide ready cash and a bit of stability without your spending power being drained continually by interest payments.

However you raise capital, you will need a business plan, which is a brief sketch of your proposals detailing how you mean to repay the money, together with an indication of how things will be run (this includes details of the management team).

It's interesting to investigate some of the factors involved in the use of money by looking at the purchase of an aircraft. It doesn't just cost, say, two million pounds. It will also cost what you can't do with the money, having spent it — what economists call the opportunity cost. In other words, you lose the opportunity to do something else with it, even if it is only to sit in a bank account and gain interest. Sometimes it's better not to buy outright but to do it on a mortgage and let the interest gained from the money in the bank pay the interest on the mortgage! With a little shopping around for interest rates this is entirely possible.

Imagine you have the choice of two aircraft — one relatively expensive to buy, but which is cheap to operate, and the other cheap to buy, but expensive to run.

Both do the job you want — well, near enough, anyway. The difference in purchase price between the two may well, if placed on deposit somewhere, more than pay for the increased running costs if you buy the cheaper one. However, in the UK, which is not an aviation-minded country in general, this may be low on the list of priorities, as often the purchasing of an aircraft will tend to be a personal decision on behalf of the Chairman.

The magic figure to survive properly in the small charter world is 500 hours per aircraft per year — that is revenue hours, ten a week. Remember, the object of the company is not to fly, it's to make a profit so that you can live, or to provide the investor with a return on his capital (not profit necessarily, although sometimes they can coincide). Far too many people forget this, set themselves up in an airfield having done no research, don't market their product and then expect the world to beat a path to their door just because they have an aircraft.

Even if work does come, more often than not by accident, the same people undercut everybody else around, thinking to put the opposition out of business then put the prices up again. Unfortunately, it doesn't happen like that — they are the ones who go out of business first because they have no cash flow, and are left with a mountain of debts wondering vaguely what went wrong.

A lot of aviation companies owe their existence to a larger parent company that bought an aeroplane possibly as a way of spending excess money that can't otherwise be used (there is such a thing), but it's not impossible to survive purely on Aviation without assistance from a Big Brother. Whether it is or not depends on the existence of competition, how big you expect your Company to be and the availability of the work itself (if there's no competition, have you thought of the fact that there might not be any work?).

Whatever happens, you will have to get your hands on an aircraft. Expensive machinery like that (while being an asset in itself) will create massive debt which will require servicing, which in turn means interest. Which company will take care of that? If the aviation company itself buys the machine then it will have that much more to worry about.

What is more likely to happen is that an outside company will actually own the aircraft and lease it to your Company, giving the additional benefit of the equipment being one step removed in case of disasters (outside aviation it's common practice to place all valuable assets into a holding company that trades only with associated ones, thus insulating them from unplanned contingencies. Where aviation is concerned, it also legally separates the registered owner from the user).

The leasing cost to you will be a total of maintenance costs, spares or engine replacement costs, insurance costs plus a bit on top for contingencies (the spares or engine replacement costs are similar to depreciation, which is an accountant's way of establishing a fund for future replacement of machinery).

There are two types of lease, **wet** or **dry**. A wet lease will include fuel, while a dry one doesn't (neither will it normally include maintenance or insurance). A wet one is useful, because there's less squabbling over who put what fuel in what aircraft. It's easier just to let the owner pick up the tab, provided he's not overcharging. Leasing costs are charged hourly and the total cost over the year is **variable**, that is, dependent on the amount of hours flown. There is a chance that the anticipated costs above turn out to be less expensive than you anticipate, but that will be the lessor's good fortune, not yours. Of course, things could go the other way and it will cost him more — this will happen if he buys a bad machine in the first place and/or it's flown badly. Leasing means that you have no asset to fall back on, which you would have if you raised a mortgage and bought it. If you ever end up leasing an aircraft to somebody else, you will make the most money by stumping up at least fifty per cent yourself and financing the rest.

When evaluating an aircraft, first establish what you want it to do. What's the maximum range, and where is the nearest airfield to the factory? What's its optimum cruise height and will you get a 'wet footprint' if you have to go lower over water if an engine stops (see Chapter 5)? Do you want an aeroplane, or would a helicopter be better? How many passengers will you normally carry, and will they want to hold meetings in the back? The bigger and faster it is, the more money it will cost. True cost-effectiveness lies not in fulfilling all your needs, but compromising on some, so that you're not in a situation where your most demanding tasks (which are five per cent of the requirement) take up ninety-five per cent of the facilities offered.

However, deciding on the most cost-effective aircraft ever won't help if you can't afford even that. Your budget may stop you dead and restrict your choices further — don't forget you have to run it as well. The previous remarks in *Financial Matters* about major purchases are relevant here.

The problem now is that the Arthur Daleys of this world exist in aviation as well. Where do you find a trustworthy dealer, and could you do your purchasing yourself? You've already done most of the work by establishing the tasks you need to perform and what you can afford. One tip is, don't believe brochures or salesmen. Take time to talk to pilots and engineers who actually work with the type of machine you're after — you may find that what you're looking at is OK until the turbocharger goes, which then takes at least three days to repair because it's hidden behind the engine which has to come out completely; on the other hand, another type of aircraft could have similar work done in less than half a day and doesn't go wrong in the first place because the turbocharger is not in such a stupid place. Similarly, a particular helicopter could be cheaper to run on paper, but its shorter range on full tanks means that you're paying out for landing fees and dead flying more often, thereby bringing the total operating cost nearly equal to that of something more comfortable with more endurance.

You need to take account of the data for propeller, rotor or engine Times Between Overhaul (TBO), the Mean Times Between Failures (MTBF) on avionics equipment, the retirement age of parts that are life-limited and inspection intervals. There are other costs involved, such as engineering unfamiliarity and the availability of spare parts, especially where new aircraft are concerned.

If you do get professional help to look for an aircraft, it will cost you money. What you need to do is aim what it's going to cost at the best target. The proportion of the cost to the actual purchase price will be larger with smaller aircraft because there's just as much work involved in selling them as there is with larger aircraft, and the total price is substantially less.

A **broker** will be selling somebody else's plane on their behalf, essentially taking money for the introduction and the paperwork, so you will probably never meet the seller. A **dealer**, on the other hand, will have bought the aircraft into stock and will be the owner. There is also the private advertiser, who is just selling his own aircraft, or maybe a bank or financial institution who are repossession agents.

Once you let it be known that you're after an aircraft of any description, you will then get every man and his dog ringing you up with what they have to offer. On the one hand, this could save you a lot of work, but on the other, it could be a pain in the neck. Another tip: get the registration number of what they're trying to sell — it could be the same machine several times over. If they won't give it to you, then treat them with the appropriate suspicion. They will have registered with the seller and will try and get a cut of the deal as an 'introduction fee'. Nice work if you can get it.

Like a car, shiny paint may disguise all sorts of troubles. There's nothing wrong with sprucing something up for sale, it's common practice, but make a thorough examination anyway. Do not do what one buyer of my acquaintance did — looked at a helicopter and took it away to lunch, leaving the engineer he'd taken along (at great expense) alone to look at books which were written in German! Yes, he bought the wrong aircraft; and deserved it!

You should expect professional help to do the following at the very least (make him work for his money):

a) Provide a complete analysis of your requirements
b) Carry out a market survey to fit your budget
c) Advise on pitfalls relevant to particular types
d) Select samples of the type decided on
e) Inspect shortlisted ones on site
f) Have a well-developed bullshit detector
g) Negotiate on your behalf — bring the price down or the concessions up
h) Advise on contract matters

Obtaining an AOC

Now if you still think you'll be some sort of success, you will need your Air Operator's Certificate. An AOC is required to be held by all operators of UK-registered aircraft that are engaged in Public Transport (**not** Aerial Work, but watch out for crop spraying, where a similar scheme is in force).

It's applied for on a form, together with a cheque for £3,000 or so made payable to the CAA. This charge will cover all types you wish to include initially, but subsequent additions will cost the same again, so if you know you'll be adding a new machine later, it makes sense to try and include it from the start. However, this will cause its own trouble in the form of additions to the Ops Manual and further training costs, as the Chief Pilot may be expected to be qualified on the new type as well. Beware of having too many types belonging to different Performance Groups.

The application form itself is quite easy to fill out. If the Operator is an incorporated body, you will need to know the directors' names, addresses and nationalities, and if not, you will need to know the same information with regard to the partners. If there's a trading name separate from the Company name, then that will need to be given as well. This bit is quite important, because the AOC is issued to the parent organization trading as whatever they care to call themselves. The CAA will want to know exactly which trading names are to be adopted.

Otherwise, the only other thing that may need a bit of research is the Maintenance Schedule reference for each aircraft that you propose to use. This will be found in the aircraft log book, and will look something like CAA/LAMS/FW/1978 Issue 2, if you're using an aircraft below 2,730 kg.

The application form and the fee should be sent to the Flight Operations Inspectorate at the CAA in Gatwick Airport at least six weeks before operations are planned to commence. Together with all that, you will need a copy of your proposed Operations Manual . . . .

The Operations Manual (Again)

Although you don't have to send the Ops Manual with the application form, things will happen considerably quicker if you do, because the CAA reserve themselves a minimum of six weeks to read it. If it's ready at the time of applying, then some parts of the form need not be filled in (just refer the reader to the Manual).

Production of the Operations Manual, which is your way of indicating to the CAA how you intend to operate, is (to use the CAA's words) 'an onerous task'. The quick way round is to buy one ready made (from me, if you have my phone number), but there is a pitfall here in that just because a manual has been approved once, there is no guarantee that it will be so again (and that goes for the contents of this book, although the relevant parts have been in an Ops Manual at some stage or other).

This is because each company is assigned a different Flight Operations Inspector who will have risen through the Industry in his own way, thus having different experiences to fall back on. His job is to advise you in the light of that experience (more than being a 'policeman', although that is another function) and assist in the formation of the Company. What one Inspector thinks is OK is not necessarily what another will accept.

A typical Inspector will have several companies under his wing, and thus will have to guard against giving away any confidential information that he may be party to (the CAA must not be seen to give commercial advantage). He will normally be the only routine contact that a company will have with the CAA, and his main function when you're up and running is to inspect, report and make recommendations on your performance. On his routine visits to the Company, he is empowered to examine any documents or records which must be kept (by law), discussing and resolving any problems that may have arisen during your operations. Your AOC is reviewed annually by the Flight Operations Inspectorate on the basis of his reports and is non-expiring, provided that the annual charges are paid up to date (based on the throughput of traffic that a Company has) and you keep your nose clean.

Only specific parts of the Ops Manual are actually 'approved', namely the form of certain documentation (such as the aircraft Technical Log) and the Flight Time and Duty Hours Limitations Schemes. All the rest is an indication to the Authority of how your Company intends to operate, which naturally varies according to circumstances, and they grant or withhold an AOC taking due note of the contents. Despite the apparent flexibility, however, there are definite indications as to what is and isn't allowed, most of it in CAP 360 and the ANO.

The CAA requires a copy of your Ops Manual for its own records and for instant reference in case of queries. As it is the primary indication (to them) of your operating standards, it makes sense, therefore, to produce the Manual in the best possible way. This is psychological — if the Flight Ops Department see a brilliant Manual on the shelves, then they're likely to be more convinced that the rest of the Company is likewise (well, wouldn't you?). So you are doing yourself down if you skimp on the Ops Manual, no matter how boring it may be to produce it.

The CAA have produced their own document — CAP 450 (in two volumes) — dealing with the production of Ops Manuals which will give you the source of information for any subject that you may wish to include.

It also offers guidance (the operative word — not directions as such) on such things as quality of printing, binders, etc (they do suggest a thirteen-hole binder — the only problem is they don't tell you where to get one!). Other sources of information on Manual contents include CAPs 360 and 371. All these are sent free on receipt of your formal AOC application. You may find the Alphabetical Index of Civil Aviation Publications at the back of this book some help here.

You will need to put everything in that bears any resemblance to Operating Staff instructions, including prepared forms, rostering instructions, etc. — essential information for day to day running, in other words.

Each page should be dated with the Company name on it and there should be a systematic system of numbering (page and paragraph) to make it as easy as possible when searching for anything (this is really helpful to the CAA in the early stages and a good index will speed things up more than anything else). A Table of Contents will also be required, but any good word processing program should be able to cope with this easily (if anyone is interested, this book was initially produced in Wordstar on a BBC (Torch Z80) and finally moved to a Victor VI. Ventura Publisher can be recommended for its ability to index a book by Sections).

Each copy of the Manual must also be numbered so that amendment procedures can be controlled.

Back to the AOC

Having submitted the application form and the manual, you then sit and wait for the CAA to respond (for which you should allow anything up to six weeks from receipt) during which time the Chief Flight Ops Inspector allocates you to whichever FOI he thinks will suit you (trying to match his experience with your level of operations). Your Inspector then reads everything and produces a long list of things that need comment. They're quite efficient, so any delays are usually down to you, but they still have to fit you in around their other duties.

For instance, there's no system of handovers — if your Inspector goes on leave for three weeks, there's no procedure for allowing another to take over temporarily. The same goes when your man is detached to the outback somewhere. In some cases, the grant of an AOC may take as much as five months through no fault of yours. It's no good delivering a finished Manual as fast as you can if there's nobody in the office to read it!

There is naturally a conflict of interests here, in that an aircraft owner is forking out money while an aircraft is sitting idle, so obviously he's keen to get on. He is also paying you for what he thinks is idleness (generally, if you're not flying, you are thought not to be working, which you and I know is blatant nonsense). Your job here is to (tactfully) slow him down and speed the CAA up, but they have been there well before you have and know the problems. Also, they do like an empty desk, so the sooner they get you off the ground, the quicker they can relax.

While the Manual is being read, you can get on with getting your pilots checked out by your Training Captains and the system streamlined for the proving ride. For details on setting out the office, etc, see **Running Things** later.

Eventually you will get a standard letter from the Flight Operations 7 requesting proposed Technical Log and Deferred Defect forms (don't forget the instructions). They will also need to see the Maintenance Schedule for the nominated aircraft and the contract between your Company and the Maintenance Contractor. The Maintenance Schedule is produced separately for each machine by whatever Maintenance Contractor is used (several aircraft can share the same schedule).

Also appearing through the post will be the books mentioned earlier, so you can write your Ops Manual. The ANO will also be needed, but you don't get that free.

Your Inspector meanwhile will take time to visit your proposed offices to ensure that they meet certain requirements (such as the Chief Pilot having his own office and being able to see his aircraft operate, the numbers of clerical staff and machinery relative to Management). The offices need not be on an airport, but being away from one does cause problems, for example keeping track of fuel states (knowing them allows you to know your payload instantly if you get a quick charter).

Hopefully by then he will have produced some proposed amendments to the Manual. When he is happy with that, and your offices, he will want a proving ride (preferably with a line pilot) on your aircraft.

The ride itself is not a check of the pilot's ability, at least not in the sense of a Base Check, but more a check of the Company procedures, which is why it should be done with a line pilot, to see if the system works.

It's meant to be a simulation of a complete line operation and will be about an hour or so long. The Inspector will pretend to be a passenger and will expect to be weighed, briefed and otherwise treated exactly in accordance with the Operations Manual. Almost the first thing he will make a beeline for on arrival at the office is the ANO to see if it's up to date! The same goes for maps and other documents. You don't have to have full copies of the Air Pilot or Notams, provided you can prove you have adequate access to any flight planning information you may need, including weather.

After the ride, assuming all is well, the AOC should be granted in due course, possibly after a few more changes. The issue of the Certificate signifies only that you are considered 'competent to secure the safe operation' of your aircraft — it doesn't relieve you from any other legal responsibilities that you may have, whatever they are.

Once you have your certificate, your Inspector will pop round within a month, and thereafter about every six months or so to ensure the continued competence of the Company, including any outstations or agents that you may employ.

It is worth checking to see that you do not need an Air Transport Licence as well (see **Special Events** in Chapter 6).

Running Things

Any company that operates aircraft must achieve as high a utilization as possible in order to achieve maximum cost-effectiveness — an aircraft on the ground is not earning money. While corporate flight departments do not make a profit as such, the comments here apply equally to them, as efficiency should be the goal of everybody. Also, if you are operating an aircraft by yourself and have no Public Transport experience to fall back on, you ought to realize that a good office environment back at base is very important to the overall operation. The following pages will give you some idea of what's required to run things properly, with a little information on the corporate scene that should be read as well because it's all relevant.

The various functions that need to be performed include planning, day-to-day operation and administration. The bigger the company, the larger the departments handling these will be. You may find you need none of these, but it's worth knowing what they get up to.

Planning covers everything from long term management decisions through scheduling flights, minimising dead flying and taking care of maintenance requirements, although some of this could be regarded as **day-to-day** operations. **Administration** is the only part likely to be really separate, but even here there is likely to be a lot of blurring between departments as staff are made to wear several hats.

In practice, you will find all the above activities (with the exception of Top Management matters) more than adequately looked after by the Operations Department in the average small company, and this is what we will mainly be dealing with in this chapter.

The Operations Department

Operations is in immediate control of all day-to-day business, the focal point of its activities being the Ops room where, depending on the extent of your activities, will be found the Operations Staff, secretaries and the rest (if they can all fit in).

The role of the Operations Room (the term includes staff) is to ensure that the right aircraft is in the right place at the right time, and that everyone concerned is aware of what is happening, being pre-warned of any problems which may be expected.

If this cannot be achieved for any reason, Operations must initiate remedial action and minimize inconvenience to passengers, who are (after all) the source of the Company's income.

One of the ways Operations are assisted in keeping track of events is with the use of Movements Boards (boards are quite useful, and you will find that several will be required for AOC operations, including Pilot Qualifications, Notams, and everything else you may think of that would be useful). These boards should be kept well away from prying eyes who may pinch your business if they see destinations and customer names, so keep them away from windows.

Movements Boards should be constantly updated as they're a constant reference point. What goes on them is up to you — just use whatever information you think will be needed. The biggest Movement Board of the lot is the map, which will usually have a string-and-weight arrangement with a Nav Ruler that makes it easy to calculate complicated distances.

Linked with Movement Boards is the Diary. There will be a scruffy one that's used daily, but there should also be a back-up that is updated after the day's work. In it should go all the scheduled work, upcoming pilot and aircraft checks (a week or so before they're actually due). Some people use files into which go Royal Flights, etc.

As mentioned in Chapter 5, there will be a quotes file. It is suggested that this be looseleaf, each page being filled in at the time of each query. If a trip looks like it's going to happen, then that page should be put into a pending file until confirmed, when it's put into a Diary file.

The Diary file is simply thirty-two file holders, not necessarily in one book, representing each day of the month plus one, and all prepared documentation for a flight is placed in the file for the relevant day.

The benefit of this system is that Royal Flight information (and anything else that's only valid for a day) can be put in there as well, which makes it easy to bring it to the attention of the staff concerned.

You can see that communications are beginning to be of vital importance. A good communications network is an essential part of modern aviation. Without knowing as soon as possible what's going on, it's very difficult to plan ahead and foresee problems that might arise. Many methods are used, VHF radio, telex, AFTN, fax and even HF Single Side Band radio for those longer distances.

The most common, however, is the telephone, and the correct use of it saves many problems. The first problem is that there's no record of what's been said. Therefore, important messages and decisions made on the telephone must be followed up immediately by telex or fax, since these are commonly accepted in business as a substitute for official correspondence on Company notepaper. When taking down a message, always ensure you have the correct information and names, so you know who to blame later.

The telephone should be answered as soon as possible, and before answering be sure you have a fair chance of helping the caller. When answered, they should not be left holding. If they have to be left on hold for any reason, ensure that nothing can be overheard that shouldn't be! A definite reason linked to holding is essential, and regular assurance that the problem is being dealt with is helpful as well.

Don't use jargon or be familiar with people you do not know; refer again to Chapter 1 and the comments on being an ambassador of the Company at all times. Always terminate a phone call leaving a positive impression — never be provoked by a complainant obviously out to wind you up!

Corporate Flight Departments

Here you may well find yourself actually in charge of a Flight Department in the proper sense of the word — a charter company, in fact, without the necessity of bothering with charging for your services. If charges are offset between companies within the same group (known as **chargebacks**), this will normally be handled by Accounts.

Chargebacks are used in many companies as one way of allocating time between users. It is a way of paying for the machine on paper, but if the rates are too high, the end result usually is that the departments who need it most can't afford it and therefore can't use it, which seems a bit pointless. A side-effect of this policy is that it also opens the door to small charter operators who can do the job more cheaply, and then money flows outside the Company instead of staying in it. Another is that Accounts have a chance to do a bit of empire-building, as they are the only ones who get any work out of it, namely chasing money round in a circle.

You could budget for a fixed number of flying hours, such as 300, and ration it strictly between departments, stopping when the maximum figure is reached. Fine in theory, but you will rarely get involved with the politics of allocating time.

If you're employed as a full-time pilot, your Company will probably already have an aircraft, therefore it is unlikely that they will charter in except to cover for times when they have lent their aircraft out. However, if you do charter, it will be advantageous to buy time in blocks, paying for it in advance usually, so you can get decent discounts.

It could even be worth considering leasing (self-drive) as a half-way house between chartering and owning. The cut-off point where owning an aircraft makes more financial sense than leasing is about 200 hours a year, so the average flying rate for Corporate aircraft is at least 200-300 hours per year, but some are utilized at a rate of 600 or 700.

It is possible that your Company may do things the other way round and lease their aircraft out to commercial operators. This causes problems, especially where allocating priorities are concerned, and if this is done extensively, Management

Cost per passenger-mile. Total cost divided by passenger miles (obtained by dividing aircraft miles by the load factor).

Operating Costs

Aside from the initial purchase of the aircraft, **variable costs**, such as leasing charges, are the largest real expenses incurred (depreciation is not a true operating expense). Others are:

Fuel. The shorter the average sector length, the higher the average fuel consumption. Fuel flow for budgetary purposes tends to be within five per cent of maximum cruise fuel flow for fixed wing aircraft and ten per cent for helicopters.

Oil. Only bother with consumption; scheduled oil changes will be catered for under maintenance.

Maintenance. This is sometimes the second largest direct operating cost after fuel and varies according to the type of flying undertaken. Much of it depends on the cycles incurred by an airframe or engine rather than the amount of flying hours. Wear and tear on components is felt primarily on take-offs and landings, when engines run at high power settings and landing-gear and flaps are cycled. Some jet engines (particularly helicopter ones) are therefore restricted to the number of start cycles in addition to flying hours, because of the enormous spread of temperatures incurred in the start sequence. Thus, if your aircraft does relatively short trips your maintenance costs per hour will increase as a result.

Whether maintenance is major or minor usually depends on the expense of the particular item, and the cut-off point between the two is usually left to Company discretion.

Scheduled and unscheduled maintenance needs to be catered for in the case of the airframe, engine, propeller or rotor, APU and avionics. In the case of avionics, four per cent of retail price should be held in reserve to cover maintenance (assuming 400 hours per year). Add half a per cent for every 200 additional hours flown, or subtract if need be.

Other variable charges may include hotels, taxis, landing, hangarage, handling, tips, oxygen, uniforms, cleaning, office costs (computers, telephone, fax) and freelancers.

Fixed charges

These cost the same per year regardless of the work, so the more you do, the less per hour these costs become.

Purchase/debt servicing. If you get as deeply involved as this, aircraft purchases are seldom made all at one go, a deposit and several sums following being typical.

The total costs would include basic airframe, avionics, completion and finance charges, and the figures for your annual budget would be the amount of the purchase price paid in the current financial year, whether borrowed or not.

Trade in/Resale. This (hopefully) is a plus item, just resale income for aircraft offered in part-exchange for your new one. However, the real value of this will be degraded by inflation.

Salaries. If you're an owner-pilot, you can safely ignore this, but you may have management, operations, mechanics and pilots to pay.

Storage. Outdoor storage is less expensive than hangarage, but storms and damage do happen, as do vandals. The average annual costs of hangarage to be allowed should be roughly one per cent of the equipped price of the new cost of your aircraft.

Insurance. Costs for this vary according to the experience of the aircrew and maintenance contractors, accident and service history of the aircraft, flying conditions and the amount of coverage required — you may be required to sort out any excess.

Hull insurance provides for physical damage to or loss of the aircraft. Engine coverage is more prevalent amongst airlines, but is nevertheless available for General Aviation. Third party liability, loss of licence (for crews), loss of use, and hangarage insurance may all need to be accounted for. Don't forget normal medicals, dental treatment, etc., if required.

Training. Recurrent crew and mechanic training may mean additions such as anti-terrorist training, if your Company is so disposed.

Services. Manuals, trade subscriptions, airways manuals and maps. Association memberships.

Tax. Best left to the experts, this, but there are ways of obtaining an asset on a mortgage offsetting Corporation Tax.

Being a Chief Pilot

First of all, you should not be on the Duty Roster. The job requires so much management that you become ineffective on both sides if you try and do too much — there's simply not enough time (you can see the list of responsibilities in Chapter 1). Any flying you do should be strictly to keep current and step in when there's a shortage.

As mentioned before, you will be the main point of reference for officialdom because you dictate the flying policy of the Company. Take for example something like not taking off until you reach Blue Line speed in an aeroplane (minimum control speed in case of an engine failure): most take-offs occur between stalling speed and Blue Line, but you could argue that if you don't get airborne until the latter, then you already have the speed in hand to carry on if one engine fails. However, if the nosewheel gets damaged because it wasn't built to take the strain, then it would be regarded as ultimately your fault, as you directed your pilots to fly like that.

Another plus point about being a Chief Pilot is that you also get to argue with Management when they want to put commercial pressure on.

Being a Boss
There are one or two mistaken assumptions that are commonly made by bosses.

The first is that all employees have a genuine interest in the welfare of the Company (well, it's common sense, isn't it? If they look after the Company, it will make enough money to pay them). Actually, employees are usually too busy getting what they want to worry about the Company. They will obviously look after it to the point that they get what they want, but ultimately they will always look after themselves first.

The second is that communications solve everything. They don't. They only help.

Another assumption is that conflicts are due to honest differences of opinion. In reality, it's usually selfishness.

The last is that everyone is as intelligent as you are. . . .

Chapter 11
Going for a Job

The Advert
Your C.V.
The Interview

The Advert

Advertisements are usually the last resort for companies who need staff — the best jobs are always filled by word of mouth. In fact, the way an advert is worded can tell you much about the company you may be working for.

Treat as highly suspicious the one that is obviously from a small company offering an extremely good package or reads something like 'Aztec pilot required — Gulfstream II experience an advantage'. There probably isn't a Gulfstream anywhere near the place; they're trying to wind up the opposition. Similarly, one company may advertise that, due to expansion, they want an incredible number of pilots. This will be followed hotly by another one the following week from another company which, not to be outdone, forecasts even more expansion. Of course, they may be genuine, but my point is that you can save a lot of wasted interviews and postage by being selective right from the start.

Another way of not wasting time is reading what the advert actually says. If it states definitely something like 'must have 500 hours jet experience', it means your application will go straight into File 13 (the waste bin) if you don't. On the other hand, another might say that such experience 'is desirable' or 'is an advantage'; if you think you score six out of eight on the requirements, then go ahead.

In this case, circumstances will determine what happens to your application, for instance whether there is a pilot shortage or not, or whether the Chief Pilot or the Personnel Department actually wrote the advert (Personnel probably haven't a clue what's really required, and may have just copied it from somewhere else).

However, it is quite possible that your face may fit better than many suitably qualified people, and it's a favourite hobby of some pilots to keep applying for jobs anyway, so to help you get on where you may be at some sort of disadvantage (whether you're one of many applicants or you haven't quite got the qualifications required), you may need to employ a few tactics. The best known is through your C.V., or *Curriculum Vitae* for short.

Your C.V.

Applying for a job involves selling yourself, by which I mean that you are the product to be marketed. Self-marketing starts even with the envelope in which you send your details — it is surprising how many people fail to use the C.V. and covering letter (they are, after all, a first introduction) as properly as they should be. I have seen very badly hand-written C.V.s with no idea of spacing on ragged paper that would disgrace a fish and chip shop. This type of introduction says little for your self-image and is likely to go straight into the bin.

Having said that, in a lot of aviation companies the process is relatively informal, so take the following remarks with as large a pinch of salt as you feel able. You may only be required to fill in an application form, which will also require a breakdown of hours — usually First Pilot and Grand Totals. A useful suggestion here is to keep a running breakdown going throughout your flying career, separate from your log book and updated monthly, which will help you extract these figures when required. It will also serve the dual purpose of being a back-up should your original log book get lost, but be advised that a log book must fulfil certain legal requirements to be officially accepted as such — see the ANO.

However, a large company that has a personnel department (which therefore deals with several other professions) will expect to get the full treatment. Like flying, the more preparation that goes into your C.V., the better the results you will get. Remember, you're trying to beat the opposition.

The C.V. should always be accompanied by a hand-written covering letter, which highlights as far as possible your suitability to cover the advertiser's needs, but does not detract from the C.V. itself. You could always draw the advertiser's attention to the relevant parts, which really means that you should analyse the advert properly.

As far as the C.V. itself goes, you should keep things as short as possible within the described limits, although it is recognized that you may wish to include a breakdown of hours, so a little length in your case is acceptable. If you're only going for a flying job, the tendency to include irrelevant information should be avoided. Management qualifications (if you have them) are not important to somebody who just wants a line pilot. All of the following advice should be read in this light. As with all salesmanship, you are trying to make it as easy as possible for the customer, in this case your potential employer.

For the very best presentation, your documentation should always be submitted in a folder or binder. This should appear expensive (but not gimmicky — steer clear of outlandish colour schemes) as you're trying to convey to your prospective employer that you are a person with a totally professional outlook in everything that you do and that the contents are very important.

You need to use quality paper — a minimum standard would be 'Conqueror'. It should be A4 and white, and therefore inoffensive. By all means hand-write (neatly!) the accompanying letter, but the C.V. must be typed on one side of the paper only with the script centralized. Leave at least a one-inch border at the top and bottom of the page with a good sized margin on either side. It will cost about £5 to get a two-page C.V. typed properly and not much more to get a reasonable number photocopied. It is possible to photocopy straight on to Conqueror paper.

The **first page** should be headed 'Curriculum Vitae' and must include the following information:

Name:	(In full)
Address:	(Don't forget the Post Code as mail without one goes second class)
Telephone:	(Include the STD code)
Date of Birth:	(Don't abbreviate the month)
Status:	(Married or Single — nothing else)
Children:	(Number, sex and age only)
Health:	(If you can genuinely put 'Excellent' then do so — otherwise just say 'Good')

All the above information must be well spaced in the middle as there isn't an awful lot of it. Avoid cramping it all into one half of the page.

The **second page** should contain details of your education, being broken down into four distinct sections:

a) **Section one** should list all the secondary schools you attended, plus details of further education including colleges, universities or training schools.

b) **Section two** should contain all major examinations taken (and passed). This includes O and A levels as well as degrees. If you've ever failed something, you're not obliged to mention it.

c) **Section three** is for professional qualifications. If they're good then list them thoroughly. If not, then don't draw attention to them — simply add them to Section 2 and retitle it 'Professional and Educational Qualifications'.

   List here any memberships of professional bodies, such as the Institute of Air Transport or BALPA. This shows that you pursue interests in your leisure time that have a direct bearing on your employment.

d) **Section four** should deal with your extra curricular activities. Membership of sports or athletic clubs will demonstrate your ability to operate as part of a team. Mention everything, but don't go into great detail.

If you feel able to combine pages one and two without sacrificing layout and legibility, then do so, but remember you may need to put a photograph somewhere.

The **third page** should be completed fully and could run into several pages, depending on your work exerience. Again, if some of the experience is not relevant to the job you're applying for, mention it, but don't go into great detail.

As we are now dealing with work experience, you must try to give the impression of steady and gradual advancement in a specific direction. Obviously, not everybody stays on the same path that they started on, so a move in another direction is not necessarily a drawback. As long as you can justify any changes, this will be understood.

Fortunately, the nature of aviation means that companies come and go with monotonous regularity and pilots often find themselves the victims of this, so you have a good excuse ready made. However, it's also extremely important not to give the idea that you're qualification hunting, and that as soon as you have 500 hours on turbines you'll be away to an airline.

In spite of it not being your fault, it still does nothing for your prospects to give redundancy as a reason for change. It's much better to say that your department or company was closing down, even though everyone regards it as the same thing. Similarly, rather than say you were fired, it's better to say that you left by mutual agreement because you felt your career lay elsewhere. Personality clashes also do not exist — you're supposed to be able to work with other people. All changes should be made to look like part of your Master Plan but **don't** tell a direct lie, for obvious reasons.

Your career history should commence with your first job after leaving full-time education and progress chronologically through to the present day.

The name and town location is enough to identify employers with a brief description of their activities, if needed (after all, aviation is aviation and everybody knows what a pilot does).

When it comes to your own job descriptions, it is not where you started (because everyone starts at the bottom) but how you progressed that's relevant, as well as what you've learned along the way. You must demonstrate progression and capability without chasing qualifications.

Having got to the present day, the **fourth** page will start with your reasons for leaving your current position and applying for the new job. When people read a C.V. they almost always do it with a highlighter pen in one hand so they can mark relevant passages for later inquisition. It's a fair bet that this section will be a prime target for such treatment, so prepare it very carefully.

It should be brief, have impact and be believable. Remember that most people are not so much upset at being told lies (although that's bad enough) but more so at being thought stupid enough to fall for a really bad line — it's a real insult to their intelligence. I'm afraid you will have to come up with your own inspiration for this bit, but a good tip is to ally the company's own progress with yours. Mention their own market dominance or flair which will no doubt rub off on you as you develop your career (Ahem!).

You will need to know something about the company you wish to join for the interview, so include a little about specific experience relevant to the post applied for in the this section as well.

In summary, the layout must be neat, as short as possible, well spaced and easy to read, with a positive attitude being conveyed throughout. Emphasize your achievements, strengths and successes — try to turn setbacks into advantages that you have benefited from.

The reason for having the final page referring to the position currently applied for is to give the impression of tailoring the C.V. to that employer's needs. The bulk of your C.V. can therefore be pre-printed, with only the need to change the last page every time (having mentioned photocopying before, it must be said that this is not a 'personal' method. A better idea would be to place your C.V. on a word processor, so as many freshly typed copies can be printed as you wish, each looking as smart as the other).

The Interview

Let us first of all establish what the interview is not. It has nothing to do with your competence as a professional, except for the simulator ride (if one is required). The mere fact that you've been put on any list at all, let alone shortlisted, indicates that your flying abilities are recognized (there are some employers that do not even look at log books or licences, taking qualifications for granted).

On their side, the interview is really for checking to see if your face will fit. They are about to let your personality loose on their customers and they want to see if you will help solve the problem or become part of it. As far as you are concerned, it's a chance to see if you will like the Company. You may find it useful to make a checklist of what **you** want from them.

Interviewing techniques are getting very sophisticated these days. You may be lucky and get away with a quick half-hour with someone who is just as nervous as you are, but the full-blown two-day affair with Personality and IQ/Psychometric testing is becoming increasingly common (be prepared for the question about how well you thought you did!).

Whatever type it is, you must regard it as having started whenever you walk through the main door of the building or meet any Company person, whichever is the earlier.

The interview is even more part of your sales technique. Naturally, you will be smartly dressed and presentable, and you have got to convince the interviewer that they are not so much buying a pilot as peace of mind (salesmen never sell you a washing machine, they sell you family happiness with white shirts, with the machine as incidental to it).

Although unlikely in a pure aviation company, there may be questions or situations designed to make you a stuttering wreck — in other words, to put you well and truly on the spot.

To combat this possibility, there are ways of behaving that will give you the most confidence. Don't talk too much, don't be pushy or negative and don't break silences. It is certainly not on to slate other companies or be too eager to leave your present one — if you can do either, you can do it to the one you're going for. Do not sit until invited, and if you are not, at least wait until the interviewer sits down. Do not smoke without permission, don't swear, interrupt or 'interview' the interviewer, even if he is inept.

Nor is it a good idea to argue, be familiar or apologise for yourself.

The best tactic is to avoid extremes and place you and your opinions firmly in the middle — be the ideal 'Company Person', in fact.

Going back to the C.V. and the highlighter pen, you will more than likely be asked why you are going for that particular company and the reasons for leaving any previous employment. In the first case, you **don't** want to say that you have a mortgage, kids, etc (they're not interested in your personal problems), and in the second try not to give money or better opportunities as a reason for moving on — well, not more than once early on in your career, anyway. Don't even think of mentioning personality clashes or 'philosophical differences' as they're more politely known (luckily, the nature of aviation means that those of you with a patchwork quilt for a C.V. will be able to claim that most cases of 'fluid employment' were not your fault anyway).

Bigger companies may also need you to go through their own medical (for pension purposes) and a simulator ride. This will test your knowledge of procedures as much as your ability to fly, so check this aspect out before you go.

Alphabetical Index
to Civil Aviation Publications,
including the Air Navigation Order 1989

A

271

D

I

M

P

T

U

P = paragraph   p = page   App = Appendix   C = Chapter   fwd = foreword
Sch = Schedule   Pt = Part   Sc = Scale   Sect = Section

The above index has been provided courtesy of the Institute of Air Transport.

The Institute of Air Transport was founded in 1989 as a Friendly Society to improve the professionalism and recognition of those working in the Air Transport industry. It does this by providing services (such as this publication) and by establishing its own training courses and certificates (such as Flight Despatch and computing) which will be aligned with those of the academic world.

The basic Membership grade is open to those aged over 30 with at least five years' experience in Air Transport who hold a responsible position, in that they act with a minimum of direction but are personally responsible for the outcome of their own decisions.

For more information and deails of other grades available, send a stamped, addressed envelope to:

The Institute of Air Transport   PO Box 377   ANDOVER   Hants SP11 8YA

Glossary

Anything not found here will usually be found in your favourite flight guide or the ICAO list of definitions.

Aerodrome Operating Minima
The Cloud Ceiling and Runway Visual Range (RVR) for take-off and the Decision Height (DH) or Minimum Descent Height (MDH), RVR and visual reference for landing which are the minima for the operation of the aircraft.

Air Ambulance Flight
A flight where the prime reason for its organization is to rapidly transport a person who is ill or has been physically injured to a recognized medical facility, or where a human organ required for a transplant operation is taken from one place to another.

Other persons on the flight (aside from the aircrew) are necessary medical attendants, the patient's immediate family or next-of-kin (or one close friend).

Approach Ban
A situation whereby an aircraft shall not:

a) commence or continue a descent below 1,000 feet above the height of an aerodrome where the RVR is reported to be less than the specified minima for landing, except that if this condition is reported to the aircraft Commander after he has properly descended below 1000 feet, the approach may be continued to Decision Height to assess the visual reference available (or in English: start or carry on with an approach where the RVR is reported to be below Company minima unless you are already below 1000 feet.

b) commence or continue an approach to landing at an aerodrome outside the UK when any of the elements included in the State Minima are reported to be below the prescribed limits and National Regulations prohibit any attempt to land, or commence an approach to landing (or: start or carry on with an approach to a foreign airfield where any State minima are below limits and State regulations forbid you to try).

c) commence an approach to landing at any aerodrome either inside or outside the UK at which RVR is not reported, or is not available for the time being, when the Met visibility or factored Met visibility is less than the equivalent specified RVR (or: start an approach anywhere where no RVR is reported and the suitably converted Met visibility is less than Company minima).

d) continue an approach to landing by flying below the specified DH or MDH unless from that height the specified visual reference is established and maintained (or: go below DH/MDH unless you can see what you're doing).

During single-pilot operations, an approach shall not be continued below the specified limits for the type of autopilot fitted to the aircraft. If the autopilot is unserviceable, an approach shall not be continued below 800 feet unless the specified visual reference to the runway concerned has been made.

NOTE: An approach ban does not apply in the UK when, on a non-Public Transport flight made solely for training purposes, the Captain elects to make a letdown followed by a Missed Approach procedure, having first declared such intention. Neither does it apply where the reported cloud base is below Decision Height — you may approach and descend to DH to assess the cloud base for yourself, but only twice. Except in emergency, you may not make a further attempt unless the controlling authority has reported a significant improvement.

Approach to landing
That portion of the flight in which the aircraft is descending below 1,000 feet above the Decision Height for that particular landing.

Avoid Curve
A graph relating to helicopter performance which indicates combinations of speed and height in which it is dangerous to fly. It is a function of the pitch angle of the blades — if you're in flat pitch, then it doesn't exist. When it does, those in Flight Manuals are derived from flight testing so as to determine

limiting cases. This involves flight at maximum weight, high density altitudes and high power settings, this last when testing is done at the lower part. Any changes in those parameters will result in corresponding changes in the shape of the avoid area, though these will not be detectable from the graphs supplied. See diagram on page 181.

Balanced Field Length
The distance within which an aircraft can either accelerate to V1 and then either stop or continue to a height of 35 (or whatever) feet with one engine out at V1.3.

Circling Minima
The lowest conditions of circling heights and in-flight visibility in which a circuit (using visual reference only), may be carried out within a fixed radius or sector of an aerodrome at which landing is intended (RVR, when applicable, is that for the landing runway).
   Circling Minima apply to: any instrument approach made for the purpose of landing on a runway other than that directly served by the approach aid being used ('directly served' means that the final heading of the approach is within thirty degrees of the runway QDM); purely visual approaches where you decide to dispense with an available letdown aid; visual circuits following overshoots from either instrument or visual approaches.

Climb Compliance
With reference to take-off, covers the situation after an engine failure at V1 or later during take-off with requirements for reasonable climbout on one engine.
   The take-off weight of an aircraft may be limited by climb compliance in one of the take-off segments.

Cloud Ceiling
The vertical distance from the elevation of the aerodrome to the lowest part of any visible cloud that obscures more than half the sky.

Days off
Periods available for leisure and relaxation free from all duties. A single Day Off shall include two local nights. Consecutive days off shall include a further local night for each additional consecutive day off. A Rest Period may be included as part of a Day Off.

Decision Height
The minimum height above the aerodrome elevation to which an approach may safely by continued without visual reference to the ground.

Defined Area
The whole of a circle of four nautical miles radius centred on the aerodrome, or a prescribed segment of this circle if visual manoeuvring can be confined to a smaller area with the intention of avoiding a predominant obstruction.

Duty Period
Any continuous period throughout which either a crew member flies in any aircraft, whether as a crew member or as a passenger, at the behest of his employer, or otherwise carries out a required duty in the course of his employment. It includes any FDP, positioning at the behest of the employer, ground training, ground duties and standby duty.

Early starts/late finishes
Any duty period that impinges upon 0100 and 0700 local acclimatized time.

Flying Duty Period (FDP)
Any duty period during which a crew member flies in an aircraft as a member of its crew. It starts at the time the crew member is required by the operator to report for duty (other than standby) and finishes at on-chocks or engines off at the end of the final sector.

Indirect Approach
A circling procedure established for some airfields (notably French), where prescribed tracks are flown to establish an approach on the runway in use after an approach to another runway. Similar to Circling Minima, but more precise.

In-flight Visibility
As seen from the cockpit. As a guide to making a circling approach, an IFV equal to the diameter of a Rate 1 turn is required. A reasonably accurate assessment is given by the formula: IFV (metres) = 20 x circuit speed (knots).

Local Night
A period of eight hours falling between 2200 and 0800 local time.

Long Range Flight
Over water in helicopters, where the overwater sector exceeds thirty nautical miles.

Minimum Descent Height (MDH)
The minimum height to which a non-precision approach can safely be continued without visual reference to the ground. Similar to Decision Height, but in this case it refers to levelling off and not a decision to commence a missed approach. You must not descend below this height unless the specified visual reference has been obtained, and go around must be initiated at the time the aircraft is calculated to be above the runway threshold.

Minimum Weather Conditions
In relation to an aerodrome, this means the Cloud Ceiling and RVR for take-off, and the Decision Height and RVR for landing, below which an aircraft cannot safely take off and land.

Notified
'As set forth in a document entitled *Aeronautical Information Publication* or *Notam* published by the Civil Aviation Authority (for the UK) or by a country other than the UK (when abroad) for the time being in force'.

Obstacle Clearance Height (OCH)
The height above aerodrome or threshold elevation for any given final approach direction and instrument approach aid below which separation from obstacles cannot be maintained either on approach or in the event of a Missed Approach.

Positioning
The practice of transferring crews from place to place as passengers in surface or air transport at the behest of the Company.

Public Transport
Defined in the ANO, Article 96A, as being where **valuable consideration** is given or promised for the carriage of passengers or cargo on a flight. The definition also covers anyone or anything that may be carried free on that flight having nothing to do with the **employees** of any air transport undertaking (i.e. the Company) that may be involved in its operation (company directors and anyone working on behalf of the CAA are

considered to be employees for this purpose and therefore outwith the terms of Public Transport).

Reporting Time
The time at which a crew member is required by the Company to report for duty.

Rest Period
A period before starting a Flying Duty Period which is intended to ensure that a crew member is adequately rested before a flight.

Rostered/Scheduled/Planned duty
A duty day or series of duty days with stipulated start and finish times notified by the Company to the operating crews in advance.

Runway Visual Range (RVR)
In relation to a runway (or landing strip), this is the maximum distance in the direction of take-off or landing at which the runway (or landing strip), or the markers and lights delineating it, can be seen from a point 15 m above its centreline.

Sector
The time between an aircraft first moving under its own power until it next comes to rest after landing on the designated parking position.

Short Range flights
Over water in helicopters, where the overwater sector is between 10-30 nautical miles.

Specified
In relation to aircraft, this means specified by the Operator in, or ascertainable by references to, the Operations Manual.

Specified Visual Reference
    a) For approaches using full ILS or PAR, the specified visual reference should contain at least six consecutive lights, which may be approach lights or runway lights, or a combination of both.
    b) For approaches using aids other than full ILS or PAR when approach lighting is not available, the specified visual reference should include the aiming point, i.e. the desired point of touchdown on the runway of

intended landing. If approach lights are available it is not essential that the aiming point should be in view at decision height, but the segment of lighting specified should contain at least seven consecutive lights, which may be approach lights or runway lights, or a combination of both.

c) For a visual circuit of the aerodrome based on visual manoeuvring minima, a pilot should have continuous sight of ground features which will enable him to establish the position of the aircraft in relation to the aerodrome and subsequently to remain within the notified visual manoeuvring area.

Split Duty
A Flying Duty Period which consists of two or more sectors separated by less than a minimum rest period.

Standby Duty
A period of time when an operator places restraints on a crew member who would otherwise be off duty. However, it shall not include any time during which an operator requires a crew member to be available for the purpose of notifying him of a duty which is due to start ten or more hours ahead.

State Minima
In some countries (e.g. France), the controlling authority lays down mandatory minimum weather conditions for take-off and landing, which may relate to the type of aircraft and nature of the operation, as well as the aids in use. The more stringent applications between State and company minima apply.

Travelling
All time spent by a crew member between his place of rest and his normal operating base on the day.

V-speeds
Vs   Stall speed
Vmc Minimum Control Speed, or the minimum speed at which it is possible to control the aircraft in the air, with one engine inoperative and the other at take-off thrust.
V1   Critical Engine Failure Speed. The speed above which the take-off is continued, and below which it is abandoned, in the case of engine failure.

Vr   Rotation Speed, at which the aircraft is rotated to the take-off attitude. VR must not be less than V1 or 1.05 x VMC. It must also be high enough to allow V2 to be attained before reaching screen height.

V2   Take-off Safety Speed, to be achieved before screen height.

Vso Stall Speed in landing configuration.

Very Short Range flights
Over water in helicopters, where the overwater sector is less than ten nautical miles.

Visual Contact Flight
A flight conducted under VFR (or IFR) such that the aircraft remains below and clear of cloud and during which the crew are in continuous visual contact with the surface. As a result of this, they must be able to assess the aircraft attitude and separation from the surface by external reference by day, and by reference to a clearly distinguishable external horizon by night.

Visual Reference
For operations is, for descent below DH, a continuous or successive reference to a segment of at least seven consecutive lights which may be approach or runway lights or a combination of both, or a segment of the runway established to be not less than 1,000 feet (300 m) long which includes the touchdown point. When the approach has been made using a full ILS or PAR, the number of consecutive lights to be contained in the segment is reduced to six; for a visual circuit or part circuit of the aerodrome based on circling minima, a pilot should have continuous sight of ground features which will enable him to establish the position of the aircraft in relation to the aerodrome and subsequently to remain within the notified visual manoeuvring area.

Week
A week is a period of seven consecutive days starting at any set time on any set day of the week, as determined by the operator. A rostering period will normally comprise four consecutive weeks.